INTRODUCTION TO POWDER METALLURGY

Joel S. Hirschhorn, Ph.D.
Associate Professor Metallurgical Engineering
University of Wisconsin, Madison, Wisconsin

AMERICAN POWDER METALLURGY INSTITUTE
Princeton, New Jersey

First Published 1969
Second Printing 1976

Library of Congress Catalog Card No.: 76–83260

PRINTED IN THE UNITED STATES OF AMERICA
by
THE COLONIAL PRESS INC.

FOREWORD

There comes a time in the evolution of every technology-based industry, when it must reveal, it must discuss, and it must educate in order that that industry shall achieve the fulfilment of its destiny.

It must reveal its technology because that which is hidden and kept secret becomes distorted and even more attractive to the curious, if only because of its very mystery.

It must discuss its techniques within its own confines to cross-pollinate with ideas its own creativity.

And it must educate. Because only through enlightened understanding can an industry advance and build itself upon a strong foundation of acceptance. Only the knowledgeable can make intelligent decisions when that technology and its practitioners must compete with other techniques.

This is the purpose of this book. To contribute to discussion. To reveal. To educate. And above all, to help foster the progress of powder metallurgy and the industry based upon it. That is why it is published by the American Powder Metallurgy Institute and its parent organization, the Metal Powder Industries Federation.

Kempton H. Roll

Executive Director
Metal Powder Industries Federation

National Director
American Powder Metallurgy Institute

CONTENTS

CHAPTER ONE

INTRODUCTION

1.1 SCOPE OF TEXT

The term *powder metallurgy* as used in this text is defined as the *material processing technique used to consolidate particulate matter, both metals and/or nonmetals, into discrete shapes.* Although the emphasis will be on the metallic materials, the principles of the process apply, with little modification, to ceramics and other types of nonmetallic materials used in increasing quantities in our modern technological society. Complex composite materials composed of both metallic and nonmetallic phases are also being designed and fabricated by this technique in increasing quantities to provide the exceptional properties required in the highly sophisticated and demanding aerospace, electronic and nuclear energy industries.

An important distinction is the concept of using powdered materials to produce shaped products rather than using such materials in their divided form. The latter type of application is both significant and varied, but will not be considered in detail in this text. For example, powders of copper, bronze and aluminum are used in large quantities in paints and printing inks to provide "gold" and "silver" hues and metallic luster. And aluminum powder in some paints provides corrosion resistance to the base material. There is also a considerable market for powders of aluminum, magnesium and their alloys in illuminating and explosive materials applications because of their ability to produce a considerable amount of heat upon oxidation. Iron powders are employed in welding electrodes and in metal cutting and cleaning (scarfing) operations. Many types of metallic powders are widely used in chemical processing operations. Chapter Two on the characterization of powders, including their manufacture, will of course pertain to the particulate materials used for these and countless other applications.

Nor is it the purpose of this book to provide detailed information for use in production operations or to serve as a source book of innumerable references and experimental data for researchers. Although there is some descriptive material and data in all segments of the text, the basic approach has been to emphasize the scientific and engineering principles upon which are based the methods used to manufacture and characterize metal powders, the processing techniques and the design and application of the powder metallurgy products.

The primary objective of this text is to provide an introductory treatment of this subject for both the university student taking a formal course in powder metallurgy or some related subject and the engineer in industry. Problems have been provided at the end of each of the subsequent chapters to aid the reader in his comprehension, evaluation and application of the subject matter. References for further reading are also presented to facilitate the continuing education of the reader, to provide a means for in depth study of areas of particular interest, and to obtain the detailed information necessary for application of the powder metallurgy technique.

1.2 THE BASIC PROCESS

The subject matter which falls within the scope of this text has been divided into its logical components to allow a simplified presentation. However, the discussion of these isolated topics should be preceded by an introduction to the fundamental aspects of the overall process. In this way the relevance and significance of the material subsequently discussed will be better appreciated.

The conventional form of the process together with some of the more common variations are illustrated in the process flow diagram of Figure 1-1. Additional variations that are not illustrated will be considered in later sections of the text. To begin with, raw powders having the desired size, shape and other characteristics of importance are either blended by themselves or with additives

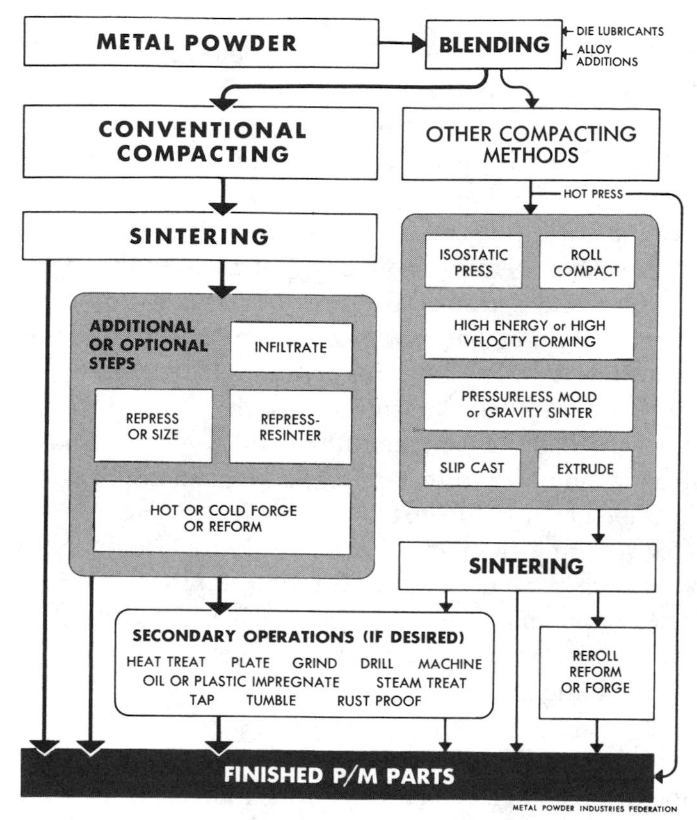

FIGURE 1-1.
Basic steps in the powder metallurgy process.

such as lubricants or alloy additions, in a device which ensures the production of a homogeneous powder or mix. In the most widely used form of the technique the powder is then compacted under pressure within a rigid die at room temperature. Compaction is done to consolidate and densify the loose powder into a "green" compact that has sufficient strength for handling; the desired size and shape of the product are basically determined in this step. After ejection of the green compact from the die cavity it is heated in a furnace at a relatively high temperature in a protective atmosphere; this step is termed sintering. In most cases no liquid or molten phase is formed during sintering; it is a solid state process. One of the most important results of sintering is the development of true chemical or metallurgical bonds among the original particles. This leads to the attainment of integrity and a high level of strength in the compact. A protective sintering atmosphere is necessary to cleanse the original green compact and to prevent any undesirable chemical reaction between the compact and its environment.

The two basic steps of compaction and sintering may be combined into one operation consisting of the simultaneous application of heat and pressure to a powder mass within some type of die. This variation has not been used extensively for metallic materials but is widely used for ceramics. Hot pressing is the term generally used to describe this approach.

Other methods of compacting metal powders, shown on the right hand side of Figure 1-1, are less commonly used. They will be described later in the text.

After sintering the part may be ready for use or secondary operations such as repressing, resintering, infiltration with a molten metal or impregnation with plastic or liquid lubricant, or a combination of these may be performed to achieve specific properties. More conventional operations such as machining, tumbling, plating and heat treatment may also be carried out. Two very important factors should be noted: (1) the process offers the greatest economic advantages when very few, if any, secondary operations are necessary, and large quantities of a part may be mass produced at rapid rates; and (2) the process variables may be adjusted to produce parts with controllable types and amounts of useful porosity or with densities approaching the theoretical value that are analogous to and competitive with conventional cast and wrought materials, including forgings. Additionally, a multitude of alloys and complex multiphase materials can only be economically manufactured by powder metallurgy techniques.

1.3 SOME HISTORICAL FACTORS

True understanding and appreciation of past and future process changes, or lack of them, can be greatly improved by some knowledge of the historical development of the process. Such a knowledge is also of great assistance in communicating with the variety of people that a practicing engineer working in this area comes in contact with.

Certainly one of the unique characteristics of powder metallurgy is the absence of fusion or melting of the material in all but one or two variations of the process. If we consider making a solid shaped object without fusion from a powdered material, then many of the metallic products of older civilizations are believed by many to be examples of the application of powder metallurgy principles. These would include the Egyptian iron implements which date from at least 3,000 B.C., the Delhi column in India weighing 6.5 tons and made of reduced iron, and articles of precious metals made by the Incas. Not until about 1800 was there any way of obtaining temperatures high enough to melt pure iron or higher melting point materials. Consequently, these early products are not believed to have been made by casting of a molten metal. But it was possible to reduce iron ores by heating them with carbon to produce sponge iron in a powder or very friable form, and subsequently to beat and work this material into the desired shape, possibly when they were heated.

The first modern significant development was the production of platinum ingots from compacted, reduced platinum powder. The compacts were sintered and subsequently hot worked. Credit for this work is given to Wollaston in England and Sobolevskii in Russia who performed about the same experiments during 1826 to 1829. During the early 1900's methods were developed by Coolidge and others to compact and sinter tungsten powder to produce ingots that could be used to make filaments for incandescent light bulbs. The successful production of large quantities of very high strength tungsten products without fusion was a dramatic demonstration of the potential of powder metallurgy.

During the subsequent years prior to World War II powder

metallurgy techniques were applied to the production of: copper-graphite brushes for electric motors and dynamos, a unique combination of two materials with divergent characteristics; refractory carbides for wire drawing dies which soon developed into tungsten carbide-metal (cermet) type cutting tool materials; bronze and iron bearings prepared by infiltrating porous compacts with oil, known as oilless or self-lubricating bearings; contact materials for electrical devices consisting of a hard refractory phase and either silver or copper; and finally small parts for engines and various types of machinery. Clearly the emphasis in this early period was in producing rather complex multiphase and exotic materials and not common parts and metals.

During the war period and subsequent years the process was applied to a greater variety of ferrous, nonferrous and composite materials. The increasing cost of labor and the need for very large quantities of parts with close control of dimensional tolerances spurred the use of powder metallurgy. A number of novel methods of compaction, including hot pressing, were developed, but the oldest and simplest method of cold compaction still remains the most widely used. There has been a steady increase in the capacities of presses, from the original 5 to 50 tons to the thousands of tons range today, and this has resulted in the ever increasing size of powder metallurgy products. Sintering furnaces have been increased in size and productivity; the use of continuous conveyor systems passing through the furnace hot zone is commonplace. Instrumentation for very precise control of sintering atmospheres and temperatures, and automation of the entire operation have been developed. And another development is the use of vacuum sintering furnaces for certain applications.

During the past decade there have been significant advances in powder manufacturing techniques. A major innovation is the production of powder directly from the ore. This results in lower raw material costs and greater attractiveness for continuous powder metallurgy processes capable of making mill shapes such as powder rolling and extrusion. New types of powders with superior properties allow the production of larger and higher strength materials. Careful control of the structure of the original powder particles has allowed more intelligent manipulation of the structure of the final sintered materials. Very complex multiphase powder particles facilitate the manufacture of composite materials by economical powder metallurgy techniques.

The increasing use of large powder metallurgy parts for structural applications by the automobile industry represents a very important contemporary development. At the outset all P/M (the acronym for powder metallurgy now widely used) parts were small, less than a few square inches in cross section, and the mechanical properties were considered barely comparable to more conventional materials. Today the size has increased many times and large parts of a foot or more in diameter and weighing ten to fifty pounds are being produced in large quantities. Materials with mechanical properties far exceeding those of more conventional materials have been developed by using new alloying elements for iron base materials, by improving heat treatments, by using improved powders and by achieving higher densities. Not only can high strengths be obtained but also high levels of ductility and toughness in P/M parts are available. The old notions of completely brittle and fragile powder metallurgy materials are completely invalid today.

Although the application of powder metallurgy materials for somewhat exotic uses, such as nuclear reactors and rockets, will continue to be an important aspect of this field, the truly great increases in P/M parts consumption will come from the more mundane uses, such as the parts in automobiles and all types of consumer products.

CHAPTER

TWO

CHARACTERIZATION OF POWDERS

2.1 INTRODUCTION

The success of any materials processing technique depends to a great extent on the complete characterization and control of the initial raw materials. In some respects this is unusually critical for powder metallurgy. The process, particularly with regard to compaction and sintering, is usually geared to produce large quantities of a uniform product. Such uniformity is best achieved by the use of unchanging raw materials. Often the problem is not so much how to control the raw material, but rather what to control. There are many characteristics of powders, some interrelated, that can be considered. Not all may be critical for a given application; but the choice of the ones that are can only be made on the basis of a complete understanding of all the major characteristics. In this chapter we will consider those factors which characterize powders, stressing the fundamental methods of description and the scientific principles upon which methods of processing or experimental determination are based. It should be emphasized that the characterization of powders must be considered in its broadest sense; the obvious factors such as particle size and shape are indeed important, but the methods of manufacture and their influence on particle chemistry and structure, and the precise nature of particle size distribution are examples of equally significant factors.

2.2 POWDER MANUFACTURE

The basis for characterizing any powder begins with a knowledge of the method of manufacture. The exact techniques used will ultimately determine many particle characteristics, including particle size and shape, the behavior during compaction and sintering, and the composition, structure and properties of the sintered material. In many cases powders are referred to simply in terms of their method of manufacture rather than by actual experimental data. Consequently, it is important to be aware of the general characteristics of a powder prepared by a specific method.

The subject of powder manufacture is a very extensive one; in this section we will attempt to briefly summarize the most important principles and processes. First we may note that the significant methods of manufacture may be classed as follows:

(a) chemical reactions and decompositions
(b) atomization of liquid (molten) metals
(c) electrolytic deposition
(d) mechanical processing of solid materials

Virtually any material can be made into a powder by one or more of these methods. The exact method chosen must be related to an intended market or type of application and the desired properties and structure of the final product, limitations imposed by the specific type of powder metallurgy process used to make the product, and the economics of the entire powder manufacturing process. The first two methods noted above are the most widely used; however, there are many cases where it is necessary or advantageous to use one of the others. Past process and product innovations and future major developments in the field of powder metallurgy can be linked to the important changes made in powder manufacturing technology in a surprising number of cases.

Chemical Reactions and Decompositions Any metal may be produced in the form of a powder by suitable chemical reactions or decompositions. Decomposition is possible for any material containing a metal element. The material will decompose into its elements if heated to a sufficiently high enough temperature. However, the problem is to separate the metallic component desired after the decomposition. There have been relatively few applications of this principle of thermal decomposition to the commercial production of powders. On the other hand, much use has been made of chemical reactions which act to decompose a material or compound containing the desired metal. Such processes will involve at least two reactants: a compound of the metal and a reducing agent. Either reactant may be in the solid, liquid or gaseous state or in a solution. It is convenient to breakdown the methods in this general classification into the following subclasses:

(i) decomposition of a solid phase by a chemical reaction
(ii) thermal decomposition of a phase
(iii) precipitation from a liquid
(iv) precipitation from a gas

However, before delving into these various methods it is appropriate to review some basic thermodynamics and kinetics of use in this and subsequent topics. These principles must be well understood by anyone particularly interested in the details of powder manufacture.

The basis for deciding whether any chemical reaction or decomposition will actually take place involves a consideration of the changes in energy and entropy which correspond to such a process. The difference between the total energy (or enthalpy) H of a system and the "bound" or unavailable energy TS, where S is the entropy and T the absolute temperature in degrees Kelvin, is the energy available to do useful work or the "free energy" F. This fundamental relationship is written as

$$F = H - TS \tag{2-1}$$

When considering a change in state or a reaction at a constant temperature the significant quantities are the differences ΔF, ΔH and ΔS between the values for the reactant(s) and for the product(s) of the reaction or decomposition; that is,

$$\Delta F = \Delta H - T\Delta S \tag{2-2}$$

If ΔF is negative the process can occur, while if ΔF is positive the process is impossible. The driving force for the change or process is the reduction in free energy.

The direction of the process is also important to consider. The reaction

$$A + B \rightarrow AB \tag{2-3}$$

can occur if the appropriate ΔF is negative, but this also signifies that the reverse reaction

$$AB \rightarrow A + B \tag{2-4}$$

will then have a positive ΔF (of the same absolute numerical value) and cannot occur. Equation (2-3) represents what is meant by a chemical reaction, while equation (2-4) represents a thermal decomposition. Tables of free energy of formation values as a function of temperature for many types of compounds are available and can be used to evaluate the potential usefulness of a given reaction or decomposition. Some such data are given in problem (2-1) at the end of this chapter. Methods are available to obtain ΔF values for complex reactions involving several products and reactants; these are reviewed in any text on elementary chemical thermodynamics.

The extent to which a reaction or decomposition will proceed is assessed by considering the appropriate equilibrium constant K which is given by

$$\ln K = -\Delta F/RT \tag{2-5}$$

For equation (2-3) the equilibrium constant is also given by

$$K = a_{AB}/a_A a_B \tag{2-6}$$

where the a values represent the activities of the reactants and product, and may also be given as partial pressures for gaseous species or as unity for solids remaining at constant composition. These quantities would be raised to a power corresponding to any numerical number of moles preceding the chemical species in a real reaction.

The numerical value of K gives us the relative concentration of products over reactants. If a reaction, such as equation (2-3), proceeds far to the right as written, then the concentrations of the reactants are much lower than those of the products at equilibrium, and K has a large value. A small value of K indicates that equilibrium (natural cessation of the reaction) is reached when there are only small concentrations of the products. For the reverse reaction, such as equation (2-4), the new equilibrium constant becomes the reciprocal of the other. By control of the environment, such as removal of the products from the reaction zone, the reaction may be made to produce a greater yield.

As an example of the importance of this basic type of thermodynamic consideration, the reduction of a simple metal oxide by either hydrogen or carbon monoxide will be illustrated. For hydrogen reduction we may write

$$MO + H_2 \rightarrow M + H_2O \tag{2-7}$$

and

$$K = P_{H_2O}/P_{H_2} \tag{2-8}$$

For the carbon monoxide reduction we may write

$$MO + CO \rightarrow M + CO_2 \tag{2-9}$$

and

$$K = P_{CO_2}/P_{CO} \tag{2-10}$$

In view of equations (2-2) and (2-5) it is seen that these critical ratios of partial pressures have a specific equilibrium value at any temperature for a particular metal oxide. Consequently, if a reduction reaction is to continue, then the actual gas ratio present in the system must be less than some critical value.

Naturally as a reaction proceeds and the reducing gas is kept at a constant pressure the product increases in concentration and will, in a static system, reach the equilibrium value in time. In actual practice such products as water vapor and carbon dioxide must be continuously removed from the reaction zone. If this is not done, then the real value of the partial pressure ratio will exceed the equilibrium value of K and the metal will be oxidized; that is, the reaction is forced in the opposite direction. Care must also be taken with regard to cooling. If the equilibrium pressure ratio decreases with decreasing temperature, then a ratio which is reducing at an elevated temperature may be oxidizing at a lower one.

Thermodynamic considerations help us to decide whether a reaction can take place and, if it can, what its extent will be. And the subject of kinetics attempts to evaluate the speed of a reaction. The rate at which a reaction will proceed is given by its rate constant k, which defines the number of atoms or molecules reacting per unit time. This is related to the energy (usually considered as thermal) which must be supplied to the atoms or molecules of the reactants to allow them to rearrange themselves and reach the final state corresponding to the products by the following equation

$$k = A \exp\left(-\Delta U/RT\right) \tag{2-11}$$

where A is a constant determined by the precise nature of the process, ΔU the energy to be supplied termed the activation energy for a specific atomic process, T the absolute temperature and R the gas constant. The lower the activation energy and the higher the temperature, the faster the reaction will proceed. If the logarithm of the reaction rate (or something proportional to it) is plotted against the reciprocal of T, then a straight line should result, the slope of which yields ΔU. If a curve results, then several individual reactions may actually be taking place simultaneously, each influenced by temperature in a different way. Similarly, several straight line portions on such a plot would indicate that the basic atomic mechanism of the reaction is changing as a function of temperature.

Although thermodynamic considerations may tell us a reaction is possible and kinetic considerations may predict that the rate of the reaction is sufficiently rapid, it may become apparent that the problem is to get the reaction started. This involves a consideration of the problems associated with the nucleation of a new phase or reaction product. The simplest case to consider is the formation of a new solid or liquid phase. The change in free energy for the process must of course include the change due to the chemical reaction as given by equation (2-2). In addition, it must be realized that the formation of the new phase also corresponds to the formation of a new interface (the surface of the particle or drop).

There is a positive free energy associated with every interface or surface due to the incomplete bonding of the surface atoms as compared to the internal atoms. The free energy change for the system is then given by

$$\Delta F = \Delta F_c + \Delta F_s \qquad (2\text{-}12)$$

where ΔF_c represents the volume free energy change due to the chemical aspects of the reaction and ΔF_s represents the free energy change due to the new interface.

The simplest geometry to consider is the formation or nucleation of a spherical particle for which

$$\Delta F = F_c(4\pi/3)r^3 + F_s(4\pi)r^2 \qquad (2\text{-}13)$$

where r is the particle radius and F_c and F_s are numerical constants (for a particular reaction and temperature) representing the chemical free energy per unit volume of material and the surface free energy per unit area of interface, respectively. In order for the reaction to proceed ΔF must be negative. Although F_c will be negative (assuming we are dealing with a possible reaction), F_s is always positive. At very small radii the value of the surface free energy contribution to the total free energy change can be greater than the chemical contribution; if this is the case, then ΔF becomes positive and increases with increasing particle radius. Eventually, as the radius increases, the situation is reversed and the chemical (volume) term becomes dominant; then ΔF begins to decrease and eventually becomes negative. This situation is thought of in terms of a "critical radius". Corresponding to this size there is a maximum in ΔF, below which the small particles if formed are unstable and disappear so as to reduce ΔF. Particles of the new phase above the critical size, if formed, are stable and grow; they allow the reaction to proceed at a rate dictated by k and to an extent dictated by K and the nature of the environment. The actual value of the critical radius is obtained by differentiating equations such as (2-13) and obtaining the value of r when $d\Delta F/dr = 0$. In most cases it is desirable to have a small critical radius; this is promoted by having a very negative value of F_c (a high thermodynamic driving force).

In any real system in which new particles are forming as a

result of a reaction some particles will be formed with radii above and below the critical value. The energy necessary to form a particle with the critical radius is the value of ΔF (the maximum value) when r equals the critical value; this is termed the activation energy N for stable nucleus formation. The relative probability of a chance energy fluctuation occurring in the system which will produce a critical nucleus is equal to $\exp(-N/RT)$. The probability increases as N and ΔF decrease. If the probability of forming a stable nucleus is the same at every place in the system, then a state suitable for homogeneous nucleation exists. However, this is a very uncommon situation. In most cases there are numerous sites (such as the sides of the reaction chamber) where the energy necessary to form a stable nucleus is much lower than expected. This can result from a lower interfacial energy between the new particle and whatever is in contact with it; this acts to reduce F_s. Because N is lower at these places nucleation leading to stable growth of the new phase occurs preferentially on them and a state suitable for heterogeneous nucleation exists. The nucleation or formation of the new phase may take place within a solid, melt, solution or gas. Manipulation of the environment in such a way so as to promote heterogeneous nucleation is often done to promote a reaction and possibly to control the particle size of the reaction product as well as its structure.

There is yet another possible difficulty in making use of a reaction or decomposition. After the process has been initiated a reaction product may act to inhibit the physical contact between the reactants. Consider a particle of metallic compound reduced by a gas to produce the metal and a new gas. After some time an envelope of metal will form around the metallic compound. The metal may form as a continuous skin around the compound, a very porous mass or fractured and semi-adherent layer. The actual case will depend on the relative specific volumes of the metal and compound and on the precise nature of the reaction. Continued contact between the compound and the gas (necessary for the reaction) must now take place by one of the following:

(a) diffusion of gas through the metal to the compound, allowing the reaction to proceed at the compound-metal interface and subsequent removal of the reaction product by diffusion through the solid metal or by transport through pores and cracks in the metal;

(b) diffusion of the nonmetallic component of the compound, or the compound itself, through the metal to the metal-gas interface where the reaction may proceed and the reaction products allowed to escape;

(c) both (a) and (b);

(d) movement of the gas through pores or cracks in the metal to the metal-compound interface where the reaction proceeds and subsequent removal of the reaction products as in (a);

(e) movement of the nonmetallic component of the compound, or the compound itself, through the pores or cracks in the metal to the metal-gas interface as in (b);

(f) both (d) and (e).

Several factors are now apparent. The overall speed of the reaction is equal to the slowest step in the process; this can be the actual chemical reaction or the material transport which allows the reactants to come in contact. The metal particle resulting from the reduction of a compound particle can very likely correspond to a porous or spongy material. This is a consequence of factors (b) and (e) and of the possible metal rupturing due to product removal as in (a) and (d). Additionally, the metal particle may contain some residual amount of the original compound due to the common difficulties associated with material transport and complete reduction, especially near the center of the particles.

The best example of the decomposition of a solid by a chemical reaction is the reduction of metallic oxides by solid carbon or reducing gases. Oxide reduction is employed to produce iron, copper, tungsten and molybdenum powders. This method is often used because of the low cost of carbon, the availability of relatively cheap metallic oxides, the ease of controlling the original oxide particle size by mechanical means and consequently the final metal particle size, the ability to produce porous powders with certain characteristics, the relative flexibility with regard to the size of the operation and the adaptability of either batch or continuous techniques.

The disadvantages of the reduction type of process include the cost of pure reducing gases, the cost of large volumes of reducing gas, the fact that the purity of the final metal powder depends on the purity of the original oxides and is usually relatively low (especially when the original oxides are ores) unless special and costly procedures are employed, and the inability to produce alloy powders.

The production of iron powder is feasible for any process involving the manufacture of sponge iron. Sponge iron is simply the product resulting from the reduction of an iron oxide ore by suitable reducing agents to form a spongy mass of metallic iron. In one major iron powder production process magnetite concentrates, Fe_3O_4, are reduced by mixing with coke or anthracite breeze, with limestone added to absorb sulphur. The mix is heated in ceramic containers to about 2200°F by combustion of the CO resulting from the reduction and from an external source. After the operation is completed, the sponge iron cakes and residual coke and ash are separated. The sponge iron cake is then pulverized, the powder annealed in hydrogen to reduce the oxygen and carbon contents and to remove the cold work in the particles due to pulverizing, and finally sized. The complete process is given in the process flow diagram in Figure 2-1. This process is of the batch type, produces a very uniform product and is relatively slow.

Another process of iron powder production consists of the reduction of iron mill-scale by hydrogen in a continuous belt furnace. The mill-scale must be carefully selected to keep impurities low; it is ground, heated in an oxidizing atmosphere and then enters a reducing furnace. Reduction is carried out at about 1800°F in a hydrogen stream. The reduced powder is then milled and sized. The time of production is relatively fast, the carbon content of the powder low because of the hydrogen reduction, but the overall purity is dependent on the purity of the original mill-scale which can be both high and nonuniform. Because of the large quantities of hydrogen needed there must be an economical source available. This process is summarized in Figure 2-2.

In still another process steel scrap and pig iron are melted to produce a material with 3.2 to 3.4% carbon; the molten metal is then atomized with compressed air at about 100 psi. The resulting powder is collected in water, dried and sized. The unique aspect of this process is that during atomization oxidation takes place and CO is formed within the liquid metal, causing the atomized droplets to form hollow spheres. During the next step the powder is heated in closed containers at about 1740°F and if the $C:O_2$ ratio is 1:1.5, then reactions between Fe_3O_4, Fe_3C and CO take place producing a deoxidized, decarburized sintered cake. The

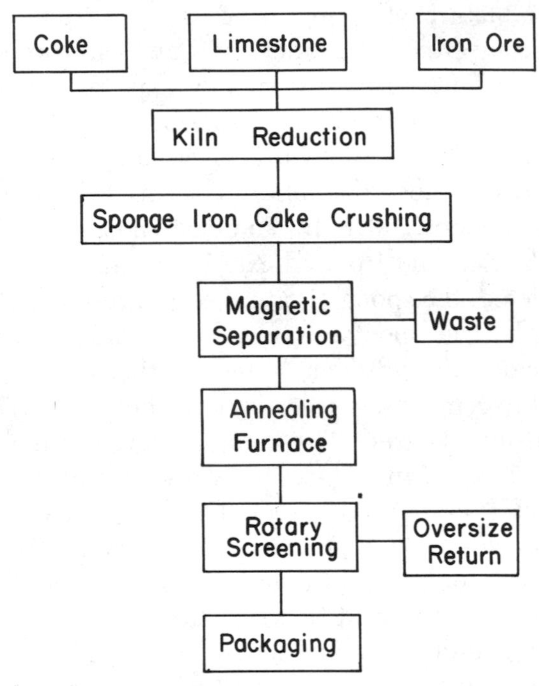

FIGURE 2-1.

A process used for the production of sponge iron powder based on reduction of an ore.

cake is then pulverized and the powder sized. Figure 2-3 summarizes this process. Although the process is somewhat complex, the production rate is relatively fast and the product has low levels of nonmetallic impurities.

A newer method of producing iron powder based on the fluidized bed concept makes use of high grade iron ore or mill-scale as the raw material and the availability of large quantities of hydrogen. The raw material is pulverized into powder. The iron oxide is reduced by preheated hydrogen in a fluid bed at a temperature less than 1000°F and at a pressure of 500 psi. The oxide is processed in a semi-batch manner in three fluidized beds. The high pressure and low temperature permit a high rate of reduction without allowing sintering of the particles to each other. The iron

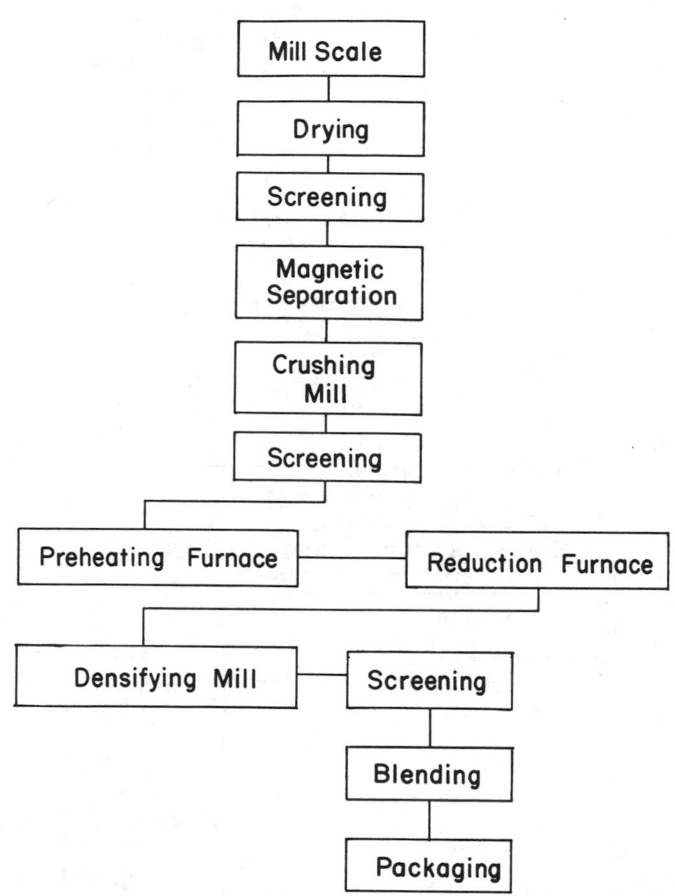

FIGURE 2-2.

A process used for the production of iron powder based on hydrogen reduction of mill-scale.

powder recovered from the reaction chamber is pyrophoric (to be discussed in a later section) and is conveyed and stored in nitrogen. To render the powder nonpyrophoric it is heated to 1500 to 1600°F in a nonoxidizing atmosphere and subsequently sized.

Typical chemical compositions of these four basic types of iron powder are given in Table 2-1. These values are given to indicate the general nature of the typical low price iron powder, made by

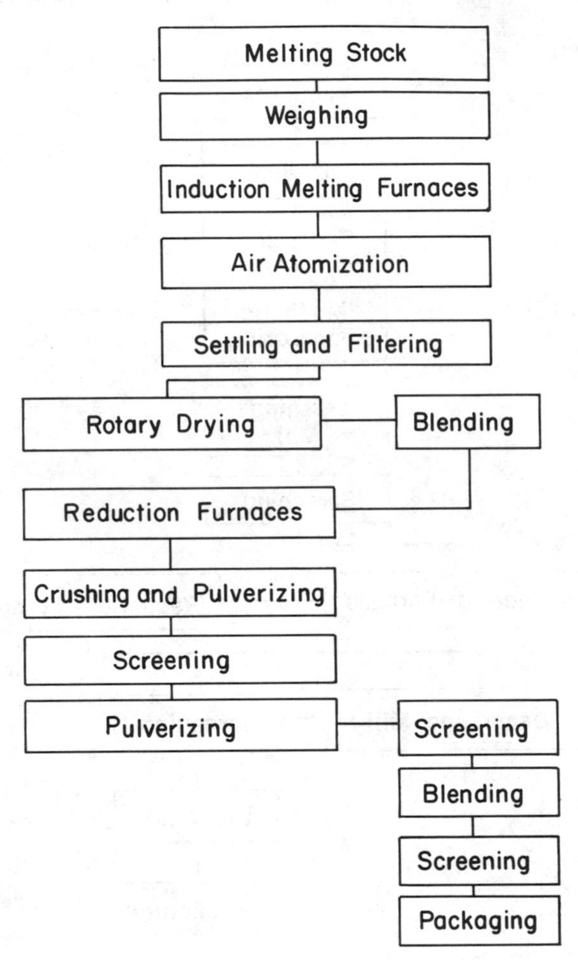

FIGURE 2-3.
The process used to manufacture atomized/reduced iron powder.

reduction techniques, used in great quantities. The actual chemical analysis for any particular lot may differ significantly due to differences in the raw material and variations in the process. All powder producers can manufacture higher purity powders at a

TABLE 2-1. Typical Chemical Compositions of Iron Powders Produced by Chemical Reduction Techniques

	Sponge	Hydrogen Reduced	Atomized/ Reduced	Fluidized Bed
Total iron	98.8 %	98.0 %	98.7 %	98.8 %
Hydrogen loss	.30	.95	.53	.63
Carbon	.04	.02	.06	.06
Phosphorus	.010	.012	.011	.013
Sulphur	.007	.005	.022	.021
Manganese	—	.55	.15	.43
Acid Insoluble	—	.33	.12	—
Silica	.10	—	—	.20
Silicon	—	—	.04	—

higher cost, by making use of additional annealing treatments, and these are also readily available. Special properties are also obtained by heat treatments of the powder, sieving to produce desired size distributions, in some cases by alloying, and by blending the iron powder with various types of other powders to produce premixes. Although not a great deal of detail has been given about these processes, the exact nature (such as gas composition and temperature) of any of these techniques is substantially based on the thermodynamic and kinetic considerations discussed previously. More will be said about the chemical composition and structure of these powders in later sections. Lastly it should also be noted that other variations of the reduction type of process, such as using compounds other than oxides, are quite feasible for iron powder production.

Copper and Other Powders Copper powder is made by the reduction of copper oxide by flowing cracked natural gas at 1110 to 1240°F in a continuous furnace arrangement. The original copper oxide is usually manufactured by melting and air atomizing ingot copper, followed by grinding and sizing. The reduced and sintered cake is ground and sieved. This is not the most widely use method to produce copper powder.

Tungsten powder is made by the reduction of tungsten oxide or ammonium paratungstate with hydrogen or cracked ammonia in tube furnaces on a batch basis. Most tungsten powder is produced in the 1 to 7 microns range by using fine oxide particles, reduction at about 930°F, a high gas velocity and short times. Another development consists of preparing the original raw materials by freeze drying of the appropriate solution of the organic or inorganic metal salts and compounds. Tungsten and tungsten alloy powders have been prepared in this manner.

Metallic carbides are made by several chemical reaction techniques. Tungsten carbide is made by heating tungsten and carbon powders together at temperatures between 2640 and 2910°F, and titanium carbide is made by heating TiO_2 and carbon black together at temperatures up to 3540°F in vacuum.

Thermit reactions, or the reduction of metallic oxides by exothermic reactions (heat generated) using metallic reducing agents, are used to prepare metals which are not reducible economically by carbon or by gases. This method presents several problems: (a) because high temperatures are needed the desired metal will melt unless a phase such as a slag is present which can hold the particles in suspension; (b) it is difficult to maintain intimate contact between the reactants; (c) an excess of the reducing agent is usually required and this, together with the slag, reduces the purity of the product; (d) special precautions and equipment are necessary because of the high temperatures and risk of explosions. Some examples of the application of this method include: production of Cr by reduction of Cr_2O_3 with Mg, production of Th by reduction of ThO_2 with Ca, production of U by reduction of UO_2 with Ca or Mg.

Another development has been the selective reduction of oxides by hydrogen. For example, if it is desired to produce a dispersion strengthened alloy containing fine particles of ThO_2 in a Ni-Mo alloy matrix, then examination of thermodynamic data would indicate that particles of NiO and MoO_2, in the presence of ThO_2 particles, can be reduced by hydrogen below 1832°F without affecting the ThO_2. In this way a good distribution of fine particles of a dispersoid within a metal matrix can be prepared. Variations of this method have been successfully employed to produce ceramic particles, such as ZrB, ZrC, Al_2O_3, $ThO_2$and MgO, with metallic coatings such as W and Mo. Complex particles, each containing a dispersion of a fine oxide have been made by dissolving a metal and a metal salt in a suitable solvent, flash drying the solution, calcining the solid to insure solvent removal, grinding the solid to fine powder, reducing the solid with cracked ammonia, and grinding the somewhat agglomerated mass. For example, to produce a Ni-Cr-ThO_2 particle the initial materials would be Ni metal, chromic acid and thorium nitrate. Although oxides of Ni and Cr are formed, they are preferentially reduced and only ThO_2 remains in the final powder. Very complex materials with extremely small dispersed particles have been prepared by this method.

Thermal Decompositions The simplest type of decomposition is the condensation of a metal from its vapor. The basic principle is that metal atoms will evaporate from a surface at an elevated temperature until a critical equilibrium pressure of metal vapor is reached in the space above the surface. This critical pressure is only a function of the temperature and is independent of the pressure of any other vapor in the system. By condensing the metal vapor the process is made to continue. The rate of evaporation increases with increasing metal vapor pressure, decreasing amounts of other gases or vapors which cause interatomic collisions, increasing concentration between the metal surface and the condensed surface (the latter is kept at a lower temperature), and decreasing distance between the evaporating and condensing surfaces. Usually the necessary conditions can only be obtained in a relatively high vacuum where the rate of condensation (or distillation) is given by

$$G = 0.05833(p)(M/T)^{1/2} \tag{2-14}$$

where G = weight of material deposited in gm/cm²/sec
p = metal vapor pressure
T = absolute temperature
M = molecular weight of the metal

The most severe practical problem is to obtain the condensate in the form of powder. This is promoted by having sites, such as impurities, where nucleation is favored and by inhibiting the coalescence of the nuclei, perhaps by mechanical means. Both Zn and Cd conventional type powders are produced by this technique. Extremely small particles, less than 500 angstroms in diameter, are now produced by this method. Both pure metals and intermetallic compounds (using two sources of metal) are produced; the individual particles are spherical but are usually agglomerated due to the high adhesive forces present for such a high surface-to-volume ratio type of material.

Both iron and nickel powders are produced by decomposition of the respective carbonyls. The process consists of preparing the carbonyls, $Fe(CO)_5$ and $Ni(CO)_4$, by passing CO at high pressure over the heated metallic material, followed by condensing to a liquid and storage under pressure. $Fe(CO)_5$ boils at 217°F and $Ni(CO)_4$ at 109°F at atmospheric pressure. Powder is produced by boiling the carbonyls in heated vessels at atmospheric pressure under conditions which allow the vapors to decompose within the heated space and not on the sides of the container. The powder is collected and sieved, and may be milled and annealed in hydrogen. A detailed summary of the production of nickel carbonyl powder is given in Figure 2-4. The chemical purity of the powders can be very high (over 99.5%) with the principal impurities being carbon, nitrogen and oxygen. Particle size and shape can be controlled very closely. Iron carbonyl powder is usually spherical in shape and very fine (less than 10 microns), while the nickel powder is usually quite irregular and porous and fine.

More complex carbonyls such as the carbonyl halides can also be decomposed. For example, $Pt(CO)_2Cl_2$ can produce platinum powder. The hydrides of several metals also thermally decompose. Similarly, organometallic compounds have been used to deposit Cu, Fe, Ni, Co, Cr and Pt. Pyrolytic graphite is produced by the decomposition of organic compounds and can be used to coat other materials.

Precipitation from a Liquid Copper powder is produced by displacement by the more reactive iron from a copper-bearing solution on to iron. Scrap iron or steel, or sometimes even iron powder, is used and a variety of salt solutions are possible, but sulphates are quite common. The acidity of the solution is important in de-

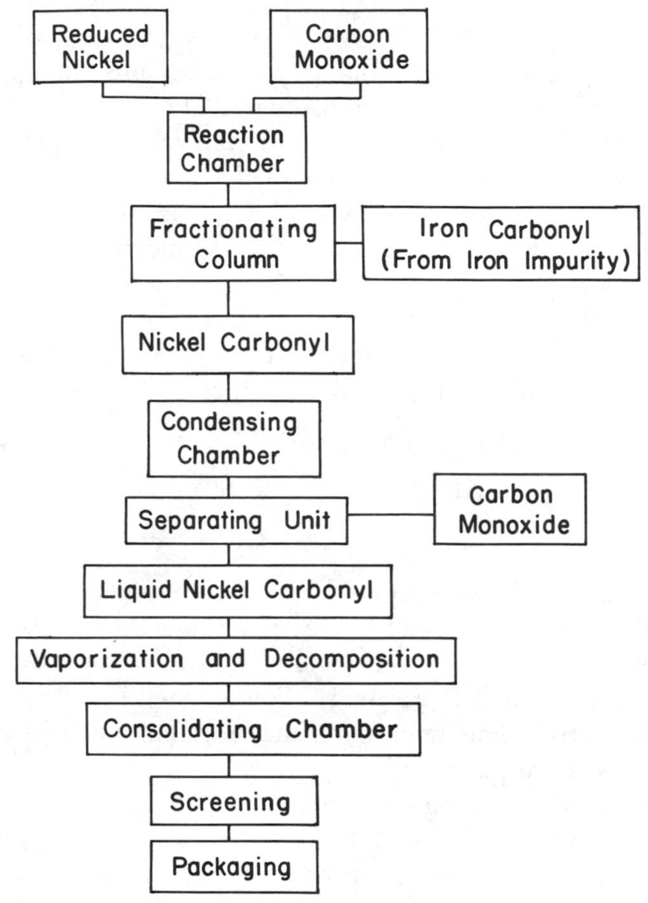

FIGURE 2-4.

A process used for the production of carbonyl nickel powder.

termining the rate and quality of the deposit. Quite pure and fine powders are produced. The raw material may be a copper ore.

A number of metals are produced by precipitation from an aqueous solution using hydrogen or other gases. The basic concept is that a metallic ion (an electrically charged atom), such as Ni, Co and Cu, in the solution reacts with a gas such as hydrogen by the following type of reaction

$$M^{++} + H_2 \rightarrow M^{\circ} + 2H^{+} \qquad (2\text{-}15)$$

with an equilibrium constant given by

$$K = [H^+]^2/[M^{++}]p_{H_2} \tag{2-16}$$

where the brackets denote molar concentrations and p is the pressure of the hydrogen in atmospheres. The extent of the reaction is determined by the appropriate ΔF value (dependent on temperature) and the manipulation of the components within the system. There are many other complex factors which also determine the feasibility of such a process; these include chemical and kinetic factors pertaining to other species in the system and the actual material transport mechanisms operating.

Copper powder may be produced from $CuSO_4$ solutions by reduction with H_2 by the following sequence

$$Cu^{++} + H_2 \rightarrow CuH^+ + H^+ \tag{2-17a}$$

$$CuH^+ + Cu^{++} \rightarrow 2Cu^+ + H^+ \tag{2-17b}$$

$$2Cu^+ \rightarrow Cu^o + Cu^{++} \tag{2-17c}$$

The first step is the slowest and controls the overall rate of the reaction. These reactions indicate that the reduction to copper powder is favored by a low H^+ concentration, a high Cu^{++} concentration and a high H_2 pressure. Powders with high purity and good size distributions have been made. A number of variations of the process are possible.

Nickel powders are now produced in large quantities directly from their ore by this method of precipitation. Leaching and purification of the ore results in a sulphate solution which is then put in a reduction autoclave with agitators. Nickel powder from processing of the previous batch of solution is put into suspension and hydrogen at about 200 psi is injected into the solution. The nickel in solution precipitates on to the nickel particles in suspension. After a relatively short time the agitators are stopped and the nickel powder allowed to settle at the bottom of the autoclave. The depleted solution is drawn off and another batch introduced, and the cycle repeated. When the particles become relatively coarse, after about 40 cycles, the powder is removed and sized. The powder has a purity of at least 99.8% with the major impurities being Co, Fe and S due to their presence in the original ore. The powder can be produced in a variety of size distributions and is quite uniform. Similar techniques have been developed for Co, and the selective reduction of Ni and Co when both are present in a solution in significant quantities.

One of the most interesting developments has resulted from the successful use of these precipitation techniques. Because they require seed particles to act as nucleation sites for the precipitating metal, it is relatively simple to make composite powders; Fe, Cu, Cr, Al, graphite, TiB_2, Al_2O_3, Cr_2O_3, ThO_2, WC and many other materials have been coated with nickel. The core material can be less than one to over 100 microns in diameter. In this way complex dispersion strengthened materials may be easily fabricated directly from the composite powders with no bonding or mixing problems. Because the use of sulphate solutions has sometimes resulted in high levels of sulphur in the final product, carbonate systems have been developed. Various organic and inorganic addition agents may also be added to the solutions to control particle size and shape.

Metal powders are also produced by precipitation from fused salts. The method is useful for rather reactive metals. To produce Zr powder the salt $ZrCl_4$ is mixed with an equal amount of KCl, in which it is soluble, and some magnesium. When heated to 1380°F the magnesium replaces the zirconium, and particles of the latter settle to the bottom of the chamber. In a different method $ZrCl_4$ vapor is passed through a salt bath of NaCl and $MgCl_2$. Both thorium and beryllium powders have been produced by similar techniques. Increasing use is being made of inorganic compounds, a particularly good example is boron nitride. This can be made by the reduction of molten B_2O_3 by ammonia. Various intermetallic compounds have been produced in powder form by the reaction of two amalgams.

Precipitation from a Gas Reactive metals such as Zr, Ti, Hf and V can be produced by this technique. A basic problem is that the raw materials must be free of certain elements that easily contaminate the given metal; for example, oxygen in the case of Ti, Zr and Hf. An additional problem is the high chemical reactivity of the freshly produced powders of these metals. The basic principle employed is the reduction of the gaseous anhydrous chlorides of such reactive metals by reducing agents such as Na and

Mg. Metallic sponge materials are produced which are then pulverized. Mo, W and refractory alloy powders have been prepared by the reduction of their gaseous hexafluorides and oxides with hydrogen. Extremely fine powders can be produced by these methods. Spherical tungsten particles, with extremely fine grains, have been used to obtain very good properties and are made by reduction of tungsten hexafluoride.

Similarly, a metal bearing vapor can be placed in contact with a different material in the form of powder. The base material may displace the metal from the vapor and the latter thereupon precipitates upon the powder. The material from the powder is swept away in the gas stream. Using this method ferrous materials can be coated with Cr, Al, B, Ti, Cb, Mn and many other materials; Mo can be coated with Cr, Si and B; graphite may be coated with Ti, Zr, Cb and Ta. Because diffusion takes place at the high temperatures employed, the surface layers of the particle will be very rich in the deposited metal and there will be a concentration gradient of this element in the particle beneath the surface.

Hydrogen may be used to reduce metal halide vapors in the presence of a different type of powder whereby the reduced metal is deposited on the powder particles. By using more than one metal halide vapor simultaneously, metal alloys may be deposited on the particles. Either in this method or the previous one, deposition on graphite at sufficiently high temperatures may result in the formation of carbide powders.

Atomization of Liquid Metals Virtually any material that can be melted can be made into powder by disintegration of the liquid. Aside from chemical reactivity, which may necessitate special atmospheres or materials, the process is independent of the normal physical and mechanical properties associated with the solid material. The method is being widely adopted, especially because of the relative ease of making high purity metals and prealloyed powders directly from the melt. The basic procedure most often employed is to force a liquid through an orifice, possibly at the bottom of a crucible, and impinge a gas or liquid stream on the emerging melt. A great deal depends on the exact design of the orifice. It may induce turbulence in the melt which atomizes the material directly and allows the impinging gas or liquid to reduce the size of the particles still further.

The theoretical aspects of this technique must take into consideration the velocity, v, of the emerging liquid and this is given by

$$v = c[2g(p_1 - p_2)/d]^{1/2} \tag{2-18}$$

where c = a constant which depends on the exact configuration of the orifice
g = the gravitational acceleration
p_1 = the injection pressure of the liquid
p_2 = the pressure of the atmosphere into which the liquid emerges
d = the density of the liquid

The emerging liquid may atomize at some distance from the orifice, depending on the disturbances within the jet. However, if the emergent velocity is sufficiently high, then the jet may atomize at the orifice. It has been suggested that the critical velocity at which this happens depends on the Reynolds number R which is given by

$$R = dvD/n \tag{2-19}$$

where d = the liquid density
v = the velocity
D = the jet diameter
n = the absolute viscosity of the liquid.

It would be expected that factors such as D and n would determine the nature of the process. Atomization at the orifice would occur above a critical R value, and the corresponding velocity would increase with increasing viscosity and decreasing density. The ease of disintegration of the liquid will also decrease with increasing surface tension of the liquid.

Because the degree of atomization will increase as the relative velocity between the liquid and the atmosphere increases, it is more efficient to use relatively low jet velocities and an atmosphere with a high velocity. This is why commercial techniques involve the use of external gas or liquid jets which impinge on the melt. The exact nature of the atomization with regard to the particle size and shape will depend on the precise nature of the impinging jet and on the geometrical configuration of the apparatus. The liquid may be atomized from above, below, horizontally or a combination of these. The kind of gas or liquid used to disintegrate the melt will depend on the nature of the melt and the necessity to avoid chemical contamination. The design of the orifice and impinging jet must also include a consideration of the coalescence of the droplets which are formed. It may also be necessary to provide arrangements for suitable heating of the melt to avoid premature solidification; this may involve heating the orifice or the atmosphere. On the other hand, the droplets or particles must be cooled relatively fast after the optimum atomization in order to avoid extreme particle coalescence; this is accomplished by using the correct type of gas or liquid jet and usually by allowing the newly formed particles to fall directly into a water bath.

The time of cooling which precedes freezing is one of the critical factors determining the shape of the particles. Spherical powders are promoted by the use of long cooling times which allow the surface tension forces to minimize the surface area, high temperatures of the melt and the use of gases to distintegrate the melt. Water jets promote fast cooling and the production of irregular shaped particles. The exact composition of the melt determines the surface tension and, hence, the tendency to form spherical or irregular type particles. Similarly, the composition of the atmosphere and impinging jet also influence the surface, or more correctly the interfacial, energy of the melt. Consequently, through manipulation of the chemistry of the melt and the impinging jet the surface energy or tension can be varied; in general it is relatively easy to produce spherical powders and almost all metals and alloys are commercially available in this form. However, as will be discussed in later sections, spherical powders do not have the desired characteristics for most types of commercial applications.

Both nonferrous, including aluminum, copper, lead and tin, and iron powders of relatively high purity are being made by atomization techniques. The nonferrous types usually have a very rounded particle shape while the iron powders are quite irregular in nature.

A typical atomization process, used to produce a solid type of iron powder, is summarized in Figure 2-5. Another method used to

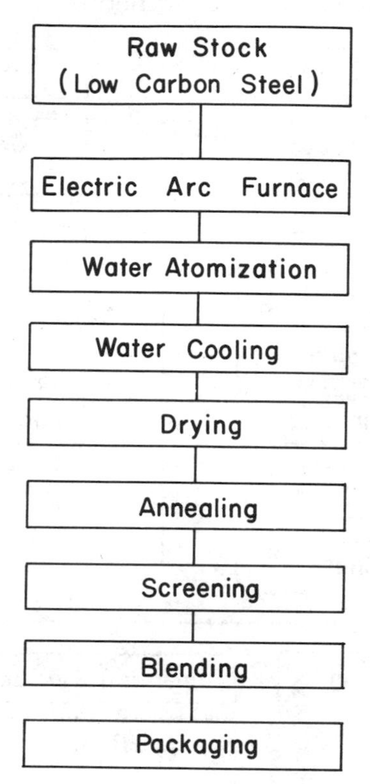

FIGURE 2-5.
An atomization process used to produce a solid type of iron powder.

produce a porous, sponge iron type of powder is reviewed in Figure 2-6. Both of these processes make use of water atomization. In some processes the particle size distribution as produced from the atomization is suited for P/M parts manufacture. In others there is a broader distribution and under-size and/or over-size fractions must be remelted. Although very high purities are possible with atomization, this is not necessarily the case. Annealing of powders to improve purity is often a part of the process. Typical chemical compositions of some atomized iron powders are given in Table 2-2.

Virtually any type of ferrous and nonferrous alloy can be made in the form of powder by atomization techniques. Various effects have been observed for atomization of alloy melts. The most important are the changes in microstructure within individual par-

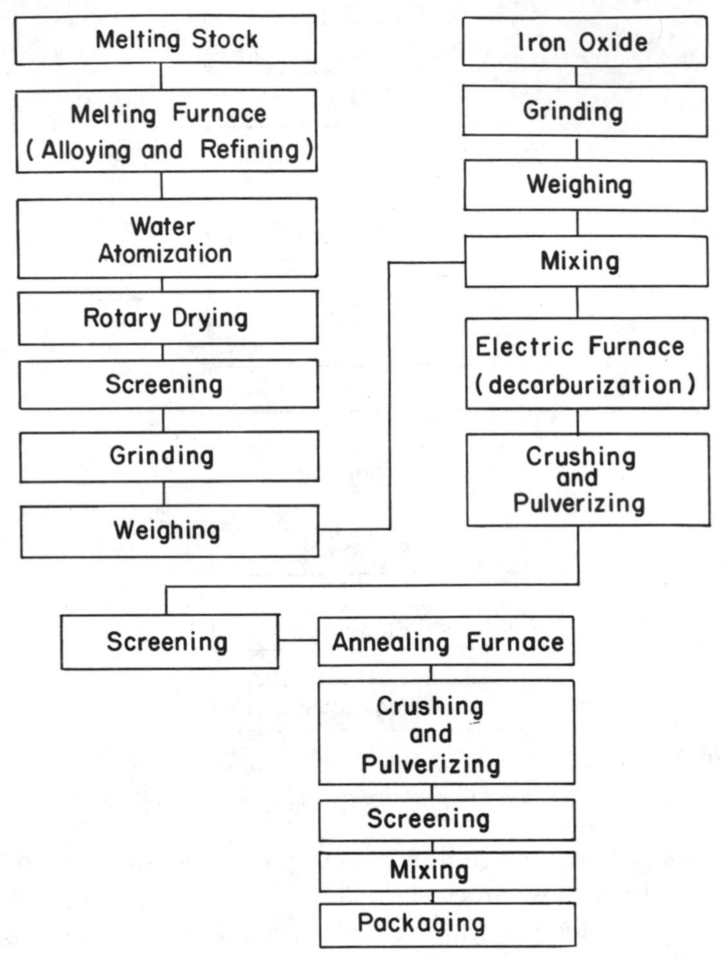

FIGURE 2-6.
An atomization process used to produce a sponge iron powder.

ticles. The rapid rates of cooling promote those features that are normally associated with very rapid solidification of a molten alloy. Segregation of alloying elements and the retention of elevated temperature phases, or the production of martensitic phases are all possible. Because the cooling rate will increase with decreasing

TABLE 2-2. Typical Compositions of Some Atomized Iron Powders

	Sponge	Annealed Sponge	Annealed Solid
Total iron	98.7 %	99.2 %	99.7 %
Hydrogen loss	.80	.45	.12
Carbon	.06	.05	.01
Phosphorus	.03	.03	.005
Sulphur	.04	.04	.01
Manganese	.15	.15	.15
Silicon	.25	.10	.03

particle size, one may expect to observe different structures in differently sized particles.

A number of variations of the atomization techniques have been developed. In one a rotating electrode is melted and the powder formed due to the centrifugal action. Or a liquid stream may impinge on to a rotating, water cooled disc to produce a powder. Plasma arcs have been used to directly melt a material and simultaneously disintegrate it or, by using powdered materials, the arc can be used to produce spherical powders.

Electrolytic Deposition A number of metals can be made to precipitate on the cathode of an electrolytic cell as a sponge, powder or in a form which can be mechanically disintegrated rather easily. Copper, beryllium and iron powders are made in considerable quantities by this technique. In general the method yields a high purity metal with excellent properties for conventional powder metallurgy processing. However this approach involves the control and manipulation of many variables and in some cases is significantly more costly than other techniques. For example, electrolytic iron powder is more costly than reduced or atomized powders with the same characteristics, while electrolytic copper powder is quite competitive with reduced and precipitated types.

A complete analysis of the electrolytic process is beyond the scope of this text, especially in view of the limited number of metals and small quantities of material produced, in comparison to other methods. It should be clear that the production of a deposit of a spongy or powdery nature may require completely different conditions than more common techniques such as electroplating for protective or decorative purposes. The factors which appear to promote a powdery deposit are: high current densities, weak metal concentrations, additions of colloids and acids, low temperatures, high viscosities, avoidance of agitation and suppression of convection. However, it may be very difficult to produce a high purity powdery deposit at relatively fast rates economically. Consequently, in many cases the deposit is a solid and must be pulverized; this is the case for iron. Electrolytic deposits, powders or solids, are usually very reactive and brittle. For both these reasons the material may be given a special annealing treatment. Particles formed during electrolysis usually have a characteristic dendritic (fir tree like) shape; however, this could be changed substantially due to subsequent processing.

Mechanical Processing of Solid Materials Although not used extensively as a primary method for the production of common ferrous and nonferrous metal powders, the technique of using mechanical means to produce a powder often is the only feasible and economic primary method. The term primary is an important distinction. In many of the previously discussed methods a spongy or semi-solid material may be produced and mechanical disintegration (or comminution) is used as a secondary step to produce the final powder product. The mechanical approach has been used as the primary process for the following cases: (a) materials which are relatively easy to fracture such as some pure metals, antimony and bismuth for example, relatively hard and brittle metal alloys, and ceramics; (b) reactive materials such as beryllium and metal hydrides which must be prepared in the absence of oxygen; (c) common metals such as aluminum and iron which are desired in the form of flake powder (in some cases the mechanical treatment would be a secondary operation).

For cases (a) and (b) the material should be neither too hard nor too ductile. The primary objective is to fracture the material into smaller and smaller pieces. A very hard material usually has a high fracture stress and would require too much mechanical energy to make this method effective and economical. If a material is ductile, then the energy is absorbed by the plastic deformation of the material and it will undergo more change in shape than actual fragmentation. Naturally for case (c) the latter factor is used to advantage in producing a flake powder.

Considering cases (a) and (b) the basic process in mechanical treatments is the nucleation and propagation of cracks in the original material. To promote mechanical disintegration the fracture stress should be lowered or, in other words, cracks should be allowed to form and grow at a low stress. This depends to a great extent on the basic chemical bonding and crystal structure of the material. Strong chemical bonding is indicated by a high elastic modulus and causes higher stresses to be required for fracture. Complex crystal structures with few slip systems restrict dislocation motion and help to promote direct fracture rather than plastic deformation. The actual fracture process involves the formation of new surfaces and, hence, energy must be supplied to create these surfaces and the concomitant increase in total surface energy. Consequently, lowering the specific surface energy of the material tends to make crack growth easier. Any structural features that tend to foster crack propagation are desirable; that is, large grain sizes and the absence of dispersed particles would usually be favorable to the fracture process.

Such considerations make it apparent that it may not be feasible to use mechanical means to produce conventional powders from bulk solids of the common ferrous and nonferrous metals and alloys. It is used for some of the more brittle alloys and exotic metals such as cast irons and beryllium, with intrinsic brittleness and not very high fracture strengths. Many ceramic materials can be successfully produced in powder form because of their intrinsic lack of ductility and their ability to cleave rather easily. The surface energy of many of these materials can be effectively lowered by chemical agents, and it is common to find various liquids used in mechanical disintegration operations. Additionally, the temperature of the material may be lowered in order to lessen the degree of plastic deformation and promote fracture.

There are a number of techniques which are used to produce powders commercially. Unfortunately all of these result in the material being under compressive or shear stresses rather than tensile stresses which would facilitate fracture. The basic principle employed is to cause an impact between the material to be distintegrated and a hard body. Either one or both may be moving before impact occurs. The greater the relative velocity and the mass of the external body (if it is in motion), the higher the stresses induced in the material and the greater the extent of fracturing.

A common method is the use of a ball mill consisting of a rotating drum in which is placed the material to be ground, usually available in a coarse divided form, with hard wear resistant balls. The critical factor is the speed of the drum's rotation. A very high speed will cause the material and balls to be pressed against the walls of the drum, because of the centrifugal forces, and prohibit relative motion between the material and the balls. Too low a speed will result in an insignificant amount of movement in the lower part of the drum. The optimum speed corresponds to a situation in which some amount of balls and material is lifted up to the top part of the drum and falls down on the remaining material. A disadvantage of this technique is the potential contamination from the balls and mill walls. The technique is used extensively for carbide-metal mixtures and for cermet materials to accomplish blending and particle size reduction.

Pure powders can be produced in vortex mills in which particles of the material to be ground are fractured by mutual contact or collision. Such mills consist of two or more very rapidly rotating propellers within a relatively small mill casing and gas flow systems which remove a desired size fraction of particles. Other variations include the rapid propulsion of the material to be pulverized against a hard object, and hammer, disc and roll mills.

Metal powders prepared by mechanical means may be annealed to remove the effects of cold work. Such powders and others produced by chemical, atomization or electrolytic means which are annealed for some reason must usually be given a moderate mechanical treatment in a crusher or hammer mill to separate the loosely sintered mass. No major changes in size or cold work are normally caused by such treatments.

It should also be noted that various ferrous and nonferrous alloys can be heat treated to produce a brittle material. This usually comes about because of carbide precipitation at grain boundaries. Powder may be produced by chemical attack followed or accompanied by mechanical treatments. Some stainless steels and nickel base alloys have been produced in powder form by such techniques.

Flake powders are produced by flattening roughly equiaxed particles produced by another method. These techniques may employ ball, hammer or roll mills. When treating the original powder lubricants are added to prevent particles from welding or sticking to each other. Larger flake powders, called "flitters", are made by disintegrating metal foil. Materials which can be made into flake powders must have a high degree of malleability; that is, the ability to laterally deform (spread out) under compressive stresses. Aluminum, copper, bronze, silver, gold, iron and stainless steel flake powders are commercially available. A summary of a process used to manufacture aluminum flake powder is presented in Figure 2-7.

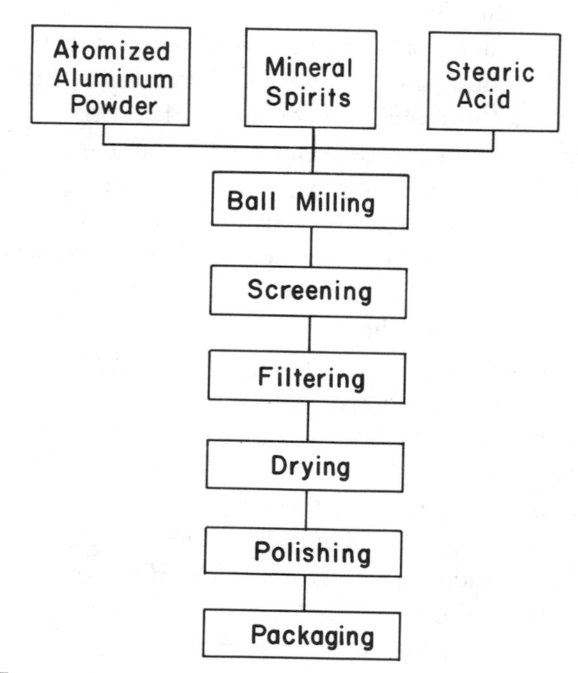

FIGURE 2-7.

A process used to produce aluminum flake powder.

2.3 CHEMICAL COMPOSITION AND STRUCTURE

Chemical analyses are usually applied to powders using normal analytical procedures. The levels of impurity elements can be very significant to both the processing and properties of the final product and should be assessed. It is important to know whether such elements are present in their elemental form or whether they are present in the form of a chemical compound. For example, as shown in Table 2-1 iron powders produced by reduction of an oxide usually contain silicon in the form of silica; however, it may not be reported as such in a chemical analysis. Other ceramic, and rather inert compounds may exist; these may be reported in terms of an acid insoluble figure. Obviously, the effect of impurity elements on the hardness of the particles and the degree of chemical reactivity during sintering will differ widely, depending on the actual form they are in.

A more subtle factor is the form of the base metal. Most analyses will report the total amount of the element present. However, some portion of the metal may be in the form of an oxide. This is particularly true for powders made by chemical reduction techniques such as the iron powders produced from iron oxide. Additionally, there is likely to be some oxides of other elements as well as some dissolved oxygen in the metal. To help clarify the situation it is common practice to report a *hydrogen loss* value for a powder. This is a very important characteristic of a powder and represents the weight loss of a powder when exposed to hydrogen at an elevated temperature. This weight loss is then an indication of the amount of oxygen in the powder. However, it can be in error due to incomplete reduction of oxides, and some oxides may not be reduced at all. In general it is desirable for both processing and the attainment of optimum final properties to have a low oxygen content. The annealing of powders referred to earlier is an effective way to reduce oxygen contents; this is readily seen by the data in Table 2-2 on the two types of atomized sponge powders for which the hydrogen loss value was almost halved by the annealing treatment.

It should be noted that there are well defined procedures for obtaining hydrogen loss and acid insoluble values, as well as a number of other properties to be discussed later in this chapter. Such procedures are given in standards of the Metal Powder Industries Federation (MPIF) and the American Society for Testing and Materials (ASTM).

It is possible to assess the presence of oxides in powder particles by metallographic examination of mounted, polished and etched particles. In Figure 2-8(a) iron oxide is readily seen along the grain boundaries within the iron particle. In reduced powders it is very common to observe small oxide inclusions near the center of a particle resulting from the incomplete reduction of the original oxide.

In general it is more difficult to produce a very pure metal powder from natural ores using non-fusion techniques because of the stability of various oxides and other ceramic phases. Methods which employ scrap materials as their raw material are prone to produce greater variation in impurity contents due to the variation of the composition of the original scrap. Powders produced by atomization techniques may have a significant oxide coating, but can be easily produced with very low impurity levels.

Many materials, both metallic and nonmetallic, absorb significant quantities of gases and water vapor from the atmosphere and this may not be indicated by chemical analyses that are performed on powders freshly produced. Such adsorption can lead to the formation of surface oxides on metals which may interfere with compaction and sintering, and possibly remain in the sintered material. Some metals such as aluminum and copper are particularly susceptible to this surface oxidation at room temperature. The amount of such surface contamination increases with decreasing particle size, because of the increase in surface-to-volume ratio, and with increasing chemical activity of the surface. The latter increases with increasing imperfection density (vacancies and dislocations), increasing purity or cleanness of the surface, and increasing angularity of the surface.

The grain structure of crystalline powders can have an extremely powerful influence on the behavior during compaction and sintering and on the properties of the final product. Many of

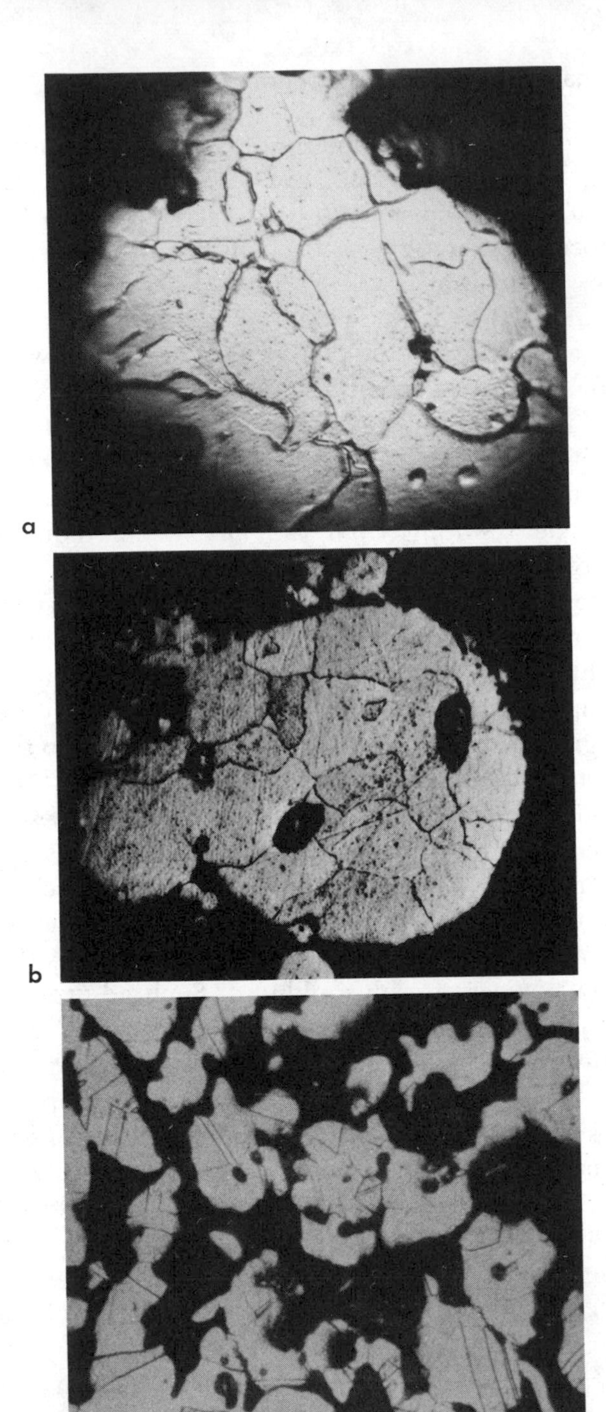
a
b
c

the most unique and important developments in powder production consist of radical changes in particle grain structure. The tendency has been to produce polycrystalline particles with a very small grain size. The two most important effects appear to be the improvement in mechanical properties, both in magnitude and directionality, in the sintered material due to a fine grain size, and the improved sintering characteristics with regard to kinetics and uniformity of dimensional changes. Although one might first expect such particles to present difficulties during compaction due to the increased strength of polycrystalline materials, this effect is probably offset by the improved ductility of the majority of the particles resulting from a greater number of grains (slip systems) being more favorably oriented with respect to the complex stress conditions in the compact. It should be realized that the grain structures of such powders are usually rather stable as compared to fine grain structures produced by plastic deformation (cold work) in wrought materials. The major driving force for recrystallization, reduction in the dislocation density, is not present in the powdered materials. They are analogous to stable grain structures in cast matetrials. Consequently, although there can be significant grain growth during sintering, the grain size in sintered materials tends to be very small and quite analogous to the original grain size in the powder. One may also note that the grain size can be dependent on the particle size. Usually the grain size decreases with decreasing particle size. This is related to the precise conditions during powder manufacture such as the more rapid cooling rates for small particles during atomization.

Photomicrographs illustrating the grain structures in several types of ferrous powders are given in Figure 2-8. It can be seen how small the grain size can be. For most powders the grain structure is roughly equiaxed in nature. An unusual grain structure exists in carbonyl iron powder as shown in Figure 2-9. It is de-

---

FIGURE 2-8.

Photomicrographs of ferrous powder particles: (a) water atomized iron (500 ×); (b) atomized/reduced iron (500 ×); (c) atomized (annealed) 316 stainless steel (250 ×).

scribed as "onion skin"; there is a series of concentric circular regions in which the grain size is extremely small.

A distinctive feature of many powders is the presence of porosity within each particle. This is quite prevalent in powders

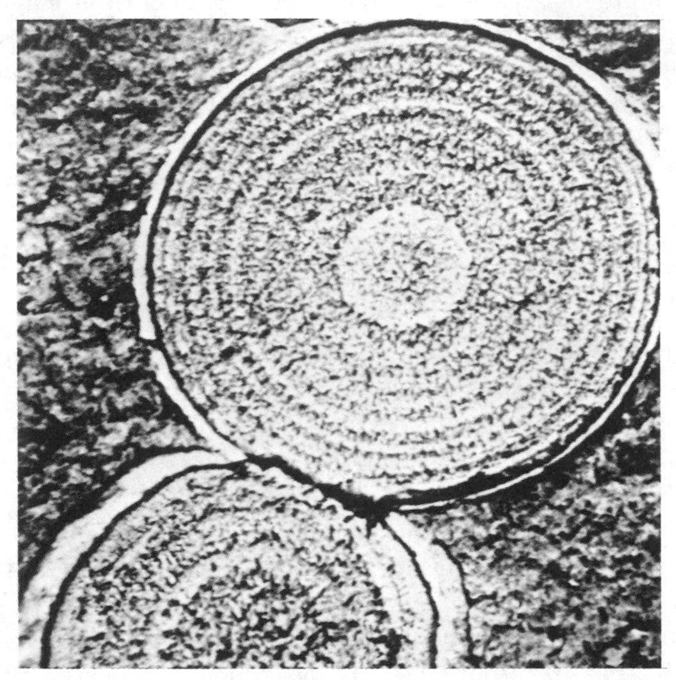

FIGURE 2-9.

Electron micrograph of carbonyl iron powder particles indicating extremely fine "onion skin" grain structure (about 10,000 ×). (from L. Delisle, Trans. AIME, vol. 185, pp. 228–232, 1949)

produced by chemical reduction techniques as discussed previously. However, atomized powders may have very significant amounts of porosity also; this can be seen in the photomicrographs of Figure 2-8. Some atomized powders, electrolytic and carbonyl type powders have virtually no porosity. This structural characteristic influences several other factors to be subsequently discussed, including the behavior of the powder during compaction and sintering, and its presence should always be known. The term *sponge* is often used to describe highly porous powders. The actual gas present in such porosity can be of great significance.

There is a general tendency for the particle porosity to increase with decreasing particle size; some data on this effect are given in Table 2-3. In this table as in many other places the concept of

TABLE 2-3. Dependence of Particle Density on Particle Size for Some Iron Powders

Type of Powder	Particle Density (gm/cc)
Electrolytic	
coarse	7.85–7.87
fine	7.70–7.85
Reduced	
coarse	7.50–7.60
fine	7.30–7.40
Carbonyl	7.85–7.87

(from H. H. Hausner, "Basic Characteristics of Metal Powders," in Handbook of Metal Powders, edited by A. R. Poster, Reinhold, New York, 1966)

porosity is given in terms of a density (in gm/cc) value; in Appendix I a tabulation of densities and percent theoretical values (100 minus the percent theoretical density value is the volume percent of porosity) for iron is given and can prove very useful.

Alloy powders may contain various phases depending on their exact composition, the appropriate phase diagram, their thermal history and the method of powder manufacture used. As noted in the previous section complex powders consisting of a dispersion of one phase in another or a coating of one phase on another may be prepared by various techniques. Photomicrographs illustrating the structure of the coated type of powder are given in Figure 2-10; these were made by a precipitation technique and it can be seen that both spherical and irregular shaped particles can be produced. Other multiphase structures may result from natural alloying such as those in steels, cast irons and superalloys. And there may be dispersions of impurity compounds such as oxide inclusions. For such multiphase particles there are two basic considerations. The effect of such a structure on compaction is usually undesirable because the material is stronger than a single phase one and requires greater pressures for densification. Some powders may be heat treated to produce a single phase structure

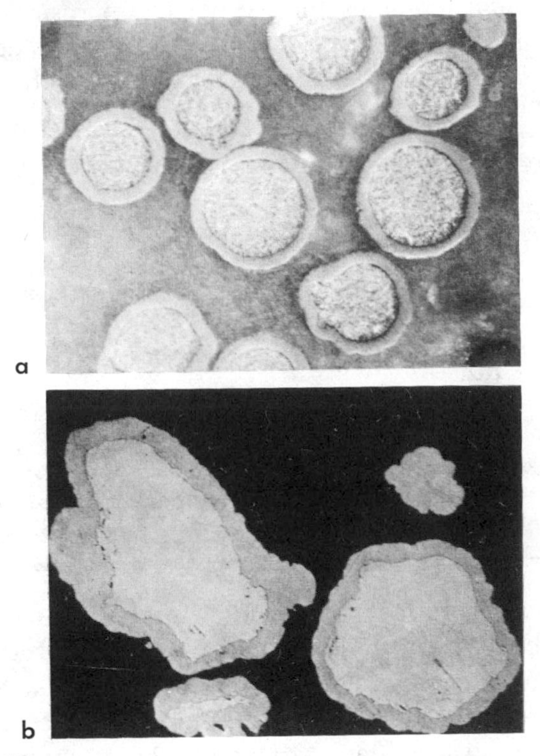

FIGURE 2-10.

Photomicrographs of coated type powder particles made by a precipitation technique: (a) a Ni/Al 80:20 spherical type powder (250 ×); (b) a Ni/Cr 80:20 irregular type powder (250 ×). (from B. Meddings, H. R. Huffman and V. N. Mackiw, in New Types of Metal Powders, H. H. Hausner, editor, Gordon and Breach, N.Y., pp. 28–44, 1964)

prior to compaction. The effects of the multiphase structure on the properties of the sintered material are usually quite favorable (except for the impurity type), but these can only be realized if such a structure is not destroyed during sintering, or if it can be produced or reformed by a post-sintering treatment.

For alloy powders made by atomization techniques one can expect to observe the same type of metallurgical structures associated with castings. For solid solution type alloys this means that cored structures, such as that shown in Figure 2-11 for a conventional stainless steel, are commonplace. Microporosity associated with entrapped gases is also common.

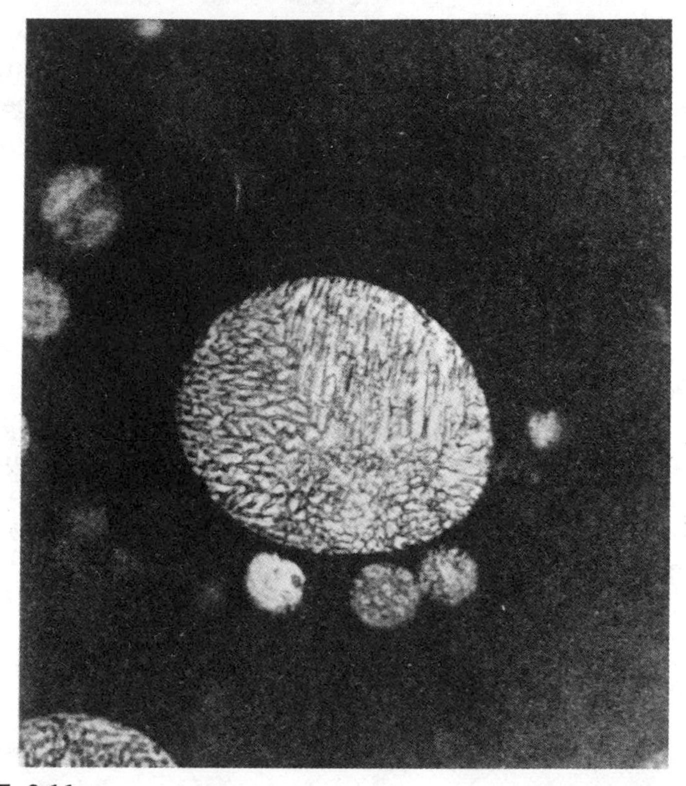

FIGURE 2-11.

Photomicrograph indicating cored structure in a spherical type atomized stainless steel powder. (from I. A. White, in New Types of Metal Powders, H. H. Hausner, editor, Gordon and Breach, N.Y., pp. 90–115, 1964)

The actual dislocation density and arrangement within powder particles can also be a significant structural characteristic for some powders. High densities and tangled networks of dislocations, characteristic of cold worked materials, can be produced in powders which undergo a mechanical treatment or severe thermal quenching accompanied by a phase transformation. Such a structure strengthens a material by inhibiting plastic flow and is undesirable for compaction. Its affect on sintering would only be significant if compaction is carried out without the use of pressure so that no structural changes are induced which would mask it. It is likely that such a structure would improve sintering kinetics because of the rapid diffusion paths provided by dislocations as well as grain boundaries that may be introduced (this will be better appreciated after the discussion on sintering). Naturally such a cold worked structure can be eliminated by annealing, which is done for some powders, or by the initial stages of sintering.

2.4 PARTICLE SIZE AND SHAPE

There can be no more fundamental characteristics of a powder than the size and shape of the individual particles. In actual fact these two factors are intimately related. It is necessary to know the shape of a particle if a reasonable method of size classification is to be used. It is customary to think of spherical particles when considering powders and the use of a diameter or radius value to describe their size. Most powders are not spherical. The two

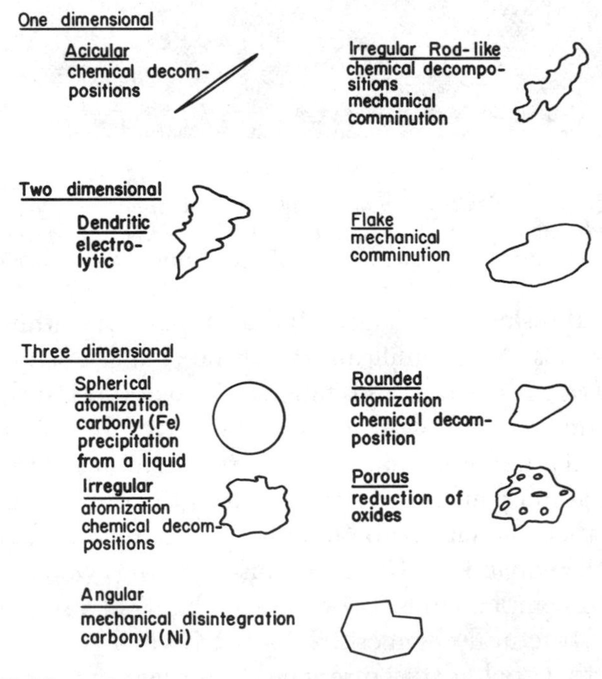

FIGURE 2-12.

A simple system of particle shape characterization.

most important ramifications of this simple reality is that the use of a single size parameter may be misleading and inaccurate, and measurement techniques which are actually based on the assumption that the particles are spherical are usually inherently in error.

First let us consider the various shapes of particles that are of significance. A somewhat ideal system of shape characterization is given in Figure 2-12, together with the major manufacturing techniques which produce such shapes. Actual photomicrographs of several different types of loose powders are given in Figure 2-13. Two basic concepts are useful in distinguishing different types of particles: they are the dimensionality of the particle and its surface contour. One-dimensional particles are usually acicular or rod-like in shape. Their most significant dimension is the length they have, which is usually considerably greater than the lateral dimensions. The aspect ratio (ratio of length-to-diameter) is also useful; metal and ceramic fibers that are being developed to a great extent would fall into this category. Flake particles may be considered as two-dimensional with the length and width being the most significant parameters and very much greater than the thickness. Dendritic particles are rather rare and are more characterized by their surface contour rather than their dimensions, but very often are flake-like in character.

Most particles are three dimensional in nature or, in other words, may be considered as being somewhat equiaxed. Spherical particles represent the simplest and most ideal example of this shape. Using the surface contour concept as a guideline it is possible to distinguish rounded, irregular and angular particles as shown in Figure 2-12. Porous particles are different than irregular ones because of the presence of the porosity, which itself may be very irregular in both size and shape. This internal porosity may be of the isolated or interconnected type. Large amounts of porosity make any shape characterization very difficult. It is best observed by examination of mounted powders for which one observes cross-sections rather than using loose powder; the latter requires much less preparation and is quite satisfactory for shape and size analysis.

For all of the equiaxed type particles it is convenient to use a single parameter, usually a diameter value, to characterize the size of the particles. In many cases only the term "size" is used as the critical parameter and this has some significance when the specific method of determination is given. Many attempts have been made

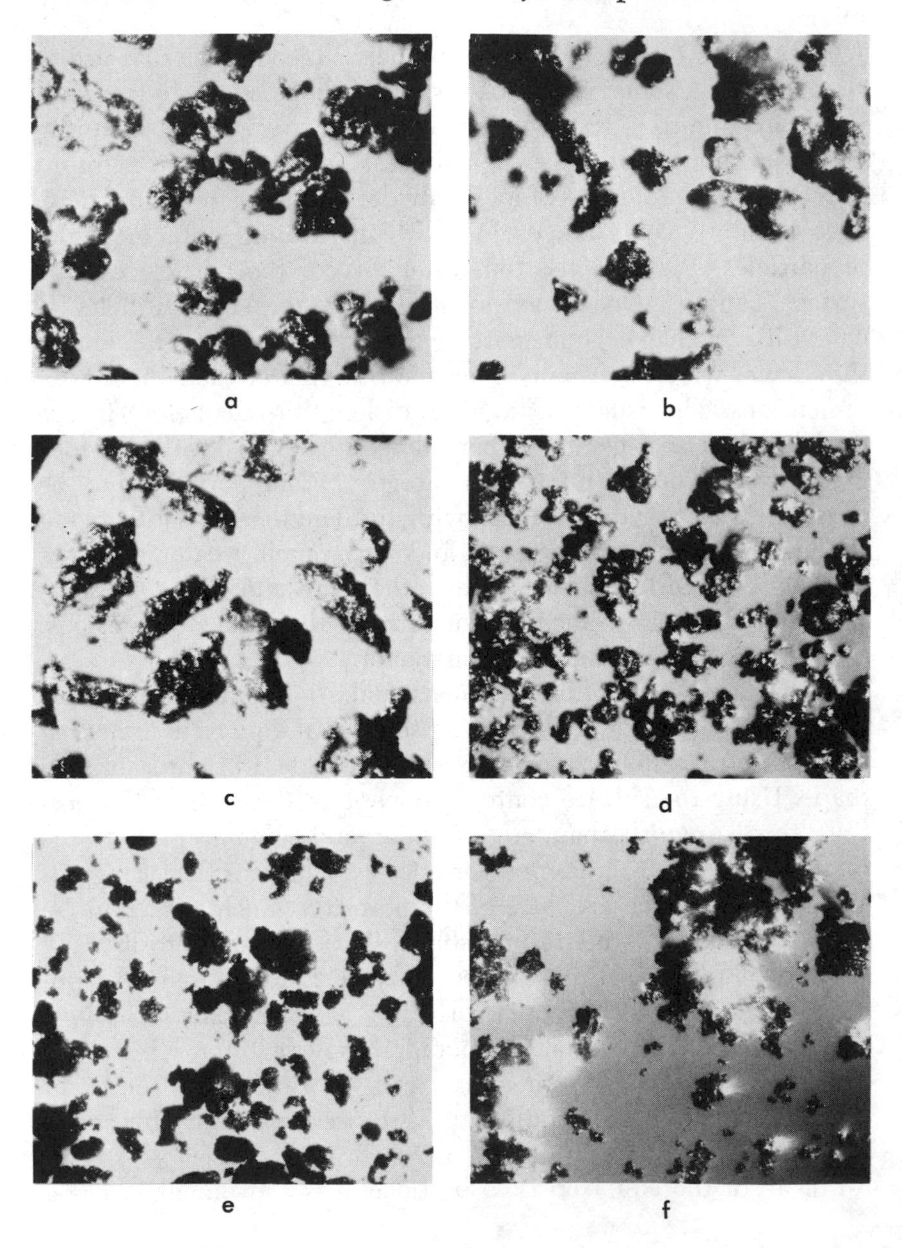

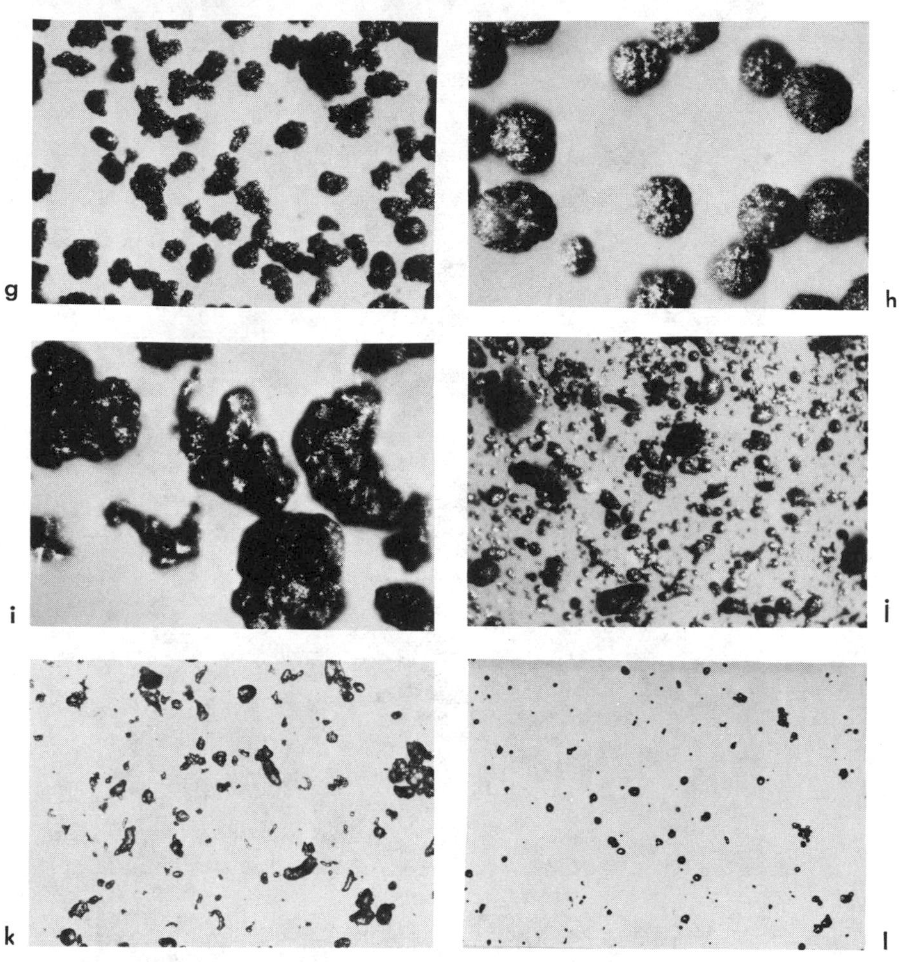

FIGURE 2-13.

Photomicrographs of loose powders: (a) reduced iron, (b) water atomized iron, (c) electrolytic iron, (d) air atomized iron, (e) electrolytic copper, (f) flake aluminum, (g) precipitated copper, (h) precipitated nickel, (i) fused salt tantalum, (j) atomized bronze, (k) atomized aluminum, and (l) atomized tin. (all except (k) and (l) courtesy of A. Adler, Easton Metal Powder Co.)

to place shape characterization on a quantitative basis by the use of various mathematical descriptions. These are difficult to apply and not particularly enlightening or accurate. The best approach is to visually observe the particles by normal light or electron microscopy and use photomicrographs to record the results.

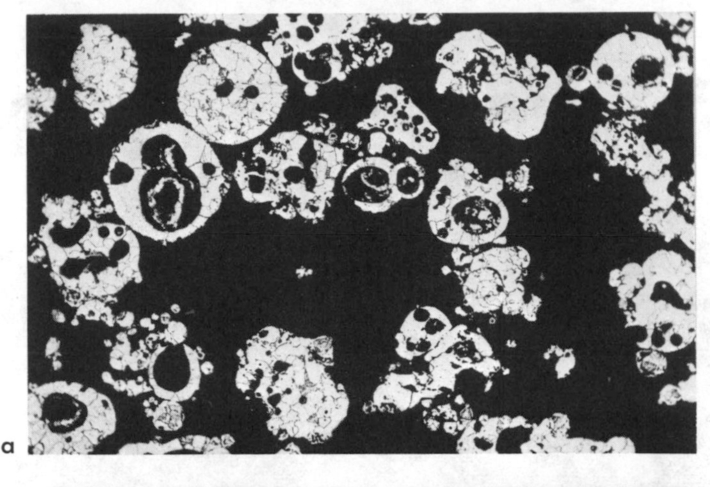
a

b

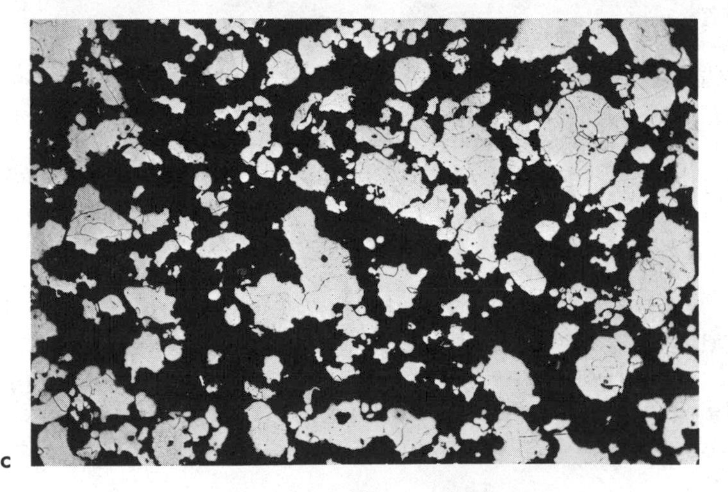
c

The difficulty of talking about particle shape is best appreciated by examination of the actual powders in Figure 2-13. Clearly there is a problem of uniformity of shape within any one type of powder. For atomized nonferrous metals and ferrous alloys, such as aluminum, tin and stainless steel, there is usually a tendency for the smaller particles to have a greater degree of sphericity than the larger ones. Very often it is believed that atomization always produces the rounded type of particle; this is not true, particularly for iron powders. The method of atomization is very important. Gas or air atomization tends to produce a more rounded type of particle, while water atomization yields a more irregular or angular type. This effect is illustrated by the photomicrographs of three types of atomized iron powders in Figure 2-14.

Quite often shape and size considerations are made very difficult because of the agglomeration of several small particles into a large one. Experimental observations of powders require adequate dispersion of the particles. An actual technique of size measurement may only "see" the agglomerate and not the component particles. This is a particularly important consideration for particle sizes less than one micron. However, it is usually possible to break up such agglomerates by mechanical or chemical means if so desired. From the viewpoint of compaction such an agglomerate will behave as a single particle with respect to bulk movement, but as component particles with respect to deformation. The latter is also true for sintering where such particles are analogous to a very fine grained material.

Very often it is convenient to use the equivalent volume concept to determine the particle size. If a particle is distinctly nonspherical and the appropriate dimensions corresponding to a simple form, or a direct measure of the volume, can be assessed, then a diameter value corresponding to a sphere with the same volume is used to characterize the particle.

In a real mass of powder, all prepared in the same manner, all

---

FIGURE 2-14.

Photomicrographs of three types of atomized iron powders: (a) air atomized —high carbon melt; (b) water atomized—low carbon melt; (c) water atomized—low carbon melt. (courtesy of A. Adler, Easton Metal Powder Co.)

the particles will not have the same exact size, even though the shape may be essentially the same. Consequently, we must deal with size distributions when accurately describing powders. All too often the tendency is to use an average value of a single dimension to describe the size. As already noted, the use of a single dimension may be inaccurate for certain shapes. Even for equiaxed particles such an average diameter value may be very misleading. There are various methods one may use to calculate average diameters. Some important ones are given in Table 2-4

TABLE 2-4. Various Types of Average Powder Particle Diameters and their Significance

n = number of particles of a given diameter, d, value
$\sum$ = summation

Type	Definition	Significance
Arithmetical Average	$d_{av} = \sum nd/\sum n$	most common value for representing a set of measurements
Geometric Mean	$\log d_g = \sum n \log d/\sum n$	a good indication of the central tendency of a log normal distribution
Mean Surface	$d_s = (\sum nd^2/\sum n)^{1/2}$	the diameter of the particle whose surface is the arithmetic mean of the surfaces
Mean Volume	$d_v = (\sum nd^3/\sum n)^{1/3}$	the diameter of the particle whose volume is the arithmetic mean of the volumes
Linear Mean	$d_l = \sum nd^2/\sum nd$	the diameter based on the total surface observed divided by the total length
Volume-Surface Mean	$d_{vs} = \sum nd^3/\sum nd^2$	total volume divided by total surface area used with surface area measurements
Weight Mean	$d_w = \sum nd^4/\sum nd^3$	associated with weight measurements

and include the arithmetical average and the diameter corresponding to the average volume or surface area; these are used frequently. Such averages differ significantly if there is a large range of actual diameters. A mean or median, corresponding to the diameter which divides the total range of values into two equal portions, is also sometimes used. Finally, a modal value can be used to distinguish the most probable or frequent diameter.

To better appreciate the significance of these parameters one must consider the actual weight percent distribution curves. Such curves relate particle size to the corresponding fraction of the powder with that size. Figure 2-15 illustrates three basic types

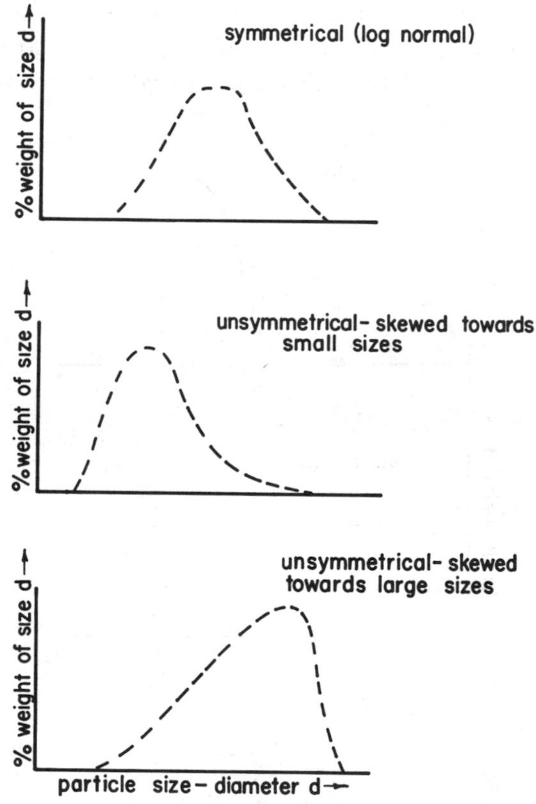

FIGURE 2-15.
Schematic illustrations of unimodal particle size distributions.

of distributions all characterized by being unimodal; that is, there is one high point or maximum amount of a certain critical size. Particles either smaller or larger than this modal value are present to a lesser degree. Figure 2-15 also distinguishes the various types of unimodal distributions with respect to symmetry considerations. A perfectly symmetrical unimodal (or log normal) distribution is characterized by having the same value for the arithmetical average, the median and the modal value. Distributions with some degree of skewness are asymmetrical and the arithmetical average and median are not equal to the modal value and not usually equal to each other.

The modal value is probably the most useful and significant parameter for unimodal distributions. However, most powders do not conform to any of these. More realistic distributions are shown in Figure 2-16. The polymodal distribution consists of two

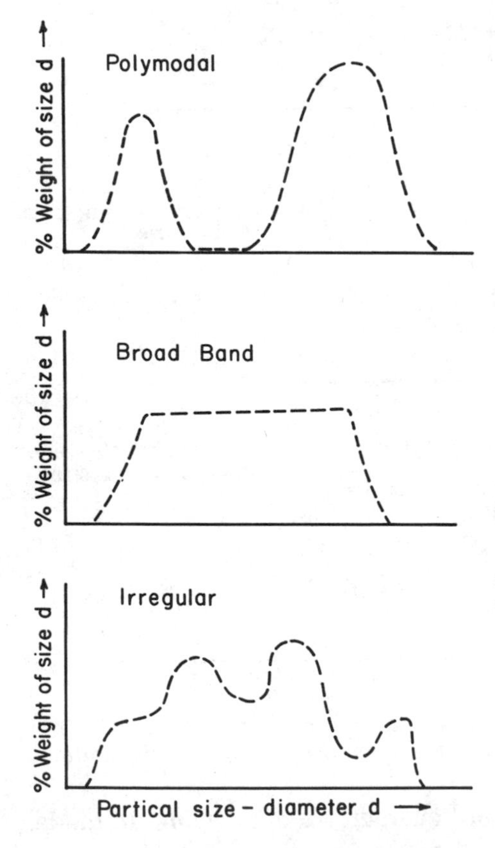

FIGURE 2-16.

Schematic illustrations of more complex and realistic particle size distributions.

or more narrow bands of particle sizes, each with a maximum, with virtually no particles between such bands. The broad band distribution simply corresponds to a uniform concentration of particle sizes over a rather broad size interval with virtually no particles having sizes outside this range. The irregular distribution represents a continuous and finite variation of particle sizes within a relatively broad range. It should be obvious that for these complex and more realistic distributions it is quite inadequate to attempt to characterize a powder by either an average value or even minimum and maximum values of size.

In Figure 2-17 weight percent distribution curves are given for

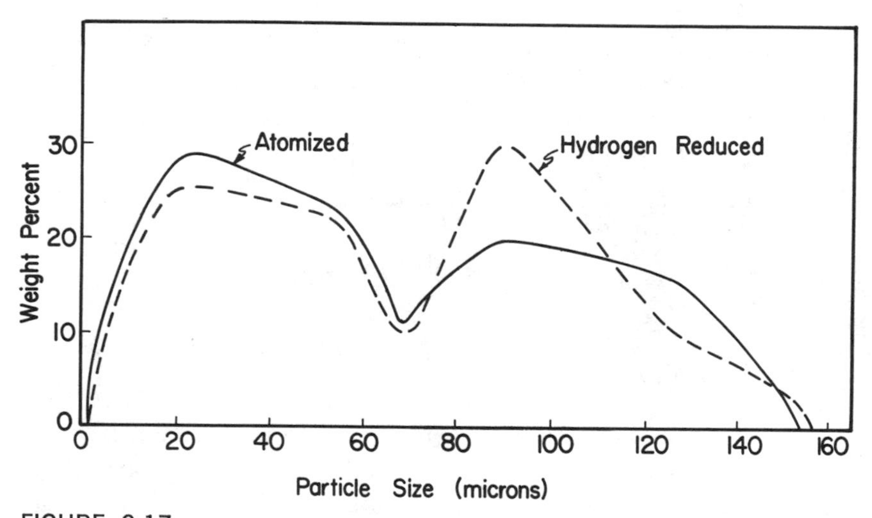

FIGURE 2-17.

Weight percent particle size distributions for atomized and hydrogen reduced iron powders.

two types of iron powders; these belong to the irregular category noted above. The broad range of particle sizes actually present in such commercial powders is also worthy of note. Instead of a smooth curve a weight percent distribution plot may be given in terms of a bar graph; such a representation is given in Figure 2-18 for an atomized stainless steel powder. In most cases this is a more realistic and enlightening type of presentation because the actual particle size data usually correspond to a size interval rather than one particular size. One of the most fundamental and critical, and as yet incompletely investigated, areas is the effect of the precise nature of the particle size distribution on compaction, sintering and other powder characteristics.

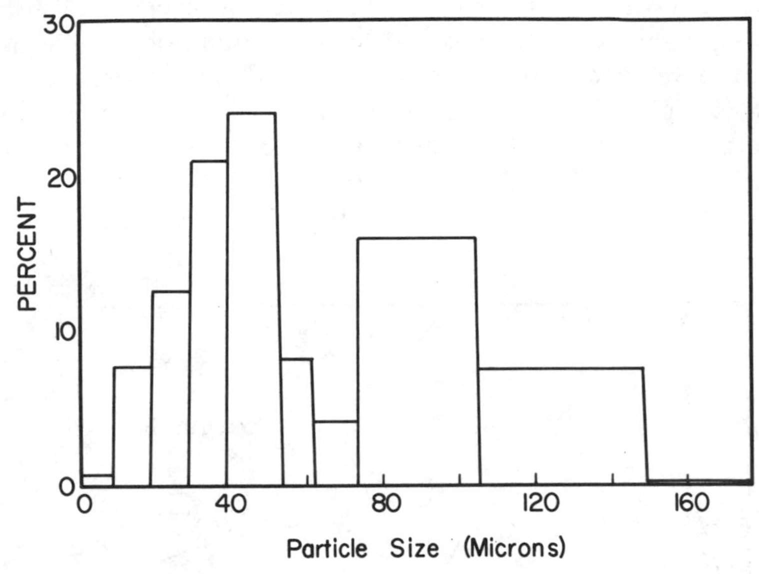

FIGURE 2-18.

Weight percent particle size distribution, in the form of a bar graph, for an atomized stainless steel powder.

Because of the limitations of some of the most common particle size measurement techniques, the actual particle size distribution curve considered above may not be obtained. Instead, a cumulative size curve may be presented as shown in Figure 2-19. Either the weight percent less than or greater than a specific size value is plotted as a function of the diameter; the latter is usually plotted on a logarithmic scale. The two types of curves shown would correspond to simple unimodal distributions. More complex distributions would be indicated by a more irregular cumulative size curve.

Actual Size Measurement Techniques A multitude of experimental particle size measurement techniques exist; some of the more common ones used in powder metallurgy and their limits of

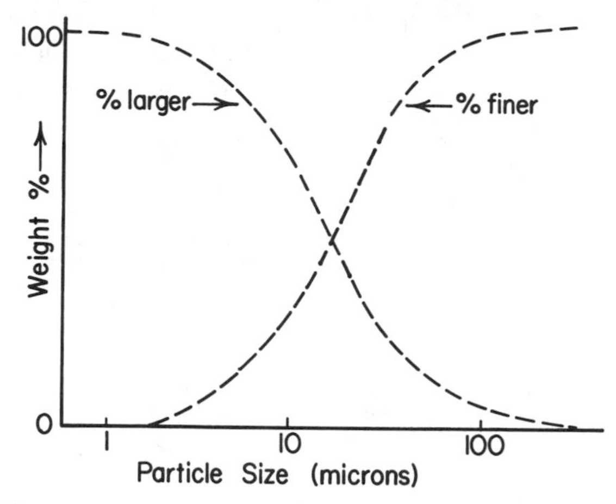

FIGURE 2-19.

Schematic illustration of cumulative weight percent particle size distribution curves.

applicability are presented in Table 2-5. They will now be briefly discussed in the order of their appearance in this table.

The most common way of describing the actual size of powders

TABLE 2-5. Common Methods of Particle Size Determination and Their Limits of Applicability

Class	Method	Approximate Useful Size Range (microns)
Sieving	Sieving using mechanical agitation or ultrasonic induced agitation and screens	44 –800
	Micromesh screens	5 – 50
Microscopy	Visible light	0.2 –100
	Electron microscopy	0.001– 5
Sedimentation	Gravitational	1 –250
	Centrifugal	0.05 – 60
Turbidimetry	Turbidimetry (light intensity attenuation measurement)	0.05 –500
Elutriation	Elutriation	5 – 50
Electrolytic Resistivity	Coulter counter	0.5 –800
Permeability	Fisher sub-sieve sizer	0.2 – 50
Surface area	Adsorption from gas phase	0.01 – 20
	Adsorption from liquid phase	0.01 – 50

is related to the most common technique of size measurement and control; that is, the screening of powder particles in standardized sieves or screens. Because of the widespread use of this method, one distinguishes between particles that are larger than 44 microns and fines or sub-sieve powder that is smaller than 44 microns. Table 2-6 gives some of the most pertinent data for both

TABLE 2-6. Information on Sieves of Use in Powder Metallurgy

Sieve Designation		U.S. Standard		
Microns	Mesh No.	Sieve Opening inches	Sieve Opening mm	Tyler Standard Mesh No.
177	80	0.0070	0.177	80
149	100	0.0059	0.149	100
125	120	0.0049	0.125	115
105	140	0.0041	0.105	150
88	170	0.0035	0.088	170
74	200	0.0029	0.074	200
63	230	0.0024	0.063	250
53	270	0.0021	0.053	270
44	325	0.0017	0.044	325
37	400	0.0015	0.037	400

the Tyler standard and United States sieve series. Sieves may be identified by the opening in inches, millimeters or microns (a thousandth of a mm), corresponding to the edge length of the square openings formed by woven wires, or a mesh designation. In the vast majority of cases the screen used with the smallest opening is the 325 mesh screen with an opening of 44 microns and, hence, the use of this size as a critical dividing point for actual particle sizes. Micromesh sieves are also available with openings down to at least five microns, but are rather difficult to use and maintain, are very fragile and have low load capacities.

It should be clear that the use of screens allows one to distinguish particle size ranges, such as −200 +270 mesh, and even broader ranges such as −325 mesh or +200 mesh, but not actual precise determination of particle size. The term −325 mesh is used to designate the fines; however, the actual powder particles can be anywhere from a fraction of a micron to near 44 microns. Such differences would surely affect all subsequent processing and material properties. Additionally, one must consider the shape of the particles and how the sieve opening is related to the actual particle dimensions.

Certainly a spherical particle can only pass through an opening which is just barely larger than its diameter. The same is true, with less accuracy, for the other types of equiaxed particles with the largest segment of the particle being the controlling factor. Consider, however, an acicular or rod-like particle. The actual process of sieving a powder involves agitation of the powder and usually the screens in both the horizontal and vertical planes. Although the length of such particles may be greater than the sieve opening, the agitation allows some particles to orientate themselves in such a way that they can pass through the screen openings. For this to happen the sieve opening (actually the opening diagonal) must be barely larger than the largest lateral dimension. Similarly, flake type powders with a thickness much less than the sieve opening may not pass through the screen because of the influence of the planar dimensions. It is for these reasons that the term size rather than diameter is most frequently used to characterize powders and why cumulative size plots rather than actual size distributions are given.

A distinct advantage of screening is that it is not only possible to obtain information about the size distribution, but one may actually fractionate (separate) powders into various size ranges and synthesize a desired distribution. In this way powder manufacturers blend powders to achieve desired properties.

Microscopic techniques are the most accurate and significant to use to ascertain the particle shape, but they are tedious to use to obtain statistically significant data on particle size distributions. Often it is necessary to use such techniques to calibrate the other types of apparatus. Direct observations provide some knowledge on the extent of agglomeration, which is often a source of considerable error in other methods unless special preliminary deagglomeration treatments are given to the powder. The use of microscopy is being facilitated by the introduction of very sophisticated electronic and computerized attachments to a basic microscope that very rapidly analyze the particles being observed. Complete size distributions can be obtained directly. Such instruments are rather expensive, require very trained personnel and often lack a high degree of accuracy on a routine basis.

Sedimentation techniques have been used extensively to obtain accurate particle size data over relatively broad size ranges. The procedure is to allow the particles to settle through a motionless fluid either as a result of gravity or of centrifugal action. The fluid may be a liquid or gas. Particle size data are obtained from the application of Stokes' law written as

$$d = [18NU/(p - p')g]^{1/2} \quad (2\text{-}20)$$

where d = the particle diameter
U = the rate of fall (equal to the settling distance divided by the settling time)
N = the viscosity of the fluid
g = the gravitational acceleration
p = the density of the particle material
p' = the density of the fluid

There are several limitations of this equation; they are:

(a) the particle size is limited by the necessity of having the particle resistance being controlled by the viscosity of the fluid and not by inertial effects; the maximum diameter d_m is given by

$$d_m^3 = 18RN^2/p'(p - p')g \quad (2\text{-}21)$$

where R is the Reynolds number of the fluid and should be less than 1.2;

(b) particles must reach their terminal velocity and this may necessitate long settling times for particles above about 50 microns;

(c) the walls of the container must not interfere with the falling particles; for particles below about 50 microns the vessel diameter should be greater than one cm;

(d) there must be no interactions between particles and this usually means a maximum volume concentration of particulate material of about 1%; any agglomeration of particles leads to serious errors;

(e) for particle shapes other than spherical the diameter obtained is an equivalent diameter and usually leads to particle size distributions quite different from the ones obtained by other methods;

(f) there must be no slip between the particles and the fluid, this is only important for very small particles settling in air, for which the true diameter is obtained by subtracting 0.08 micron from the Stokes diameter;

(g) unless the temperature of the sedimentation apparatus is kept constant, the results may be in error;

(h) the preparation of the suspension, usually a liquid for metal powders, can be a tedious procedure requiring trial and error tests to find the proper fluid viscosity leading to reasonable settling times;

(i) there must be no chemical interaction between the particles and the fluid.

The actual experimental apparatus for sedimentation may be of several types. These include cumulative techniques in which the weight of the settling particles or the height of a fluid in a manometer is measured as a function of time. Other techniques are based on measuring a change in concentration of the particulate material in the fluid at a certain level. These techniques involve the use of graphical or analytical procedures to convert the raw data into actual particle size information. An instrument which yields a cumulative weight distribution almost directly is the Micromerograph. A quantity of deagglomerated powder is introduced at the top of a long settling tube and the weight of the settling powder is recorded automatically by an electronic balance at the bottom of the tube. The sample size can be very small, much less than a gram, and the size range is from less than 1 to 250 microns, depending on the density of the material. Still other techniques make use of centrifugal instead of gravitational acceleration. These can be used to fractionate powders as well as analyze, whereas the gravitational types cannot accomplish this; however, they are not widely used. Lastly, it should be noted that when a particle density figure is needed to calculate a particle size from some raw data it is necessary to take into account the presence of particle porosity. For many powders the actual particle density is considerably less than the theoretical value for the particular material.

Turbidimetry methods involve the measurement of the decrease in intensity of a beam of light as it passes through a stable suspension of particles in a liquid. Such measurements can also be used in conjunction with sedimentation techniques, in which cases the measurement is made at a specific depth below the surface. The advantages of this method are that very small amounts of powder can be used and the data are relatively easy and quick to obtain. The basis for this method is the following form of the Lambert-Beer equation describing the attenuation of the light produced by a particulate suspension

$$I = I_o \exp(-KAcm) \qquad (2\text{-}22)$$

where I = the intensity of the beam after passing through the suspension
I_o = the intensity of the same beam in the absence of obscuring particles
c = the mass concentration of particles per unit volume
A = the projected area per gram of particles
m = the length of light path in the suspension
K = the ratio of effective scattering area to true area or the extinction coefficient

The last factor is a complicated function of particle size and particle refractive index and is very difficult to obtain. It is often assumed to be one, which is probably not too inaccurate for very small particles (less than about 20 microns), or obtained by calibrating the apparatus.

The value of A obtained leads to a calculation of a volume-surface mean diameter. Since the suspensions are very dilute one may make use of the fact that the projected area of a sphere is 1/4 of the surface area. The specific surface S_w, expressed as area per unit weight, is related to d_{vs} by

$$d_{vs} = 6/S_w p \qquad (2\text{-}23)$$

where p is the density of the particle material. The proportionality factor would be greater than 6 for shapes other than spheres or cubes. Consequently, unless used with sedimentation apparatus this method does not allow a complete size distribution to be determined, but only some measure of the average size. For either case the powder studied by this method is usually spherical or equiaxed and less than 10 microns in size. No fractionation of the powder is possible.

Elutriation methods refer to the use of an upward moving suspending fluid to counteract the action of gravity on the particles. In this way, by controlling the rate of upward flow particles of a given size will remain suspended, larger particles will settle (or fail to be lifted from the bed) and smaller particles will follow the fluid flow and can be collected. In commercial apparatus, such as the Roller Air Analyzer, the fluid is air. The method allows fractionation in addition to particle size distribution analysis, at least for size increments of 5 to 10 microns. The fluid velocity is adjusted to correspond to the terminal velocity of particles of a given size as calculated from Stokes' equation. The actual size fractions are determined by weighing the material collected. The disadvantages of the technique are the finest fraction obtainable contains particles in the range of 0 to 5 microns, the times involved are usually long, the accuracy is less than that obtainable by sedimentation techniques and the treatment of the data assumes spherical particles. Porosity in the particles can be another source of error. The chief advantage is the ability to fractionate powders and the method is well suited for analysis of commercial −325 mesh powders.

Electrolytic resistivity is one of the more sophisticated and versatile methods of particle size measurement. In the Coulter counter the powder is dispersed in an electrolyte which is forced through an aperture having an immersed electrode on each side. As a particle passes through it replaces its own volume of electrolyte and, hence, changes the resistivity between the electrodes. There is a complete electronic system which amplifies, scales and counts the resultant series of electrical pulses. It is possible to select a threshold size level and only count those particles larger than this value. By varying the threshold level, a complete cumulative particle size distribution is readily obtained. The selection of the aperture size is an important consideration. For optimum results only one particle should pass directly between the electrodes. If the size range is very broad, then two or more apertures may be necessary. Plugging of small apertures can be a problem. The basic assumption usually made is that the particles are spherical. In this way the actual data which are indicative of particle volume may be interpreted on the basis of equivalent diameters. The powder must be dispersed and various techniques have been developed to reduce particle agglomeration. The technique is very rapid, uses small amounts of powder (in the order of 5 to 20 mg) and is useful for a very broad range of particle sizes.

By making use of some fundamental principles of *adsorption* and *permeability* it is possible to obtain a volume-surface mean diameter for a mass of powder. Use is made of equation (2-23) and the value of S_w is obtained by measuring the permeability of a certain volume of powder or by measuring the amount of adsorption of a gas or a liquid on to the powder.

The permeability method is based on the concept that there is a sound relationship between the rate of flow of a fluid through a porous bed to the specific surface area of the loosely packed powder making up the bed; this is given as

$$u = f^3 g \Delta P / (1 - f)^2 k N L S_w^2 p^2 \qquad (2\text{-}24)$$

where u = rate of flow of fluid
f = fractional porosity in bed
g = gravitational acceleration
ΔP = pressure drop across the bed
k = a dimensionless constant usually taken as 5
N = fluid viscosity
L = bed thickness
p = density of particulate material

By controlling all the other parameters in the above equation it is possible to obtain a value for S_w. When a gas is used as the permeating fluid, diffusion or molecular flow is possible; this phenomenon of "slip" of the gas at the container walls where theoretically it should be stationary gives rise to a corrected value of u which is given by

$$u' = u[1 + (1 - f) S_w p Z m / f] \qquad (2\text{-}25)$$

where m is the mean free path of the gas (e.g. 5.9×10^{-6} cm at

760 mm, 0°C for air) and Z a constant about equal to 3.3. The Fisher sub-sieve sizer is widely used and is based on applying these principles to a specific type of permeability cell. The instrument is very easily used, gives a value for d_{vs} directly on a chart and is relatively inexpensive. It must be clearly recognized that the value of S_w obtained from a permeability experiment is representative of the "friction" surface presented by the powder mass to the flowing fluid. There may be many surfaces, such as pores and cracks in particles and hidden or isolated cavities, which are not seen or taken into account by the permeating fluid; hence, the value of S_w is usually smaller than that obtained by gas or liquid adsorption techniques. In most cases the value obtained from the Fisher apparatus is rather inaccurate and is usually referred to as a "number" rather than a diameter (it too assumes spherical particles); however, the instrument is quite useful as a quality control device. It is used for −325 mesh powders.

Adsorption of a species in solution may be used to obtain a value for S_w if the surface of the powder is completely covered by a monomolecular layer of the solute. From a knowledge of the area occupied by one molecule, the total area of the powder sample and finally S_w can be obtained. The basic problem is to insure complete saturation of the surface, and this is accomplished by obtaining the weight of adsorbed solute as a function of solute concentration in the solution. Analyses are then possible which allow one to ascertain at what conditions a monomolecular layer is formed. It is very important that the powder be very well dispersed in the liquid.

More accurate values of S_w may be obtained by measuring the amount of a gas adsorbed on the surface of a powder. Assuming a monomolecular layer of adsorbed gas and a value for the area covered per molecule (e.g. 16.2 square angstroms for liquid nitrogen) a value for S_w may be obtained by the use of

$$S_w = qN_vA \qquad (2\text{-}26)$$

where q = quantity of adsorbed gas in mols/gm of powder
N_v = Avogadro's number (6.02×10^{23})
A = area covered per molecule

The adsorption may be either physical, due to van der Waals

forces, or chemical (chemisorption) resulting from actual chemical bonding across the interface. The major experimental problem is determining the quantity of gas corresponding to a monomolecular layer. Adsorption isotherms representing the quantity of gas adsorbed as a function of the equilibrium gas pressure, at a constant temperature, must be obtained in order to determine this critical quantity. Theoretical analyses are available to assist with the interpretation of the experimental data. Various gases may be used, but nitrogen is very common.

Experimental procedures may be of the *volumetric* or *gravimetric* types. In the former the volume of gas adsorbed is obtained by first ascertaining a value for the volume of the space containing the powder, and subsequently the total volume of adsorbate in the same space. The adsorption isotherm is obtained by admitting increasing amounts of gas to the chamber. Gravimetric methods make use of very sensitive balances to detect the weight increase due to adsorption and are not used extensively. Both these methods are relatively complex and require very sophisticated equipment and highly trained personnel.

Comparison of Techniques Because of the importance of accurate knowledge about particle size, both distributions and average values, and the variety of methods available, there have been numerous studies comparing various techniques for different types of powders. If one takes into account the basic limitations and assumptions for each method, then it becomes clear that for some powders a number of techniques should yield virtually identical results. The most frequent assumption is the sphericity of the powder particles; hence, if one uses spherical or very equiaxed particles, then very good agreement can be obtained. Figure 2-20 shows the excellent agreement obtained for spherical copper powder by using the Coulter counter, the Roller air analyzer and micromesh sieves in terms of a cumulative size distribution presentation. Similar results have been obtained for irregular but highly equiaxed powders and also using the Micromerograph apparatus in addition to these other techniques. As the particle shape departs from sphericity more variations will be observed in the data obtained from a number of techniques.

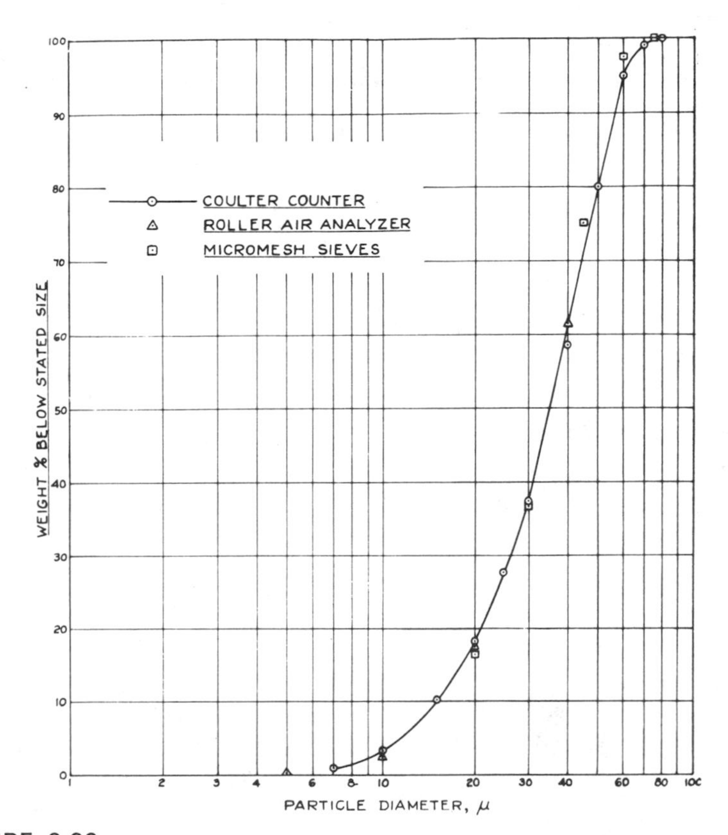

FIGURE 2-20.

Particle size distributions for spherical copper powder obtained from three different techniques. (from W. J. Ullrich, in Modern Developments in Powder Metallurgy, H. H. Hausner, editor, Plenum, N.Y., vol. 1, pp. 125–143, 1966)

A single value method, such as the Fisher sub-sieve sizer, may be compared with a technique yielding size distribution data and enabling fractionation of the powder. Such comparative data are given in Table 2-7 for the case of various size fractions obtained from a Roller air analyzer for several types of powders. It is seen that the more irregular reduced powders show greater deviations than the rather spherical atomized powders. In Table 2-8 fractions obtained from sieving and the Roller air analyzer were also measured with the Fisher apparatus and by microscopy; the latter is considered the most accurate. It can be seen that the results from

TABLE 2-7. Fisher Sub-sieve Sizer Diameters for Roller Size Fractions of Several Metal Powders

Roller Size Range (microns)	Pb Atomized	Sn Atomized	Al Atomized	Cu Reduced	Fe Reduced
0–5	3.5	2.7	—	—	1.2
5–10	9.2	6.5	7.2	3.3	2.4
10–20	17.2	14.4	12.8	6.6	—
20–40	31.4	22.2	22.7	8.0	—

(from J. Haertlein and J. F. Sachse, Handbook of Metal Powders, A. R. Poster, editor, p. 67, Reinhold, New York, 1966.)

the Roller instrument are considerably more accurate than those from the Fisher one. One may also note the decrease in the difference between the Fisher and microscopic values for the spherical powder.

TABLE 2-8. Comparison of Particle Size Data (316 Stainless Steel Powder)

Powder Fraction	Average Fisher Size (microns)	Average Size-Photomicrograph (microns)
(A) Sieving		
−325 mesh (irregular)	14.8	27.2
−325 mesh (spherical)	29.9	41.2
(B) Air-elutriation (irregular)		
30–44 micron	18.9	32.4
20–30 micron	14.4	26.6
0–20 micron	10.4	14.3

Additional comparative data for two single value types of determinations are given in Table 2-9. For the very fine and equiaxed powders the Fisher and photolometer (turbidimetry) instruments yield rather similar results.

2.5 SURFACE TOPOGRAPHY AND AREA

The nature of the surface of individual particles is also an important powder characteristic. This facet of powder characterization

TABLE 2-9. Comparative Size Data from Fisher Sub-sieve Sizer and Cenco Photolometer

Powder	Fisher Sub-sieve Sizer diameter, microns	Cenco Photolometer diameter, microns
Tungsten	1.05	0.75
Tungsten	1.65	1.5
Tungsten	2.30	1.8
Tungsten	4.50	3.1
Tungsten	3.80	2.8
Molybdenum	4.40	3.7

(from F. Clark, Advanced Techniques in Powder Metallurgy, p. 166, Rowman and Littlefield, New York, 1963.)

is even more difficult to put on a quantitative basis than particle shape. Usually what one must consider is the extent of surface roughness on a microscopic scale. It is possible to consider the topography (the relative size and shape of surface elevations or protuberances) for any shape particle. A spherical particle may appear smooth, but on closer examination at high magnifications the surface may actually consist of many protuberances. Two concepts may be used to describe such surface roughness: the relative height and width of such bulges compared to the particle dimensions, and the shape of such material extensions. A fine surface roughness would signify that the size of the protuberances are very small compared to the overall particle dimensions. Powders produced by chemical reductions of oxides usually have a highly roughened surface which is easily observed at relatively low magnifications; such surfaces can be seen in some of the photomicrographs in Figure 2-13. On the other hand, atomized powders may have a much finer degree of surface roughness. The latter type of powder may also have a rounded type of roughness rather than sharp, irregular protuberances which are more characteristic of powders made by chemical or mechanical methods. Greater appreciation of the influences of surface topography on the properties of metal powders and their behavior in the manufacture of P/M products is becoming apparent.

A very significant recent development has been the application of scanning electron microscopy to the study of individual powder particles. Magnifications up to 50,000 $\times$ and resolutions of 250 angstroms make this an invaluable tool for the study of the surface topography; and the specimen preparation is almost insignificant. The great detail that can be observed is illustrated in Figure 2-21 which contains two images obtained with this tech-

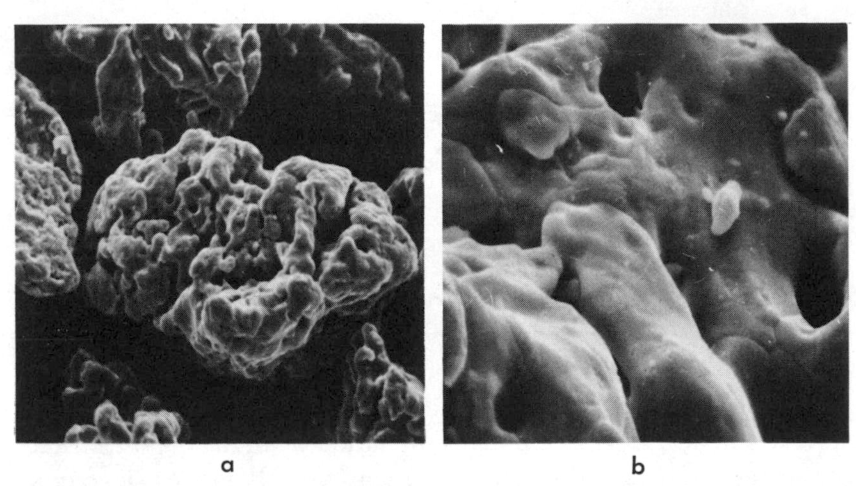

a b

FIGURE 2-21.

Images of individual particle surfaces obtained with the scanning electron microscope: (a) iron particle produced by hydrogen reduction of mill scale showing well-rounded smooth pores having surface outlets (about 1,000 ×); (b) sponge iron particle showing rounded edges and corners, smaller amount of porosity than (a) and outlines of some grain boundaries running into the pores (about 3,000 ×). (from O. Johari, Metal Progress, pp. 147–150, August, 1968)

nique. Both surface roughness and particle porosity are clearly shown; in some cases grain boundaries are also evident. Surface contamination of particles and agglomeration of fine particles can also be studied with this technique, as can the surfaces of green and sintered compacts.

The exact nature of the surface topography will influence the frictional forces between particles. This would be important in any situation in which the bulk movement of the particles is happening. For example, when powder is flowing, settling or during compaction. Then too, the extent of actual particle-to-particle contact during sintering, which is a very important consideration, will also be affected by the nature of the surface roughness. As already noted, the chemical reactivity of the powder will tend to increase with increasing surface roughness, especially the irregular type.

The actual amount of surface area per unit amount of powder can also be very significant. Any reaction between the particles, or between the powder and its environment, initiates at these surfaces and, hence, sintering will be influenced by the ratio of surface area to particle volume. This ratio increases as the particle size decreases. This may be seen by considering a spherical particle of diameter d for which the ratio is $6/d$. For flake particles with a circular surface of diameter d and a thickness h, the ratio is $2/h + 2/d$. As the particle shape departs from sphericity and the surface roughness increases, this ratio also increases significantly. Consequently, for a very irregular shaped particle with a high degree of surface roughness, the specific surface area can be very high.

Some data on surface areas of commercial types of powders are given in Table 2-10. It may be seen that the surface area is very

TABLE 2-10. Typical Specific Surface Areas of Commercial Powders

Powder	Specific Surface Area (cm^2/gm)
Reduced Fe	
Fine, 79%—325 mesh	5160
Normal blend	1500
Coarse, 1%—325 mesh	516
Sponge Fe—normal blend	800
Atomized Fe—normal blend	525
Electrolytic Fe—normal blend	400
Carbonyl Fe 7 micron size	3460
Reduced Tungsten 0.6 micron size	5000
Precipitated Ni 6 micron size	3000

high for fine powders and for those made by reduction techniques. The experimental methods of permeability and adsorption, described in the previous section, are used to determine the specific surface area. Gas adsorption methods are usually the most accurate.

2.6 APPARENT AND TAP DENSITY

The *apparent density* of a powder refers to the weight of a unit volume of loose powder, usually expressed in gm/cc. It is one of the most critical and useful characteristics of a powder. It is important because it determines the actual volume occupied by a mass of powder and this ultimately determines the size of the compaction tooling and the magnitude of the press motions necessary to compact and densify the loose powder. Additionally, the equipment used to transport and treat the initial powder is affected. In an indirect way the behavior during sintering may also be influenced by the initial apparent density. Apparent density depends on the density of the solid material, particle size, shape, surface area, topography and distribution, and how the particles are packed or arranged. It is usually in the range of 20 to 50% of the theoretical density of the solid material.

The apparent density is usually determined by flowing a mass of powder into a container of known volume and measuring the weight of the powder which completely fills the space (the Hall flowmeter apparatus is generally used and it and the appropriate test are described in MPIF 4-45 and ASTM B 212-48(1965) standards).

Naturally increasing the density of the solid material increases the apparent density of the powder. Decreasing surface area-to-volume ratios and decreasing surface roughness tend to reduce frictional forces between the settling particles and increase the apparent density by allowing the particles to more effectively fill the free spaces between the previously settled particles. To understand the significance of particle size and shape one must take a closer view of the packing of powder particles in such a mass.

First, it should be realized that a space can only be completely filled by certain types of uniformly sized polyhedral particles, such as cubes, which are exactly aligned. This situation is analogous to a brick wall. For any particle shapes with curvature or irregular contours, it is impossible to completely fill a space with the powder. Therefore any aggregation of the types of real particles discussed previously into a bulk implies the presence of porosity, or a packing factor, PF, of less than unity. The two are related as follows

$$\text{Fractional Porosity} = 1 - PF \qquad (2\text{-}27)$$

As PF approaches unity, the apparent density approaches the theoretical value for the solid material. The value of PF depends on the particle shape, arrangement and size distribution. There is also a major dependence on particle size because of the usual variation of particle arrangement with size.

The simplest way of visualizing packing is to consider spheres and the concepts used to describe how spherical atoms are arranged to form crystal structures. The four basic arrangements of atoms are simple cubic, body-centered cubic, face-centered cubic and hexagonal close-packed. These have PF values of 0.52, 0.68, 0.74 and 0.74, respectively. Both the face-centered cubic and hexagonal close-packed arrays actually consist of a number of close-packed planes (any sphere on such a plane is directly surrounded by six other spheres) and represent the highest possible PF values for uniformly sized spheres. Examples of the simple cubic and close-packed arrangements, in two dimensions, are given in Figure 2-22. The PF values for these ideal arrangements are independent of the sphere diameter. It is worthwhile to verify some of these values by performing the simple calculations. Such analyses can also be applied to other simple shapes, such as the packing of uniformly sized cylindrical rods for which the PF factor is 0.91.

A very effective way to increase the packing factor or apparent density is to fill the spaces among particles with smaller ones; that is, by using a distribution of sizes. It is easiest to consider systems containing just two differently sized particles. For the highest PF and the lowest porosity, the mixture should contain a coarse/fine bulk volume ratio of 1/(porosity of coarse fraction). In other words, the small particles should fill all the pores among the coarse ones. The voids among a uniform arrangement of spheres are called interstices; hence, this filling arrangement is sometimes referred to as interstitial packing. An example is given in Figure 2-23. However, even the smaller particles cannot completely fill the original pores. But the greater the difference in the

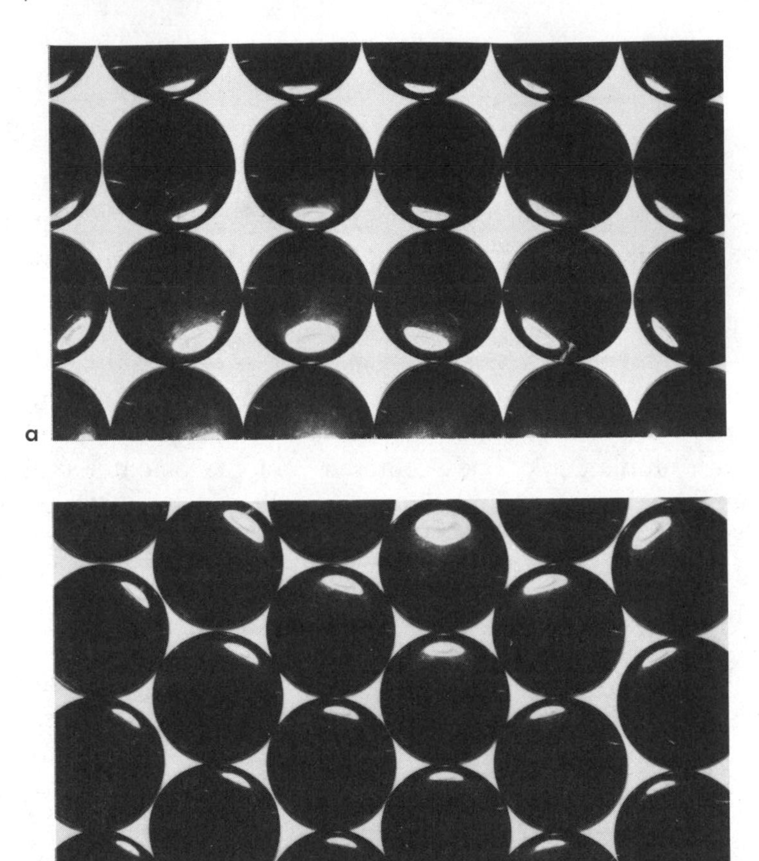

FIGURE 2-22.

Illustrations of (a) simple cubic and (b) close-packed arrangements in two dimensions for spheres. (courtesy of A. Adler, Easton Metal Powder Co.)

diameters, the greater the maximum increase in *PF*; this effect is illustrated schematically in Figure 2-24.

It is apparent that using several different size fractions can maximize the packing factor still further. Various theories assuming spherical particles and certain types of uniform packing have been presented to enable a calculation to select the proper size distribution for the highest possible value of *PF*. They are of limited significance and use because either real powder particles are not spherical or, of even greater importance, there is

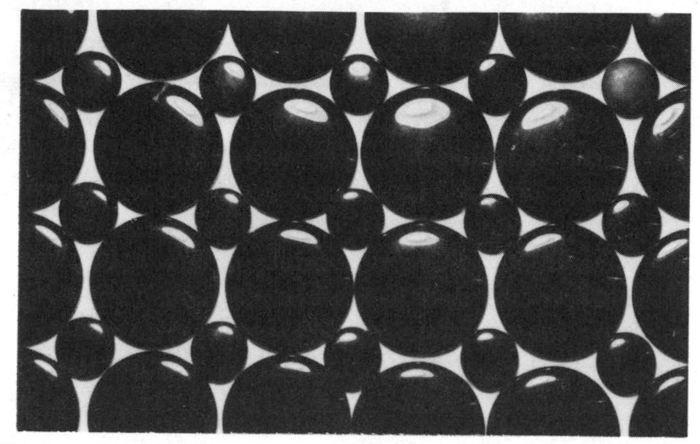

FIGURE 2-23.

An example of interstitial packing; that is, voids among large particles being filled by smaller ones. (courtesy of A. Adler, Easton Metal Powder Co.)

actually no long range uniform packing of particles according to the geometrical arrays considered in the theories. This last factor becomes increasingly pertinent as the particle size decreases, the

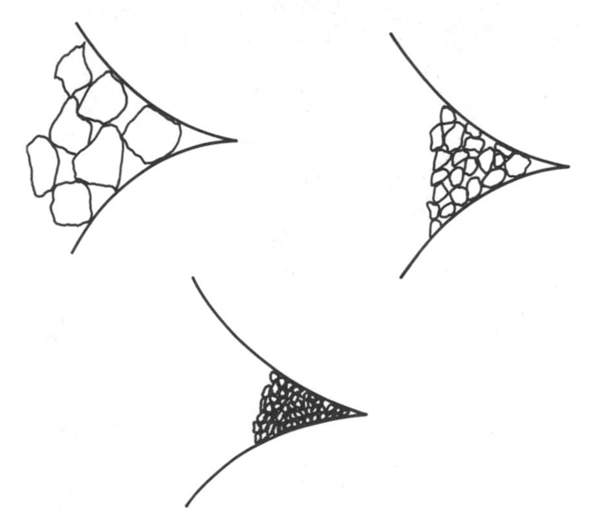

FIGURE 2-24.

Schematic illustration of the greater effectiveness of void filling with increasing difference in the sizes of the particles.

shape departs from sphericity and complete mixing of the different sized particles is not attained.

Adding small particles may not increase the *PF* of the original system but may decrease it. In relatively large quantities small particles may cause separation of the larger ones resulting in greater porosity. This is shown schematically in Figure 2-25. This

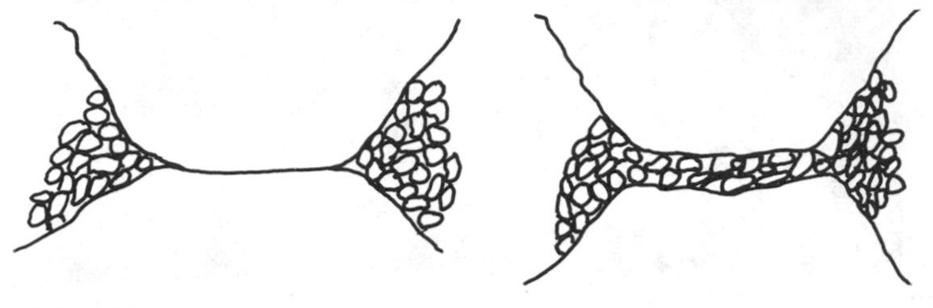

FIGURE 2-25.

Schematic illustration of particle separation or "bridging" leading to a reduction in the packing factor.

effect is sometimes referred to as "bridging" and is also shown in the model of Figure 2-26. It can be seen that this situation is gen-

FIGURE 2-26.

Model illustration of the "bridging" effect caused by small particles. (courtesy of A. Adler, Easton Metal Powder Co.)

erally associated with a quite irregular distribution or array of the particles.

If one considers adding fine particles to coarse powder of the same material, then there are four basic types of effects as shown schematically in Figure 2-27:

(1) a continuous increase in apparent density with fine par-

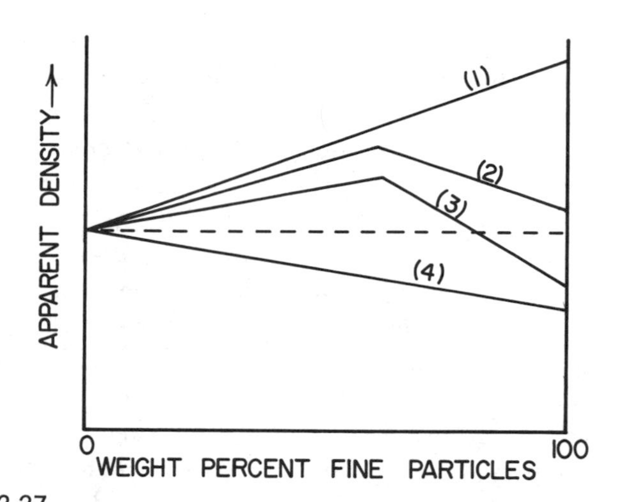

FIGURE 2-27.

Schematic illustration of the four possible effects on apparent density of adding fine particles to coarse ones.

ticle additions; this signifies that the filling of voids is more significant than any bridging effects, and that the fine powder itself has a higher density than the coarse one (this is usually not the case since the fine powder has a higher surface area-to-volume ratio, but could be the case if the fine powder had a more spherical shape or smoother surface condition);

(2) an initial increase followed by a decrease leading to a density of the fine powder greater than that of the coarse one; this is a reflection of bridging effects becoming important at some critical percent addition of the fine powder and the fact that the fine powder itself has some characteristic giving it a higher apparent density as considered in (1);

(3) the same as (2) except that the density of the fine powder is now smaller than that of the coarse powder (the more normal case);

(4) a continuous decrease in apparent density with increasing additions of the fine powder; this would result from a exceptional

amount of bridging and the absence of any significant amount of void filling; the fine powder would have such a size or shape leading to a very low apparent density in comparison to the coarse powder.

It is now appropriate to review the basic effects related to apparent density for real types of powders as well as some data for these:

(a) *The apparent density decreases with decreasing particle size.* The two factors causing this are the increase in frictional surface area which reduces the ability of the particles to settle efficiently, and the increasing departure from a long range three dimensional uniform arrangement of the particles which decreases *PF*. The first factor decreases in importance with increasing sphericity and decreasing surface roughness. Table 2-11 gives some representative data for several different powders which clearly demonstrate this dependence. The effect is particularly important for very small particle sizes (less than about 20 microns). Porosity within particles will of course decrease the apparent density. It should be emphasized that a powder consisting of very small, smooth and spherical particles, such as carbonyl iron, has a higher apparent density than the same metal when in the form of larger, more roughened and irregular particles.

(b) *The apparent density decreases as the particle shape departs from sphericity.* This is a consequence of the increase in frictional surface area and less uniformity of packing. This effect is illustrated by the data of Table 2-12 obtained for the same size distribution (this can only be an approximation because of the fundamental difference in shapes) for copper powders.

(c) *The apparent density decreases with increasing surface roughness.* In Table 2-12 the sponge iron represents the greatest, the atomized the intermediate, and the electrolytic iron the least degree of particle surface roughness.

(d) *The apparent density may be manipulated by mixing various sizes of particles.* Increases in apparent density can result from the predominating effect of void filling by smaller particles, while bridging effects can lead to decreases in the apparent density. In Figure 2-28 the effects of adding differently shaped −325 mesh powder to a standard +325 mesh blend of stainless steel powder

TABLE 2-11. Apparent Densities of Various Sizes of Several Different Powders

Material	Average Particle Diameter (microns)[a]	Apparent Density (gm/cc)
Aluminum,		
atomized[b]	5.8	0.62
	6.8	0.75
	15.5	0.98
	17.0	1.04
	18.0	1.09
	60% above 44 (+325 mesh)	1.22
	75% above 44 (+325 mesh)	1.25
Nickel,[b]		
carbonyl	3.2	0.61
precipitation	3.5	1.80
carbonyl	3.8	1.87
carbonyl	4.1	2.10
precipitation	4.4	2.09
precipitation	8.0	2.60
precipitation	−40 + 325 mesh	3.60
Tungsten[b]	1.20	2.16
	2.47	2.52
	3.88	3.67
	6.85	4.40
	26.00	10.20
Stainless Steel,		
atomized, spherical[c]	−325 mesh	4.3
	−270 + 325 mesh	4.5
	−200 + 270 mesh	4.4
	−150 + 200 mesh	4.5
	−100 + 150 mesh	4.5
Iron[c]		
reduced	6	0.97
carbonyl	7	3.40
reduced	51	2.19
electrolytic	53	2.05
electrolytic	63	2.56
reduced	68	3.03
electrolytic	78	3.32

[a] from Fisher sub-sieve sizer for single values and screens for size fractions.
[b] from data for commercial powders in A. R. Poster, Handbook of Metal Powders, Reinhold, N.Y., 1966.
[c] from H. H. Hausner, in above reference, p. 16–17.

TABLE 2-12. Apparent and Tap Densities of Various Powders

Material	Apparent Density (gm/cc)	Tap Density (gm/cc)	Percent Increase
Copper[a]—spherical	4.5	5.3	18
—irregular	2.3	3.14	35
—flake	0.4	0.7	75
Iron (−100 + 200 mesh)			
—electrolytic	3.31	3.75	13
—atomized	2.66	3.26	23
—sponge	2.29	2.73	19
Aluminum (−200 mesh)			
—atomized	0.98	1.46	49

[a] all copper powders with same size distribution; from H. H. Hausner, in Handbook of Metal Powders, A. R. Poster, editor, Reinhold, N.Y., 1966.

are shown. Fine spherical powder is very effective in increasing the apparent density, while flake additions reduce the apparent density sharply. If one considers adding fine spherical powder to coarse spherical, rather than to coarse irregular as in the previous case, then the effect illustrated in Figure 2-29 can result. Here

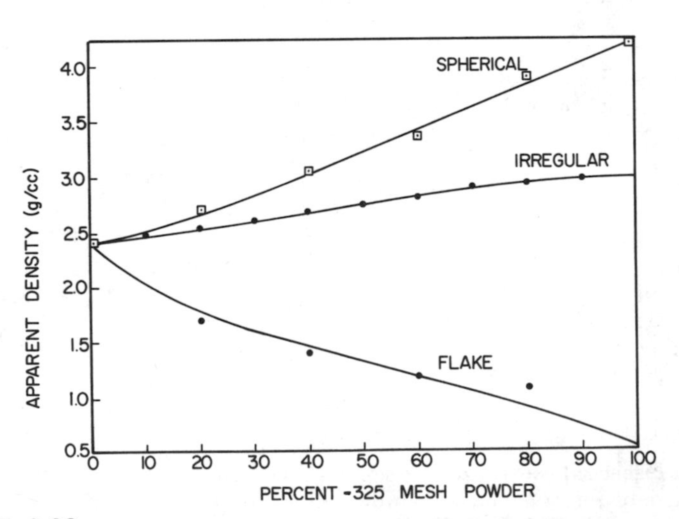

FIGURE 2-28.

The effect of −325 mesh additions to a +325 mesh distribution of 316 stainless steel powder on apparent density, for three different shapes of the addition. (from G. J. Pearson, M.S. Thesis, University of Wisconsin, 1967)

there is simply a size effect. The effect of size distribution on the apparent density is shown by the data of Table 2-13 for electrolytic iron and nickel powders. As the percentage of —325 mesh powder decreases, the apparent density increases. The exact dependence on this size fraction will be determined by the precise

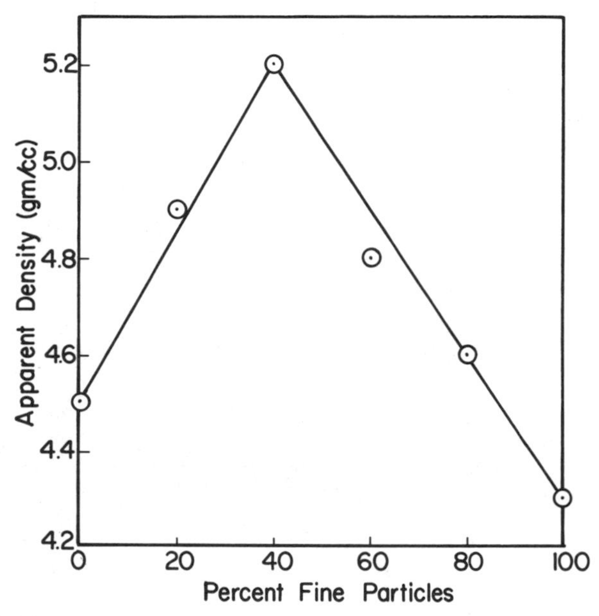

FIGURE 2-29.

The effect of adding fine (—325 mesh) spherical powder to coarse (—100 + 150 mesh) stainless steel powder on apparent density. (from H. H. Hausner, in Handbook of Metal Powders, A. R. Poster, editor, Reinhold, N.Y., pp. 9–19, 1966)

size distribution of these fine particles. In general, commercial powders with particles in the sieve and sub-sieve range contain 20 to 30% —325 mesh powder and a distribution of +325 mesh powder for optimum properties.

Tap Density Very often a mass of loose powder will be mechanically vibrated or tapped. The density of the powder increases due to this treatment and is always higher than the apparent density. This comes about by the induced movement of the particles which

TABLE 2-13. Effect of Particle Size Distribution on Apparent Density and Flow Time

Material	% Particle Size (mesh) +100	−100 +150	−150 +200	−200 +250	−250 +325	−325	Apparent Density gm/cc	Flow Time sec
Iron,[a] electrolytic	4	11	18	16	18	33	2.6–2.8	29
	3	26	18	6	16	31	3.2–3.4	24
	15	10	30	25	5	15	3.8–3.9	20
Nickel,[b] precipitation			0.4	2.0	12.2	85.4	0.58	—
			2.1	5.1	24.0	68.8	0.92	—

[a] from H. H. Hausner, in Handbook of Metal Powders, A. R. Poster, editor, p. 17, Reinhold, N.Y., 1966.
[b] from H. A. Hancock, D. J. I. Evans and V. N. Mackiw, Int. J. Powder Met., 1, 42 (1965).

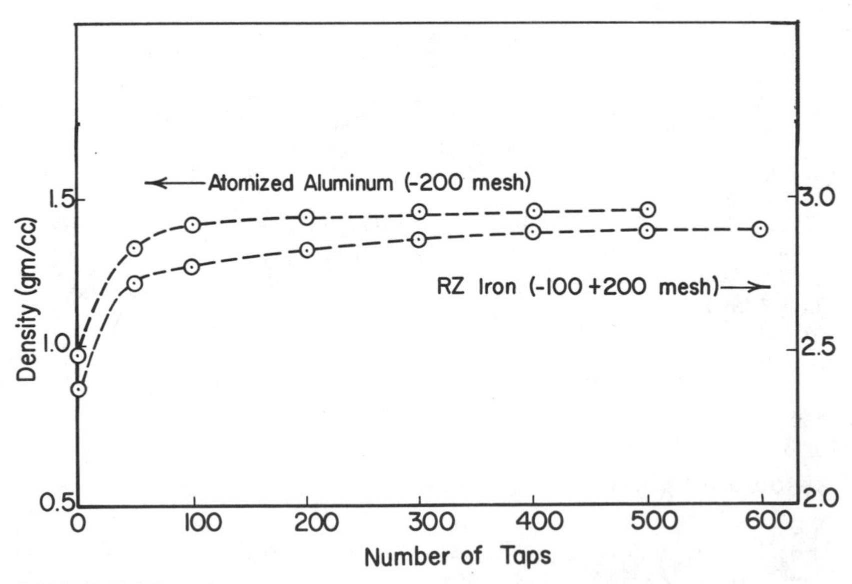

FIGURE 2-30.

The density of loose powder as a function of the number of taps, for atomized aluminum and atomized/reduced iron powders.

causes separation and allows the particles to settle to a greater extent and increase the *PF* value. The greatest increase in density occurs during the initial tapping period and eventually the density becomes constant. This effect is illustrated in Figure 2-30 for iron and aluminum powders. The final stable density is the value reported as the tap density. The amount of increase in density due to tapping depends on the extent of the original friction forces between the particles.

The greater the frictional conditions in the original powder (e.g. small sizes, irregular shapes and roughened surfaces), the greater the increase in density due to tapping. This is shown by the data of Table 2-12 for the three shapes of copper particles, and for iron powders with varying degrees of surface roughness and aluminum with a very low initial apparent density. Usually the lower the original apparent density, the higher the percentage increase in density upon tapping. An exception is the case of atomized iron powder which has a fine type of surface roughness probably consisting of rounded protuberances. Apparently this type of surface facilitates particle movement.

2.7 FLOW RATE

The flow rate of powders is a very important characteristic. Rapid rates of parts production require relatively rapid flow of powder from storage containers to dies and within the dies also. The standard method of measuring the flow rate of metal powders used by both powder producers and users consists of measuring the time necessary for 50 gms of powder to flow through a prescribed small orifice (the use of the Hall flowmeter is commonplace and is described in MPIF Standard No. 3 and ASTM Standard No. B 213-48 (1965). This test offers only a means of comparison and evaluation because in the majority of operating conditions the powder does not have to flow through a small orifice. It is common practice to report the results of this test in terms of the time in seconds for this weight of powder to completely flow through the orifice. In many cases this time is considered the flow rate. It is not. The flow rate of any material is the amount flowing per unit time per unit area. Consequently, these flow times are proportional to the reciprocal of the flow rates.

The actual mass flow rate, G, of a powder through an orifice would be given by

$$G = p_a u \tag{2-28}$$

where p_a is the apparent density (gm/cc) and u the average velocity of the powder passing through the orifice (cm/sec). The mass flow rate by definition can also be given by

$$G = w/At \tag{2-29}$$

where w is the total weight of powder flowing, A the cross-sectional area of the orifice and t the total time for the powder flow. The flow time is then given by

$$t = w/Ap_a u \tag{2-30}$$

In actual fact the powder velocity is determined by a number of factors as follows

$$u = Kc/pS_w R \tag{2-31}$$

where K = a proportionality constant
c = a constant representing the size and shape of the orifice
S_w = the specific surface area
R = a factor directly dependent on the surface roughness
p = the density of the solid powder material

The last factor determines the actual forces between particles; that is, for particles of constant size, shape, and surface roughness, the frictional forces would increase with increasing material density.

It is well known that very fine powders do not flow through a small orifice. This is a result of the drastic increase in S_w as the size becomes very small. The general effects of size, shape, surface roughness and material density on u are shown in Figure 2-31. When u becomes zero the flow time becomes infinite or, in other words, there is no flow.

For real powder materials the single most important factor determining the flow time is the apparent density. The basic effect is:

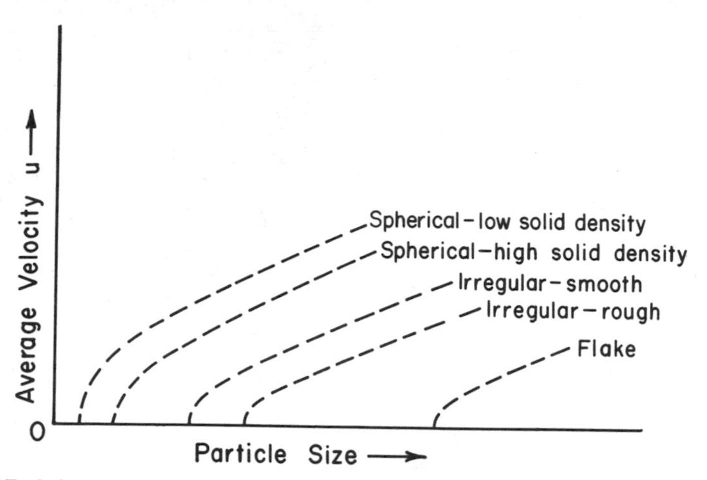

FIGURE 2-31.

Schematic illustration of the effect of particle size, shape, topography and density on the average velocity of powder flowing through an orifice.

for a given metal, the higher the apparent density, the lower the flow time. To demonstrate this effect, the flow time may be given by combining equations (2-30) and (2-31) to yield

$$t = (wS_wR/AKc)[1/(p_a/p)] \tag{2-32}$$

or taking logarithms of both sides

$$\log t = \log(wS_wR/AKc) - \log(p_a/p) \tag{2-33}$$

It is seen that t is inversely dependent on the ratio of apparent density to the theoretical density of the solid material. Data for t and p_a/p for many different types of powders, representing many methods of manufacture, have been gathered from a number of sources and plotted according to equation (2-33) in Figure 2-32. It is seen that all the data fall into a relatively narrow band. A line with a slope of -1 has been drawn through the data to indicate the agreement with the exact form of equation (2-33).

Other factors such as particle shape, and surface roughness (actually S_w or the frictional surface) are more influential in determining the minimum size for positive powder flow times. Very coarse particles approaching the size of the orifice will not flow due to the fact that they will easily block the opening. The effect of varying the particle size distribution on the flow time, as given

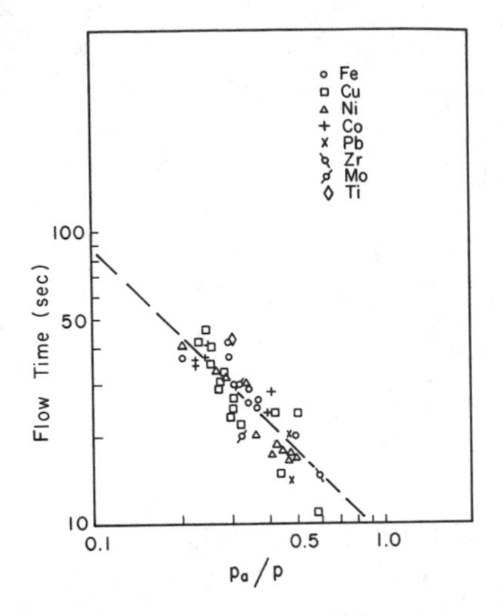

FIGURE 2-32.

Data for various types of powders illustrating the dependence of flow time on the ratio of apparent density to theoretical density.

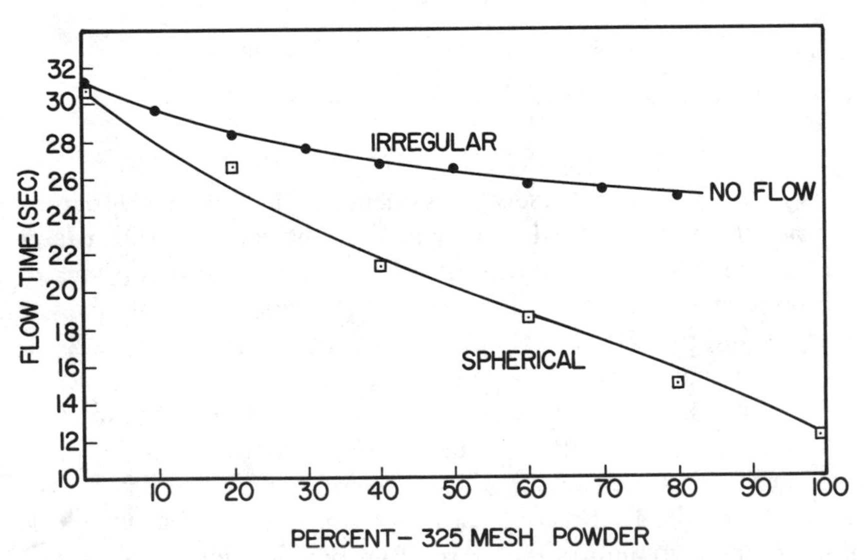

FIGURE 2-33.

Effect of −325 mesh particle additions to a +325 mesh distribution on flow time for two different shapes of the stainless steel addition. (from G. J. Pearson, M.S. Thesis, University of Wisconsin, 1967)

by the data of Table 2-13, simply is a consequence of the dependence of p_a on the size distribution. As the percentage of fine particles increases, p_a decreases and, hence, t increases. Flow time data corresponding to the type of fine particle additions given in Figure 2-28 for apparent density are given in Figure 2-33. Both the irregular and spherical fine powder additions increase the apparent density and, hence, it would be expected that the flow times are decreased. Essentially, this is the case; however, with the irregular powder additions an amount is reached for which no flow behavior is observed. This corresponds to the presence of an excessive amount of frictional surface area.

2.8 COMPRESSIBILITY

A powder characteristic of some value is its *compressibility*; that is, the amount a powder will compress or densify upon application of pressure. Its usefulness is limited because of the number of other parameters which actually determine its magnitude, and the problem of quantitatively defining it. One approach is to define the compressibility as the green density obtained at 30 tsi compaction pressure. However, this has limited value because: (a) the dependence of green density on compaction pressure is not linear and relative differences between powders at 30 tsi may be quite misleading for evaluation at other pressures, and (b) for the production of high density structural parts a compaction pressure of 30 tsi may be unrealistic.

An alternative is to define compressibility in terms of the following parameter

$$\begin{matrix}\text{densification} \\ \text{parameter}\end{matrix} = \frac{\text{green density—apparent density}}{\text{theoretical dens.—appar. dens.}} \qquad (2\text{-}34)$$

The green density to be used could be for any compaction pressure. This parameter represents the fractional densification achieved with respect to the maximum amount possible. Some data for actual iron powders in terms of the two methods of defining compressibility are given in Table 2-14. One may note the following: (a) both measures of compressibility indicate that

TABLE 2-14. Compressibility of Commercial Iron Powders

Type	Apparent Density (gm/cc)	Green Density at 30 tsi (gm/cc)	Densification Parameter[a]
reduced	2.35	6.10	0.679
reduced	2.35	6.35	0.725
sponge	2.40	6.20	0.695
atom. red.	2.45	6.45	0.738
sponge atom.	2.47	6.55	0.755
reduced	2.50	6.50	0.745
sponge	2.60	6.60	0.759
atom.	2.90	6.70	0.764

[a] calculated on the basis of a theoretical density of 7.87 gm/cc and a green density at 30 tsi.

the compressibility increases with increasing apparent density, (b) a rather large amount of densification has taken place at a relatively low compaction pressure, (c) it is not meaningful to relate compressibility to methods of powder manufacture. The first group of data in the table represents the more conventional type of iron powder, while the second group represents the newer "high compressibility" type.

Possibly the best approach to evaluation of compressibilities is to consider the actual green density-compaction pressure curves. In Figure 2-34 two such curves are given; these indicate the difference between the conventional and high compressibility types of iron powders. Such curves have the typical shape as shown in this figure corresponding to a steadily decreasing rate of effectiveness with increasing compaction pressure.

In the next chapter the physical processes going on during compaction will be considered in some detail, and a better understanding of compressibility and green density-compaction pressure curves should be attained.

For the production of structural types of *P/M* parts it is generally advantageous to use powders with high apparent density that permit high green densities to be obtained if desired. This concept may be put in terms of the *compression ratio* which is defined as the ratio of the volume of the loose powder to the vol-

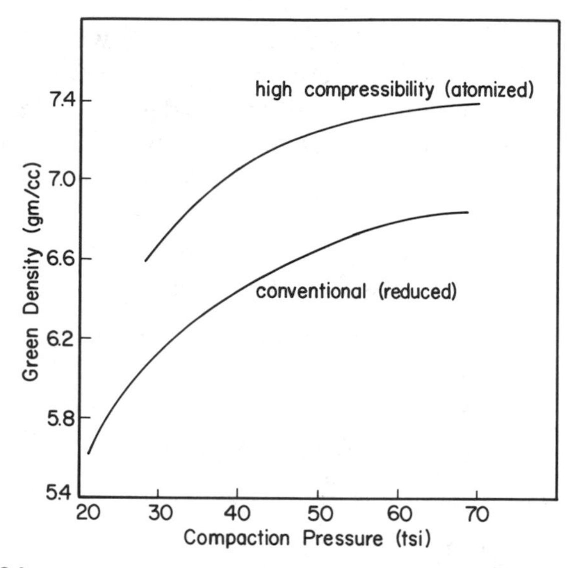

FIGURE 2-34.

Green density-compaction pressure curves for a high compressibility atomized iron powder and a conventional reduced iron powder.

ume of the compact made from it. It is closely approximated by the ratio of green density to apparent density. A low compression ratio is desirable because: (a) the size of the die cavity and tooling can be reduced, (b) breakage and wear of tooling is reduced, (c) press motions can be reduced, (d) a faster die fill and thus a higher production rate are possible.

2.9 PYROPHORICITY AND TOXICITY

Handling of certain fine powders can present several health hazards in either industrial or research operations. Pyrophoricity (spontaneous ignition or oxidation) is a potential danger for many metals, including the more common types, when they are in a finely divided form with large surface area-to-volume ratios. Toxicity of powders is normally related to inhalation or ingestion of the material and the resulting toxic effect. The basic cause of these hazards is not merely the property of the material but the ability of fine particles to remain suspended in air and resist collection and removal. A 100 micron particle will settle at a rate of about 60 ft/min; a 50 micron particle at a rate of about 10 ft/min; and a 10 micron particle at about 0.5 ft/min. In normal situations air has a turbulent velocity of about 25 ft/min. Consequently, particles in the 50 micron range float easily for extended periods in the air stream.

Data for the typical maximum permissible levels of toxic powders are given in Table 2-15. It is seen that radioactive

TABLE 2-15. Typical Maximum Permissible Levels for Occupational Exposure (8 hour day)

Material	Concentration (micro gms/m^3)
Plutonium	0.0001
Beryllium	2.0
Nickel-carbonyl	7.0
Uranium	80.0
Cadmium	100.0
Chromium oxide	100.0
Mercury	100.0
Tellurium	100.0
Thorium	110.0
Lead	150.0
Arsenic	500.0
Zirconium oxide	5000.0
Iron oxide	15000.0
Titanium oxide	15000.0
Zinc oxide	15000.0

(from F. Clark, Advanced Techniques in Powder Metallurgy, p. 161, Rowman and Littlefield, N.Y., 1963)

plutonium is highly hazardous due to radiation poisoning. Even common metals such as nickel when in extremely fine powder present a serious threat. Many of these toxic effects are cumulative and even short time exposures can add up to a toxic dose in time. Exposures to certain metals can be toxic no matter how little the time of exposure; for example, 25 micrograms/m^3 of beryllium.

The chemical reactivity of a material increases as the ratio of surface area-to-volume increases. For this reason fine particles of many materials combine with oxygen, ignite and result in explosive conditions. Surface roughness and particle porosity are important contributions to the total surface area. Many materials behave in this way at room temperature while others require a higher tem-

TABLE 2-16. Ignition and Explosibility of Powders

Material	Size Microns	Ignition Temp. (°C)[a] Cloud	Ignition Temp. (°C)[a] Layer	Minimum Explosive Concentration oz/ft³	Index of Explosibility[c]
					Severe
Aluminum, atomized	−44	650	760	0.045	>10
Al-Mg Alloy	−44	430	480	0.020	>10
Magnesium	−74	620	490	0.040	>10
Thorium Hydride	3	260	20	0.080	>10
Zirconium	3	20	190	0.045	>10
Uranium Hydride	3	20	20	0.060	>10
Titanium	10	330	510	0.045	>10
Uranium	10	20	100[b]	0.060	>10
Thorium	7	270	280	0.075	>10
					Strong
Zirconium Hydride	−44 (98%)	350	270	0.085	3.7
Iron-Carbonyl	−74	320	310	0.105	1.6
					Moderate
Boron	−44	470	400	−0.100	0.8
Chromium	−44 (98%)	580	400	0.230	0.1
Manganese	−44	460	240	0.125	0.1
Tantalum	−44	630	300	−0.200	0.1
Tin	−53 (96%)	630	430	0.190	0.1
					Weak
Lead	−53	710	270	—	≪0.1
Molybdenum	−74	720	360	—	≪0.1
Cobalt	−44	760	370	—	≪0.1
Tungsten	−74 (99%)	730	470	—	≪0.1
Beryllium	1	910	540	—	≪0.1
Copper	−44 (98%)	700	—	—	≪0.1

(a) These data apply to relatively coarse dust (−200 mesh) but not to submicron powder

(b) In this test less than one gm of powder was used; larger quantities ignited spontaneously

(c) IE = Ignition sensitivity × explosion severity

(from M. Jacobson, A. R. Cooper and J. Nagy, Explosibility of Metal Powders, Bureau of Mines, Report 6516, 1964)

perature. Particles below one micron are particularly dangerous and generally the 50 micron range is considered hazardous. Some materials are ignited by a spark or flame, while others are only ignited in a furnace or hot air atmosphere. Table 2-16 contains recent data describing the explosibility and ignition conditions for some materials. Particle size is a very important factor; for example, Zr powder of 3 microns is pyrophoric, at 12 microns it does not ignite at red heat, and in massive form it can be heated to 3000°F without igniting.

If one is aware of the potential hazards of toxic or pyrophoric powdered materials, then adequate facilities can be established for safe material handling. These include dry boxes, hoods for safe ventilation, use of inert atmospheres, and procedures involving careful cleaning of equipment, clothes and rooms.

REFERENCES FOR FURTHER READING

2-1. W. D. Jones, Fundamental Principles of Powder Metallurgy, Arnold, London, 1960. Chapter One contains detailed descriptions of the various methods of powder manufacture; contains many references and data.

2-2. B. Meddings, H. R. Huffman and V. N. Mackiw, Technology and Application of Coated Powders, in New Types of Metal Powders, H. H. Hausner, editor, pp. 28–44, Gordon and Breach, N.Y., 1964. Excellent review of newer methods to make composite powders.

2-3. C. L. Mantell, Electrodeposition of Powders for Powder Metallurgy, J. Electrochem. Soc., 106, 70–74, 1959. Basic discussion of this method.

2-4. R. L. Probst, Spherical Metal Powders—Production and Characteristics, in New Types of Metal Powders, as in 2-2, pp. 45–49. Discussion on atomization techniques and powder characteristics.

2-5. I. A. White, Stainless Steel Powders—Manufacturing Techniques and Applications, in New Types of Metal Powders, as in 2-2, pp. 90–115. Good discussion of dependence of composition and structure of particles on manufacturing variables.

2-6. H. H. Hausner, Characteristics of Metal Powders, in New Types of Metal Powders, as in 2-2, pp. 1–8. Discussion of topic on elementary level.

2-7. C. G. Johnson, A Fabricator Views Materials for Structural Parts, Progress in Powder Metal., 20, 51–63, 1964. Good discussion of importance of powder characterization in industrial operations.

2-8. A. R. Poster, editor, Handbook of Metal Powders, Reinhold, N.Y., 1966. Several chapters on particle size determination by various techniques; discussions on more advanced level; this book is an excellent source of information on all types of commercially available powders.

2-9. R. D. Cadle, Particle Size—Theory and Industrial Applications, Reinhold, N.Y., 1965. A thorough discussion of the subject.

2-10. R. R. Irani and C. F. Callis, Particle Size—Measurement, Interpretation and Application, Wiley, N.Y., 1963. Similar to 2-9.

2-11. B. H. Kaye, Determining the Characteristics of Fine Powders, Chemical Engineering, November 7, 1966, pp. 239–246. A good modern discussion and interpretation of particle size measurement techniques.

2-12. H. H. Hausner, editor, Modern Developments in Powder Metallurgy, Plenum, N.Y., 1966. Several papers in volume one on particle size and shape determination on more advanced level.

2-13. M. Jacobson, A. R. Cooper and J. Nagy, Explosibility of Metal Powders, Bureau of Mines, Report 6516, 1964. Extensive data and discussion on this topic.

2-14. F. Clark, Advanced Techniques in Powder Metallurgy, Rowman and Littlefield, N.Y., 1963. Chapter 12 on toxicity and pyrophoricity contains useful data and discussions.

PROBLEMS

(2-1) If one considers a simple reduction of an oxide by carbon, then the free energy change for the reaction is given by the sum of the individual free energies of formation (taken with the appropriate sign); for example

$$MO + C \rightarrow M + CO$$

may be considered as equal to

$$MO \rightarrow M + O$$

and

$$C + \tfrac{1}{2}O_2 \rightarrow CO$$

The following are some free energy of formation values for various oxides at four temperatures, for use in several of these problems

Free Energy of Formation (kilocal/oxygen atom)

oxide	440°F	1340°F	2240°F	3140°F
CO	−37.1	−47.9	−58.3	−68.5
NiO	−46.1	−35.0	−24.2	−13.0
Fe_2O_3	−54.8	−44.8	−35.1	—
Cr_2O_3	−81.6	−69.7	−59.5	−49.1
Al_2O_3	−120.7	−108.2	−95.1	−82.0
SiO_2	−94.0	−83.4	−73.1	−61.9

Considering the reduction of an iron ore (Fe_2O_3) by carbon, is there a critical temperature below which the reaction is not possible? If so, what is that temperature?

(2-2) An ore contains Fe_2O_3 and 10% SiO_2. Can reduction by carbon produce a metal with less than 1% SiO_2? Explain your answer on the basis of thermodynamic considerations.

(2-3) If a small amount of Al_2O_3 and nickel powder are blended together and heated to 2240°F in a sealed vessel for several hours, what will the resulting material be?

(2-4) Considering the effect of critical gas ratios on the oxidation of iron, the following data are pertinent:

Ratio below which iron is reduced

Temperature (°F)	CO_2/CO	H_2O/H_2
2012	0.32	0.68
1832	0.37	0.64
1652	0.44	0.59
1472	0.50	0.55
1292	0.70	0.41

(from Hoeganaes Handbook, Hoeganaes Corp., Riverton, N.J.)

Is an atmosphere containing a H_2O/H_2 ratio of 0.62 in which iron ore is being reduced at 1900°F, detrimental to the final product recovered after cooling to 1200°F?

(2-5) For the situation described in (2-4) will the presence of CO_2 and CO in the ratio of 0.3 be of any value and, if so, why?

(2-6) It is contemplated to produce powder of a highly reactive metal by melting it in a high vacuum furnace and discharging the liquid into a high vacuum chamber. Disintegration of the liquid is to be induced by heavy turbulence resulting from a unique orifice design. Does this procedure appear feasible? Explain your answer.

(2-7) Discuss the dependence of grain size on particle size for atomized and precipitated powders with regard to the process variables.

(2-8) The following particle size data are obtained from some microscopic observations:

Number of particles	Diameter (microns)
5	1–5
15	6–10
11	11–15
20	16–20
30	21–30
35	31–40
8	41–50

Calculate the arithmetical average, the modal value, the mean surface diameter, and the volume-surface mean diameter. Discuss any differences among these single value indications of particle size. What type of distribution do these data represent?

(2-9) In Table 2-7 the data for the diameters obtained from the Fisher sub-sieve sizer are mostly on the low end of the range obtained from the Roller air analyzer. Discuss this observation on the basis of the principles of operation and assumptions used in each technique.

(2-10) In Table 2-9 the particle diameters obtained from the Fisher sub-sieve sizer are consistently larger than the diameters obtained from the Cenco photolometer. Discuss this observation on the basis of the principles of operation and assumptions used in each technique.

(2-11) For the atomization process shown in Figure 2-6 used to make porous iron powder, explain how the particle porosity is achieved and controlled.

CHAPTER THREE

POWDER COMPACTION

3.1 INTRODUCTION

The compaction of powders has the following major functions:

(a) to consolidate the powder into the desired shape;

(b) to impart, to as high a degree as possible, the desired final dimensions with due consideration to any dimensional changes resulting from sintering;

(c) to impart the desired level and type of porosity;

(d) to impart adequate strength for subsequent handling.

The second and third factors are not precisely the same. Chemical or metallurgical reactions during sintering may effect either the dimensions or the density, or each to a substantially different degree and level of uniformity. Hence, compaction should be considered as a means to manipulate and control each of these factors, separately. Additionally, for many applications it is more advantageous to consider porosity rather than density; the former allows one to consider both interconnected and isolated types of porosity, while the latter is only based on the total amount of porosity. Compaction can be used to selectively control either type of porosity and, hence, is very effective in achieving specific engineering properties. It is also feasible to produce a part in which the degree of porosity (or density) is purposely nonuniform.

There are numerous methods of powder compaction. To help

differentiate and evaluate them it is useful to consider the following process variables:

(a) continuity: either a specific quantity of powder is treated to produce a single object (discontinuous) or powder is continuously treated to produce a continuous form;
(b) degree of applied pressure: techniques range from "pressureless" (actually gravitational forces operate) to extremely high pressures;
(c) dimensionality of applied pressure;
(d) speed of pressure application: this may be considered from the viewpoint of the time involved in the process or as the velocity of a moving ram or punch which causes the increase in pressure on the powder mass;
(e) temperature of the powder material during the operation;
(f) fluidization of the particulate material: the particles may be in mutual contact, with only the gaseous environment present, or they may be suspended in some type of liquid (the latter technique often is used for the production of porous materials);
(g) nature of the mold or die: usually the powder is contained within some type of mold or die during compaction and this may be rigid or flexible, and solid or porous.

In order to facilitate the discussion of compacting techniques the following classification will be used:

A. *Pressure Techniques*
   Die
   Isostatic
   High Energy Rate Forming (HERF)
   Forging
   Extrusion
   Vibratory
   Continuous
B. *Pressureless Techniques*
   Slip Casting
   Gravity
   Continuous

Each of these will now be briefly considered with respect to the above noted process variables, the more important uses and limitations, and the basic equipment designs employed in practice. The engineering aspects of compaction will be more thoroughly discussed in Chapter Five. Several compaction techniques may be carried out at elevated temperatures and this approach is termed *hot pressing*. In such cases the basic nature of the process is fundamentally changed and will be considered in the next chapter from the viewpoint that it corresponds to sintering under the influence of an external pressure.

3.2 ACTUAL COMPACTION TECHNIQUES

Die compaction represents the most widely used method and is considered as the "conventional" technique. It is discontinuous, employs either low (under ten tsi) or very high (several hundred tsi) pressures, allows pressure to be applied only in the axial (vertical) direction to one or both ends of the powder mass, involves relatively slow speeds (in the order of 1-2 sec and punch movement of about 20 fps), and no liquid is used to suspend the powder, although various additives may be added for specific purposes. The die used is a rigid, solid mass with a relatively long lifetime. Both low density and high density structural parts over a very broad size range are made by this technique. The basic components of the equipment necessary for die compaction are:

(a) a source of energy or pressure, usually a mechanical or hydraulic mechanism;
(b) a die of the proper strength with the cavity of the desired shape and dimensions;
(c) upper and lower punches of the proper strength and design to contain the powder, apply pressure and assist in part removal or ejection from the die;
(d) core rods for the formation of holes within the compact;
(e) proper controls and instrumentation to manipulate the magnitude and rate of pressure application, the extent of motion and speed of the punches, core rods and possibly the die; the filling of the die with powder; the ejection of the compacted part.

The term "tooling" refers to factors (b), (c) and (d).

There are several distinctly different types of die compaction techniques, as follows:

(1) *Single action compaction* has only one dynamic pressing action; that is, the motion of the upper punch entering the die cavity, compressing the powder against the stationary lower punch, inner surface of the die cavity, and external surfaces of any core rods present. The force applied by the press is from one direction only. Ejection of the part may be carried out in either of two fundamental ways: (a) the die remains stationary and the lower punch raises the part from the die cavity, or (b) the lower punch remains stationary while the die is lowered (withdrawn) from the part, this is termed the "withdrawal" type of system. The ejected part is moved away from the compaction zone by a shoe device which also fills the die cavity with the proper amount of loose powder and levels it for the next pressing cycle. This entire single action compaction system is illustrated in Figure 3-1 for the

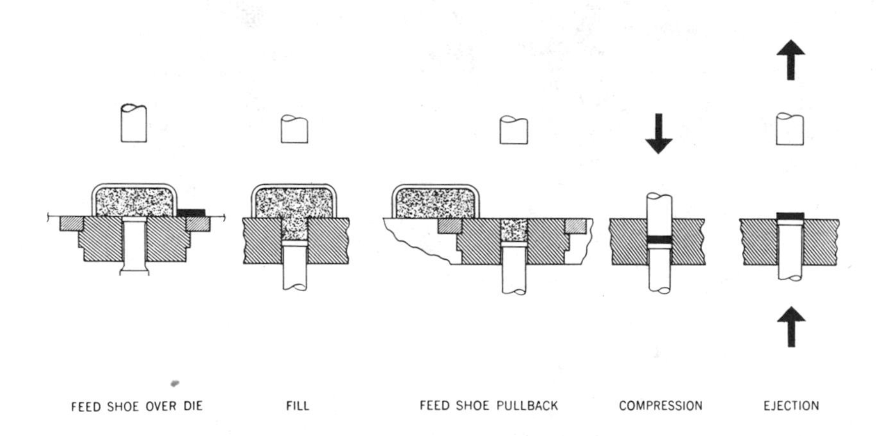

The steps in a single action die compaction system. (*from Powder Metallurgy Equipment Manual, MPIF, N.Y., 1968*)

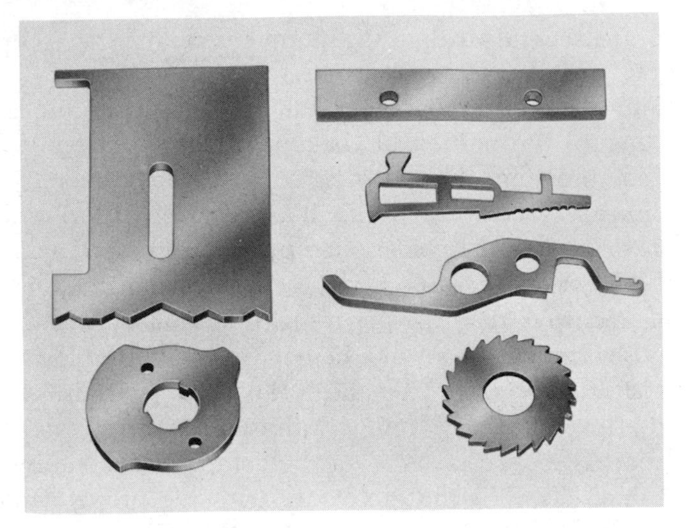

a

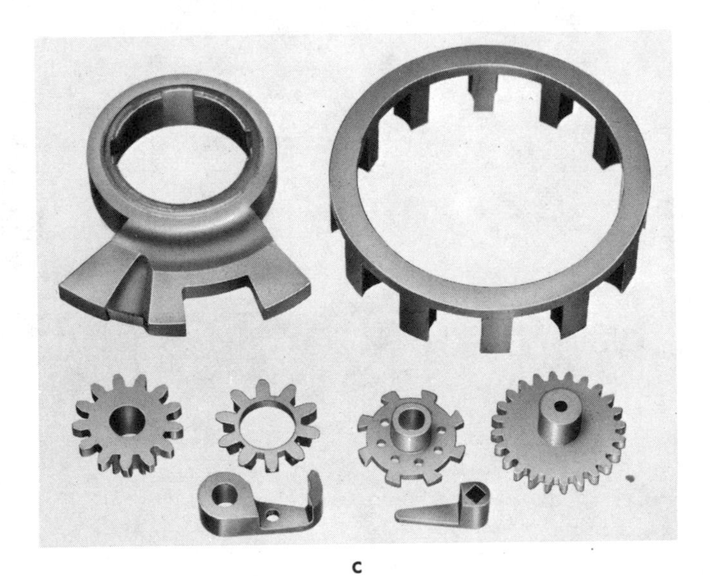

c

FIGURE 3-2.

Four basic classes of P/M parts: (a) class I, thin one level parts that can be pressed from one direction; (b) class II, thicker one level parts requiring pressing from two directions; (c) class III, two level parts of any thickness

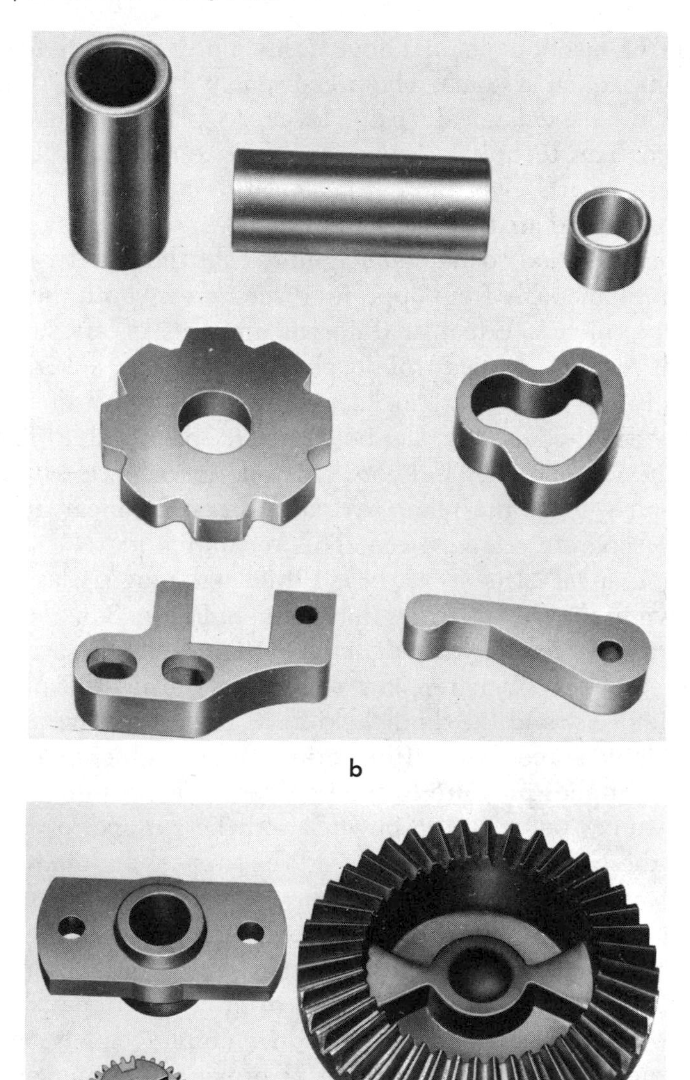

b

d

and contour requiring pressing from two directions; (d) class IV, multilevel parts of any thickness and contour requiring pressing from two directions. (from Powder Metallurgy Equipment Manual, MPIF, N.Y., 1968)

first type of ejection noted above (the more common for this simple compaction system). The pressure may be applied through a hydraulic or mechanical (cam, lever, toggle, or crank type) mechanism. This technique is used to produce relatively thin one level types of parts, over the entire density range. Such parts are termed Class I and are illustrated in Figure 3-2.

(2) *Double action compaction* signifies that the powder is compacted simultaneously from opposite directions by both the upper and lower punches. Equal or different amounts of pressure and movement may be applied from each direction. The lower punch also usually ejects the part in keeping with its upwards motion during pressing. Core rods may be stationary or movable. The actions of the lower punch and core rods may be actuated by cams or levers driven by the main hydraulic or mechanical drive or through a separate drive system. This technique may be used to produce one level parts over a broad thickness range, Class I and II as shown in Figure 3-2, and is illustrated in Figure 3-3.

(3) *Double action floating die compaction* denotes a system in which the lower punch remains stationary during the pressing part of the cycle, and the die is held in its original (top) position by a yieldable force (air, oil or springs). The upper punch descends and applies pressure to the powder. This pressure induces frictional forces between the powder and the surfaces of the die cavity. If these frictional forces exceed the supporting forces of the die, then the die descends as the upper punch moves downwards and the powder is compacted. The relative movement between the lower punch and the die, due to this movement, simulates pressure application from the lower punch. An external force may also be applied to the die so as to move it sooner (relying solely on friction may necessitate a large amount of upper punch movement) and at a faster rate. Part ejection may be achieved by moving the lower punch upward or by moving the die downward from the part in keeping with its original motion during pressing. Both mechanical and hydraulic drives are used. This type of system is illustrated in Figure 3-4 and is generally used to make Class I and II type parts as shown in Figure 3-2.

(4) *Multiple motion compaction* refers to systems usually consisting of a separate punch for each level of a multilevel part.

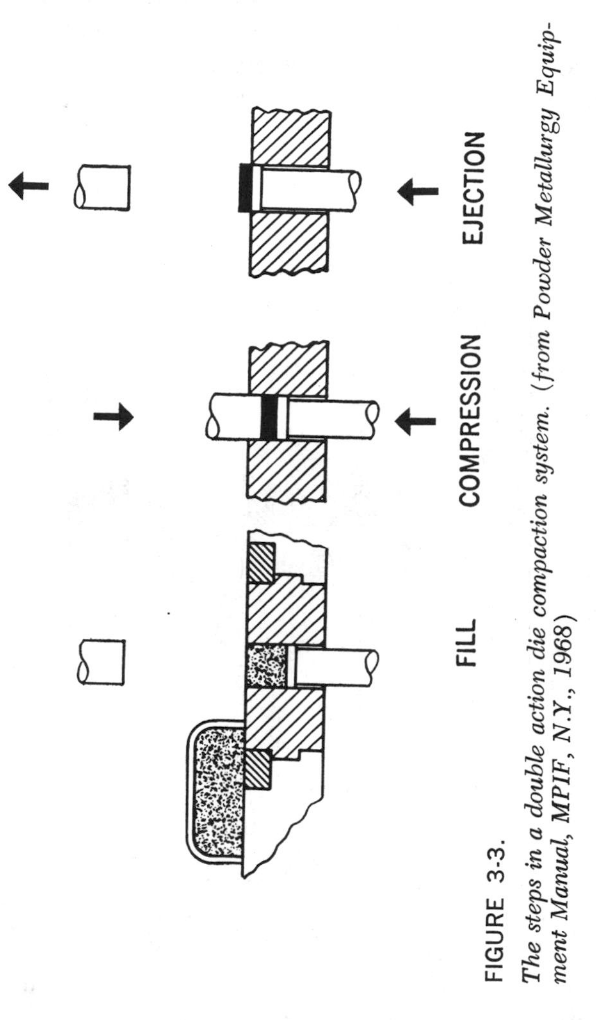

FIGURE 3-3.
The steps in a double action die compaction system. (from Powder Metallurgy Equipment Manual, MPIF, N.Y., 1968)

There are usually two or more movable lower and upper punches. The punches are positioned in precisely the manner necessary to form the various levels of the part. One or more movable core rods may be used and this represents an additional lower motion. Figure 3-5 shows a relatively simple multiple motion system for producing a flanged part. Each of the lower punches can be moved independently of each other, both to achieve the desired fill con-

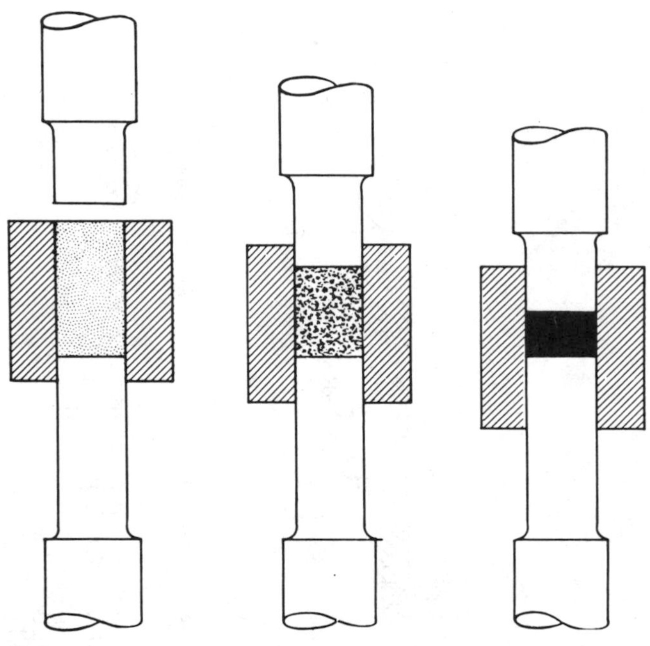

FIGURE 3-4.
The basic motions in a double action floating die compaction system. (from Powder Metallurgy Equipment Manual, MPIF, N.Y., 1968)

figuration and the desired size and density of each level of the compacted part. Various upper motions can also assist in controlling the size and density of the levels. Part ejection may be accomplished by having the lower punches move upward until they are flush with the top surface of the die. Alternatively, the die may be withdrawn and one or more of the lower punches moved to allow removal of the part from the compaction zone. Either mechanical or hydraulic drives or a combination of both may be used. This type of system is generally used for production of a wide variety of parts, Classes I, II, III and IV as shown in Figure 3-2, but usually more complex parts are made on this type of press.

(5) *Multiple motion floating die withdrawal compaction* is one of the more complex systems of compaction allowing the production of highly complex multilevel parts. All the lower punches, except the one forming the lowest surface of the part, are floating on air, oil or spring cushions and move downward as the part is being compacted. Their motion is stopped by adjustable stops. The

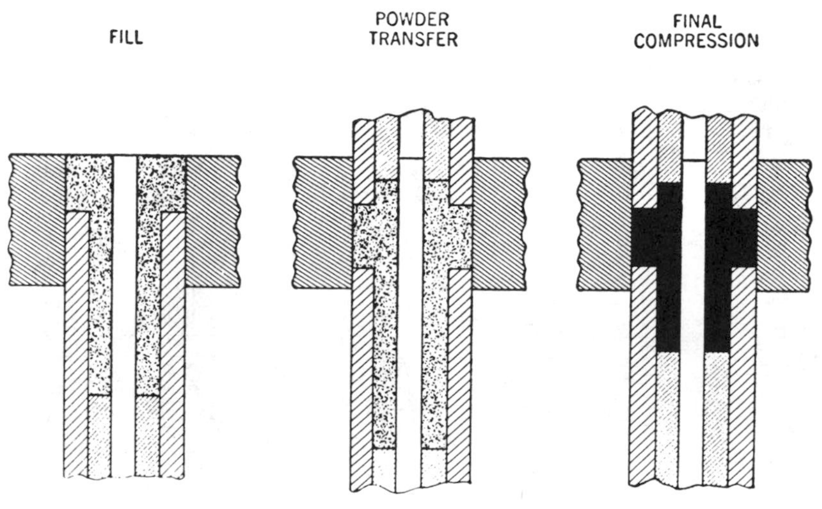

FIGURE 3-5.

The basic motions in a multiple motion compaction system. (from Powder Metallurgy Equipment Manual, MPIF, N.Y., 1968)

die also descends during compaction, either by overcoming the supporting forces by powder-die frictional forces or by an external source of pressure on the top surface of the die (or perhaps pulled down). Stationary or movable core rods may also be employed. The basic characteristic of this type of system is that all moving parts of the tooling descend during the entire pressing cycle. Only the punch forming the lowest level remains stationary at all times. Proper die fill and ejection require punch and die motion. This technique is illustrated in Figure 3-6 for a relatively simple part. Complex hydraulic or mechanical drives, or a combination of them are necessary. All the Classes of parts shown in Figure 3-2 may be made with this system.

(6) *Reflex action* systems represent a very sophisticated level of dynamic compaction and are particularly suited for complex multilevel parts, containing through holes or counterbores, with constant density throughout the entire object or certain levels. Equal pressure may be applied simultaneously from opposing directions on as many as five separate levels. The die moves upward during die filling to provide a desirable underfill action; this helps to prevent powder splashing from the die cavity when the

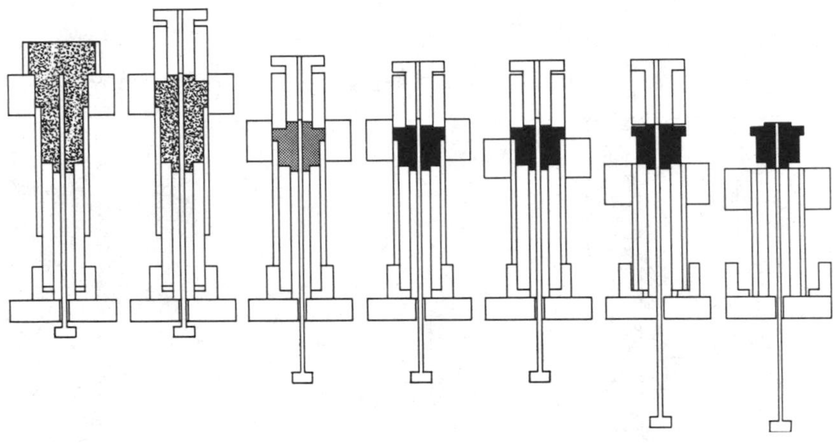

FIGURE 3-6.

The operation of a multiple motion floating die withdrawal compaction system. (from Powder Metallurgy Equipment Manual, MPIF, N.Y., 1968)

upper punches first contact the powder. During pressing the upper punches and die descend and the lower punches move upwards. Ejection is by withdrawal of the die coupled with punch motion. The movement of the press members comes about by each reacting in reflex to the original movement of the ram. This type of system is shown in Figure 3-7 for a rather complex part. A mechanical drive system is usually used to produce high pressures. All classes of parts may be made with this system; however, usually only relatively complex parts are made.

(7) *Rotary compaction* systems employ a number of identical tools mounted on a rotary table. The powder feeding device is in

a stationary position. Actual compaction is done at one position on the table. Die filling, underfilling, and ejection take place continuously as the tools move around the unit. A series of cams (upper and lower) induce proper upper and lower punch motion. The die cavities remain at the same position in the rotating table. Such presses provide a double action compaction; ejection is by the up-

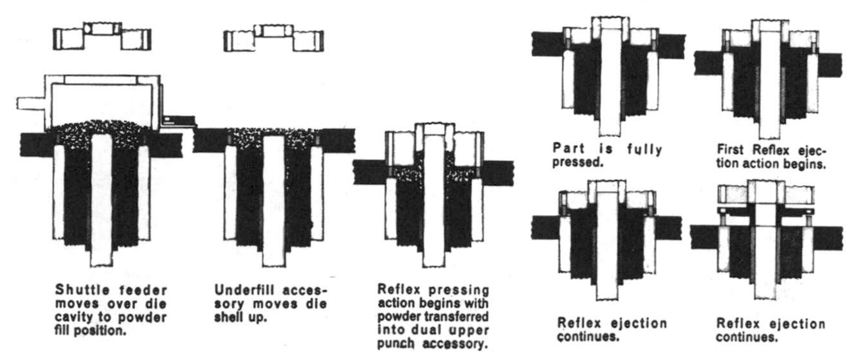

FIGURE 3-7.

The steps in a reflex action die compaction system. (from Powder Metallurgy Equipment Manual, MPIF, N.Y., 1968)

wards motion of the lower punch. The main advantage of this type of system is the high production rate. On some presses it is possible to produce two parts from each set of tools for each revolution of the table. This requires two feeding, compaction and ejection positions. An example of a rather simple system is given in Figure 3-8. As many as 50 sets of punches and dies can be mounted on one machine at one time. Production rates range from 72 to 1000 parts per minute. The chief disadvantage of this system is the high cost of tooling. The method is usually used to produce large numbers of relatively small parts of the Class I category with low to medium densities.

Isostatic compaction is the unique method in which pressures may be applied simultaneously and equally in all directions. It is discontinuous, is usually used at relatively high pressures, does not allow very high production rates and the powder is not suspended in a liquid. The most unique aspect of the method is that the powdered material is placed in a flexible rubbery container, that serves as a mold, which is tightly sealed against leakage (actually the mold may be evacuated to some extent to remove the air which would interfere with compaction, in die compaction this is not usually a problem because the air exits through the

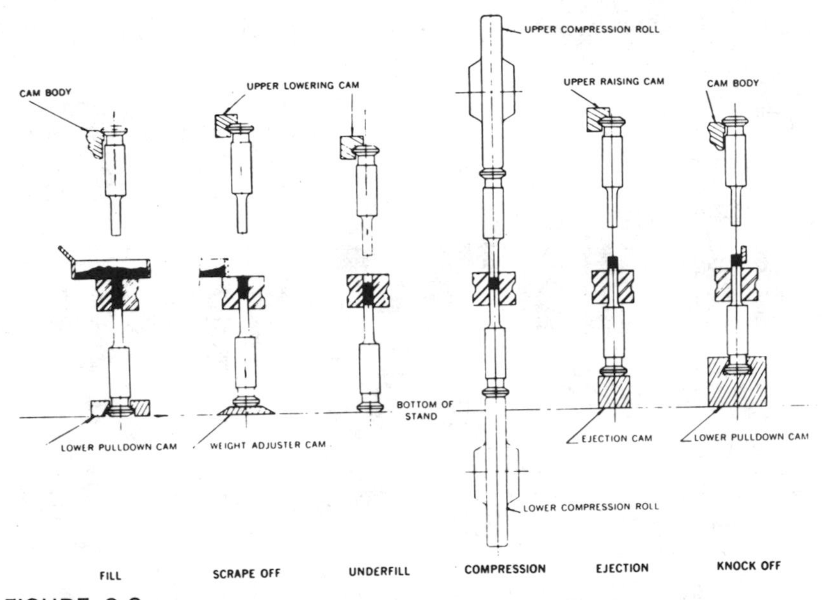

FIGURE 3-8.

The operation of a relatively simple rotary compaction system. (*from Powder Metallurgy Equipment Manual, MPIF, N.Y., 1968*)

clearances between the tooling during pressing). The container or mold is then immersed within a fluid bath within a pressure vessel, so that the fluid may be put under high pressures and, hence, exert a hydrostatic pressure on the powder. This approach is termed "wet bag tooling" and is illustrated in Figure 3-9; a perforated metal mold support may be used to give some rigidity to the mold without interfering with the application of pressure. Also shown in this figure is an alternative method of tooling termed "dry bag" in which the elastic mold may remain permanently in the pressure vessel; this approach lends itself to automated systems. In the wet bag case the mold must be stripped from each compact upon removal from the pressure vessel, and in many cases it is disposable.

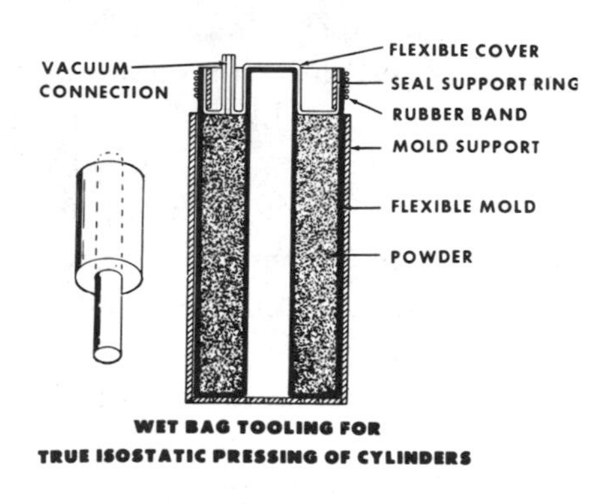

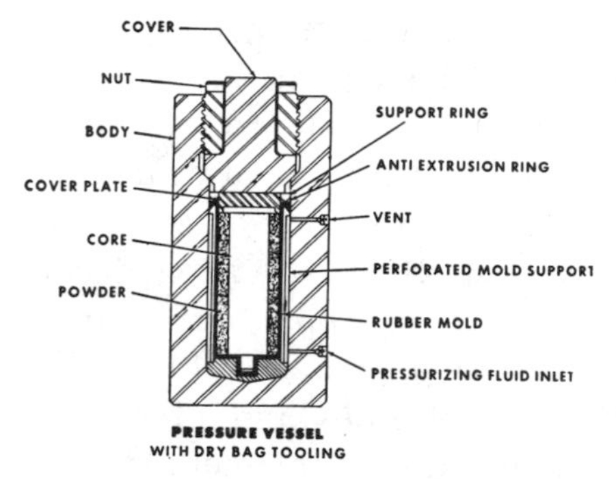

FIGURE 3-9.

Tooling systems used for isostatic compaction. (from Powder Metallurgy Equipment Manual, MPIF, N.Y., 1968)

Because pressure may be applied from all directions on to the powder mass it is possible to obtain a very uniform green density and a high degree of uniformity of properties. Powders which are in general very difficult to compact are more readily prepared with the isostatic approach than with die compaction. The method has been used extensively for ceramic materials rather than metals. Very complex shapes and high length to diameter ratios can be achieved that would be impossible to attain with conventional die compaction. Automated systems have been developed to increase production rates, but the average pressing time is in the order of 4 seconds and is relatively slow. It should be noted that the fluid used to transmit the pressure may be a liquid (usually water or oil) or a gas, the former is used for normal room temperature compaction and the latter for high temperature compaction.

High energy rate forming techniques are being used to a limited extent for closed die powder compaction. Several different methods of energy production have been developed including pneumatic mechanical, explosive and spark discharge techniques. The two unique features of this method are the very short time of pressure application, ranging from 50 milliseconds to 50 microseconds, and the very high amounts of energy imparted to the material. The latter is indicated both by the velocity of the moving ram, which may range from 10^3 to 2×10^4 fps, and the maximum pressure reached during the compaction, which may range from 10^6 to 15×10^6 psi. The most intriguing potential advantages of this method are: (1) both the lateral and axial dimensions of parts could be substantially increased; (2) both the magnitude and uniformity of density could be improved; (3) very cheap and low grade powders could be used; (4) parts might be used without any subsequent sintering due to the increased strength of the green compact. As with most other innovations in processing there are some major problems to overcome before commercial use can be made of the process; these include: (1) punch and die wear due to the high relative velocities and pressures; (2) dimensional control; (3) the automation of the method to allow rapid production rates; (4) expenses due to safety precautions and equipment maintenance; (5) adequate strength of dies, punches and core rods.

Forging of powders as a means of compaction has been used in a limited way. It is a technique developed for the production of fuel elements for nuclear reactors. It should be clear that at this time we are not considering the forging of powder metallurgy compacts (often termed preforms); this will be considered in Chapter Five. The technique of forging as applied to original compaction of loose powder consists of "canning" the powder in some type of metal container. Once the powder is within such an enclosure it can be evacuated or heated and eventually the assembly is treated in a conventional forging press. After forging the can material may be removed by chemical or mechanical means. The resulting compact can have a very high density and may require no sintering if the powder was heated prior to the forging step. The densification of the powder during the forging can take place very rapidly as shown by the data in Figure 3-10. In one stroke virtually complete densification is achieved.

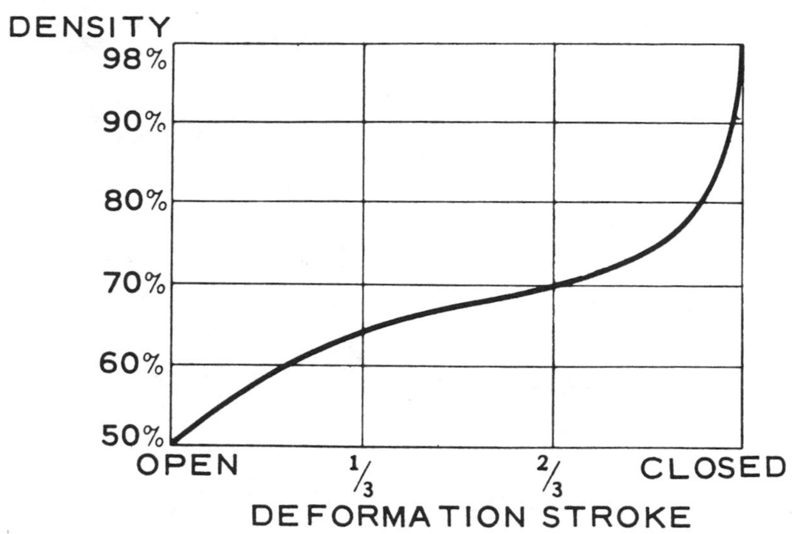

FIGURE 3-10.

Densification of canned beryllium powder during a forging stroke. (from N. G. Orell, in Beryllium, Univ. of Calif. Press, 1965, pp. 102–119)

Extrusion of a given amount of loose powder is another method of compaction that has been used in a limited way. As in the previous case the most practical procedure appears to be the canning of the powder. Once the powder is within the can it may be heated and perhaps evacuated; several variations of this approach are shown in Figure 3-11. Extrusion of the canned powder can yield extremely high densities and a product that does not have to be sintered if the powder was heated originally. Many different types of metals and alloys have been treated in this manner. Often the resulting properties are far superior to extruded materials made from cast ingots or wrought forms because segregation and excessive grain growth are avoided.

Vibratory compaction is very similar to the conventional die compaction method. In most cases the term vibratory compaction signifies the simultaneous application of pressure and vibration to a mass of powder within a rigid die. A vibratory-compacting machine is illustrated in Figure 3-12. Having both vibration and

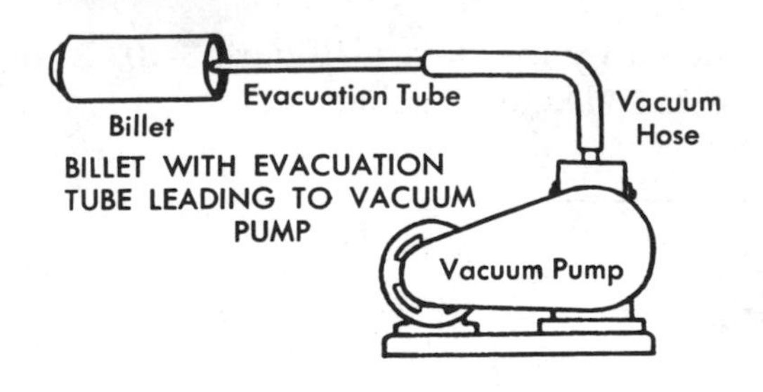

a

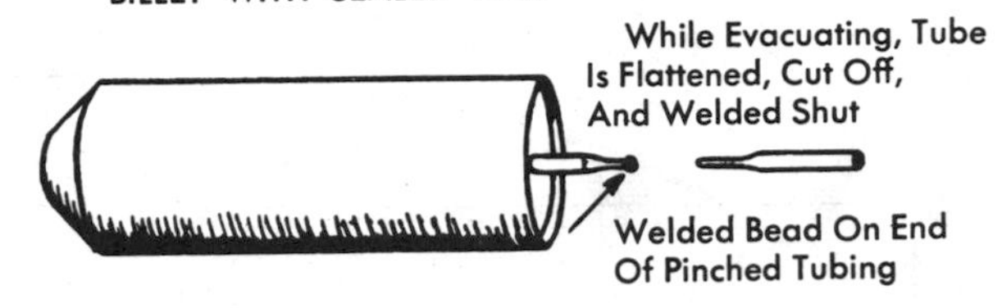

b

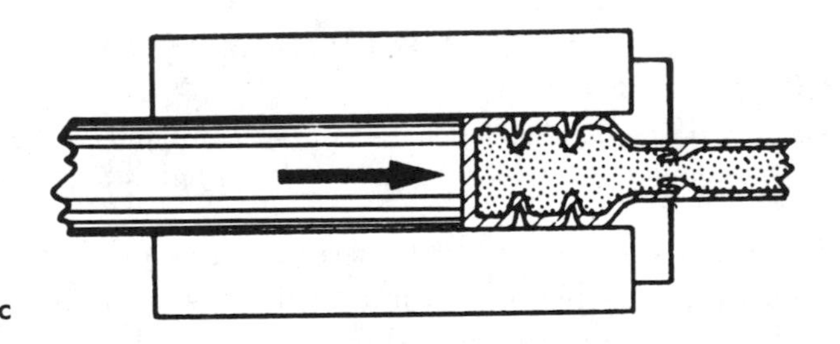

c

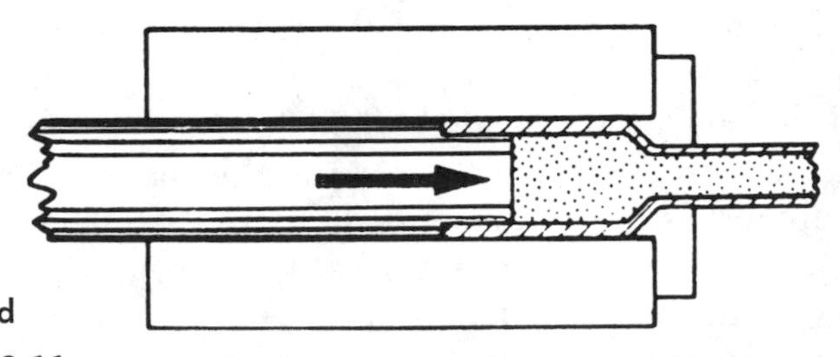

d

FIGURE 3-11.

Various techniques for extruding canned powders: (a) continuous evacuation of powder billet; (b) evacuation and sealing of powder billet; (c) folding of metal can with loosely packed powder; (d) penetrator technique to avoid folding of can. (from N. R. Gardner, A. D. Donaldson and F. M. Yans, Progress in Powder Metallurgy, vol. 19, pp. 135–141, 1963)

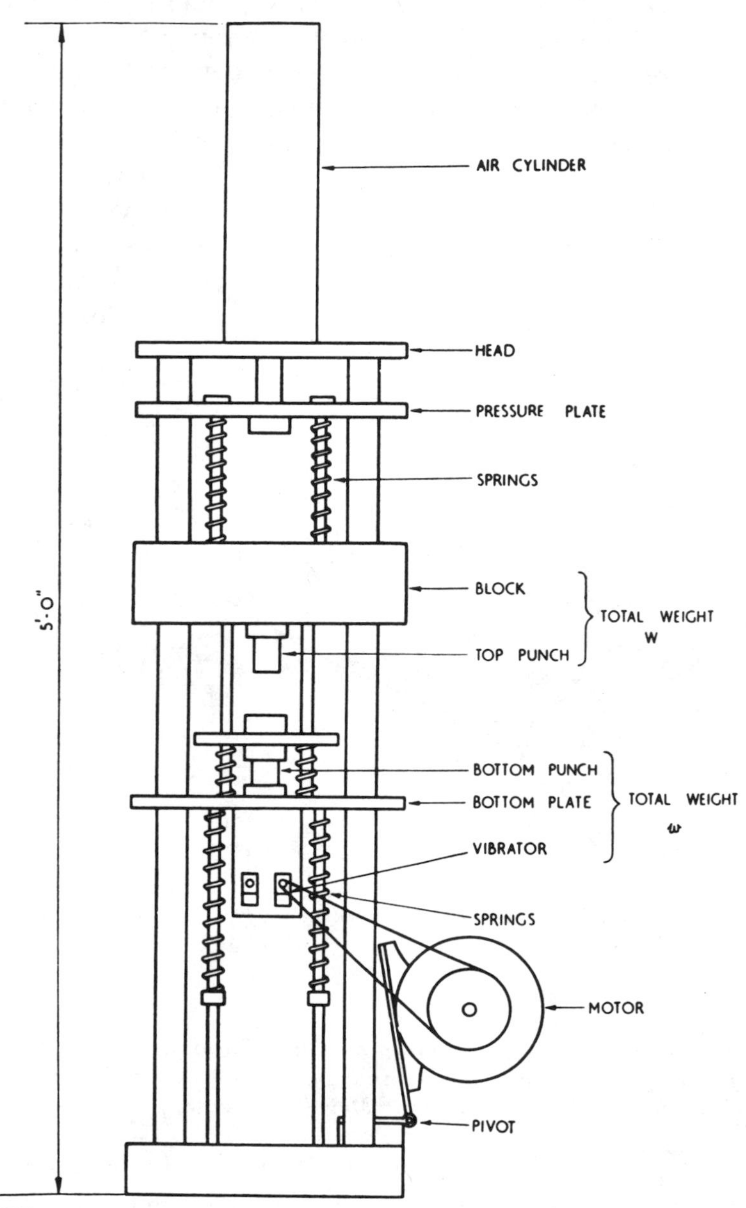

FIGURE 3-12.

Schematic illustration of a vibratory compaction apparatus. (from J. L. Brackpool and L. A. Phelps, in Powder Metallurgy, no. 7, pp. 213–227, 1964) pressure applied to the powder greatly promotes densification. In comparison to ordinary die compaction much lower pressures are required to achieve a given level of densification. The two main variables associated with the application of vibration are the frequency and amplitude. It is generally found that there is an optimum amplitude and frequency associated with any pressure, and also that there is an optimum pressure (not necessarily the greatest) for achieving the maximum densification. Some data illustrating the dependence of green density on pressure and frequency are given in Figure 3-13 for copper. One of the prob-

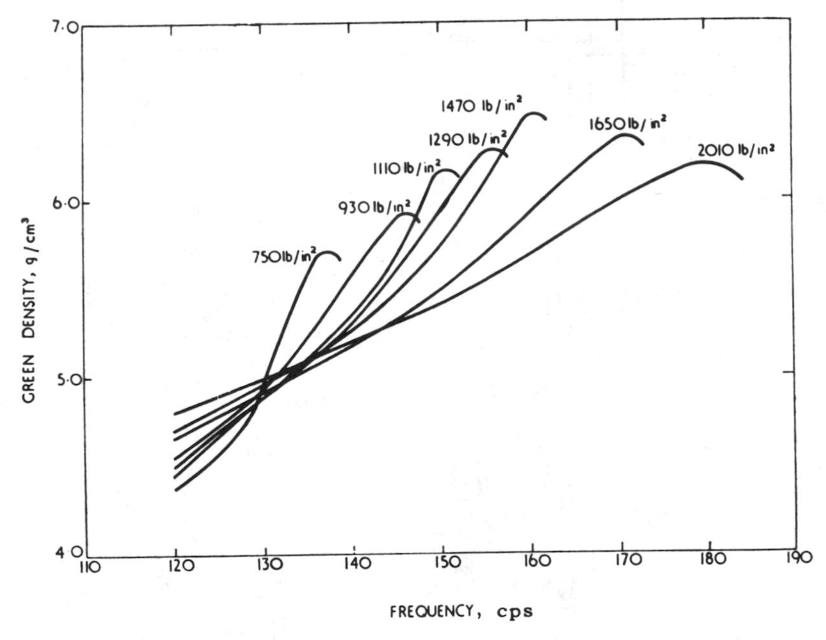

FIGURE 3-13.

Effect of variation in applied pressure on the density of copper at varying frequencies of vibratory compaction, amplitude 6.3×10^{-3} *in. (from J. L. Brackpool and L. A. Phelps, Powder Metallurgy, no. 7, pp. 213–227, 1964)*

lems associated with the difficulty in using this method commercially is the necessary equipment for achieving the vibration for practical tooling and presses. The method may offer more promise for ceramic type materials difficult to compact by more conventional means.

Continuous compaction refers to those techniques by which a relatively continuous compact is formed from loose powder (we are now considering the case of pressure continuous compaction). Usually the type of product being produced is considered a "mill shape"; that is, sheet, rod, tube and plate. Several major techniques are possible: (1) direct extrusion of loose powder, (2) direct rolling of loose powder and (3) a novel approach that may be termed "sequential motion" compaction. The continuous extrusion of loose powder to produce rods and bars has been largely experimental. Relatively few powders lend themselves to this type of treatment. The sequential motion compaction is also largely experimental at this time; the basic nature of this process is illustrated in Figure 3-14. The powder is held in some kind of form which moves along while given lengths are compacted. Powder rolling has achieved a significant level of commercial use. Nickel,

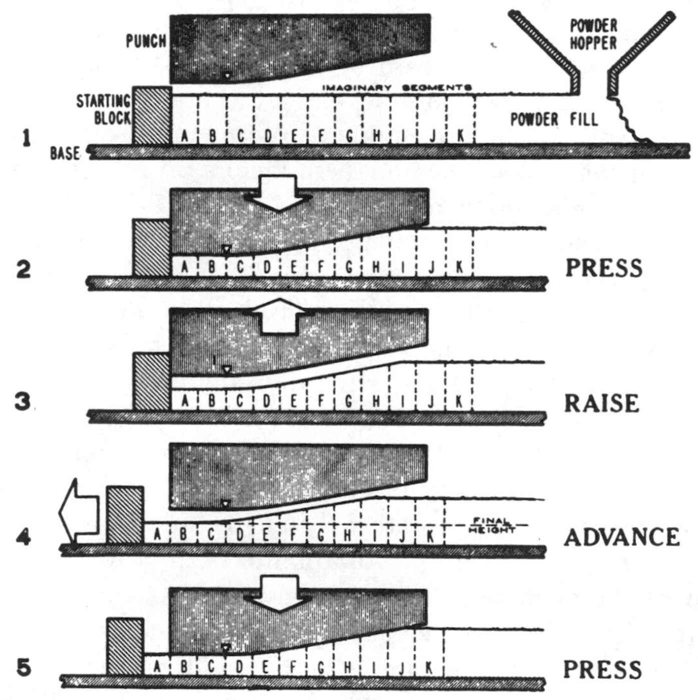

FIGURE 3-14.

The operations in sequential motion compaction. (from F. Emley and C. Deibel, Progress in Powder Metallurgy, vol. 15, pp. 5–13, 1959)

cobalt and aluminum sheet are being made in this manner, and many other ferrous and nonferrous metals and alloys have been produced on an experimental basis.

Superior properties in terms of magnitude and uniformity have been achieved by powder rolling. Very interesting layered composites (or clad materials) have also been made. Most of the commercial techniques involve flowing loose powder between a set of vertically oriented rolls. In this way gravity promotes the flow of the powder between the rolls. In most cases the rolling is done cold, although the powder may be heated somewhat prior to entering the mill. After the initial rolling the green sheet is usually sintered, then there may be additional cold or hot rolling. The green strip produced initially can easily have theoretical density. Increasing the roll diameter is an effective way to increase the thickness while maintaining a given density. The roll gap (open distance between the rolls) is a very important parameter in powder rolling. Increasing the roll gap causes a decrease in the green density and mechanical strength, an increase in thickness and weight per unit length, and ultimately a point is reached where the powder would no longer have sufficient coherency to form any sheet. Some data illustrating the dependence of these factors on roll gap for pure nickel sheet production are given in Figure 3-15. The surface roughness of the rolls is also important; as this increases the thickness of the sheet of a given density increases. Powders particularly useful for powder rolling may be considerably different than for use in die compaction. Their size and shape must be such so as to promote fast feeding of the powder in to the rolls as well as rapid compaction between the rolls. In general the speed of powder rolling is considerably slower than conventional rolling operations. The commercial use of powder rolling is very much linked to economic considerations rather than to technical ones.

Slip Casting has been used to a limited extent for metals; it is widely used for ceramics. The three basic components of a powder slip are: (1) the metal or ceramic powder, (2) a liquid vehicle to serve as a suspending medium and (3) additives such as suspension agents and deflocculants, which prevent particle settling, and binders. The process consists of preparing the slip, filling of a mold made of a fluid absorbing material, such as plaster-of-paris, with the slip, removal of the "slip casting" from the mold, drying and sintering of the compact. The most commonly used liquid vehicle is water, although alcohols and other organic liquids have been used. The three basic requirements of the liquid are proper

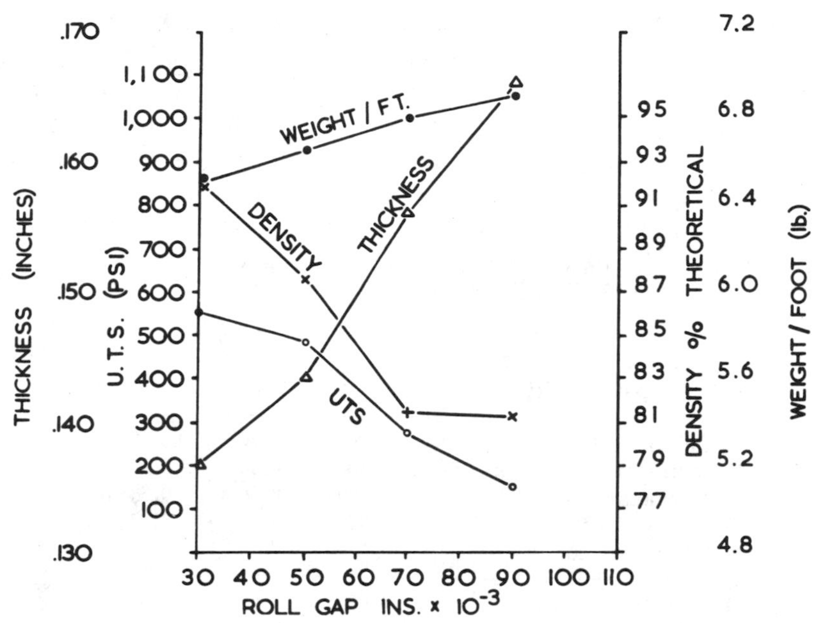

FIGURE 3-15.

The dependence of green strip properties on roll gap for pure nickel. (*from M. H. D. Blore, V. Silins, S. Romanchuk, T. W. Benz and V. N. Mackiw, Metals Engineering Quarterly, vol. 6, no. 2, pp. 54–60, 1966*)

viscosity, chemical stability, and adequate fluidity to permit proper mold filling. In order to produce a homogeneous compact, powder settling must be avoided during the casting process and, hence, the usual necessity of additives which help keep the particles suspended. Some additives act as binders to improve the strength of the green compact. Both high and low density materials may be made by this technique; however, because the green density is often quite low there is much shrinkage during sintering in order to achieve high sintered densities, and this is undesirable for commercial practice.

Because no pressures are used, dimensions and part complexity can be significantly greater than conventionally prepared parts, if adequate green strength can be obtained. The process does not lend itself to high production rates. This is due in part to the long times (usually many hours) necessary to leave the casting in the mold and allow capillary action to remove the liquid through the porosity in the mold. Many other factors enter into the proper design of the technique, these include: (a) the liquid-to-metal ratio (green strength, green and sintered densities decrease as the ratio increases; some data illustrating these effects are given in Table 3-1); (b) the type and amount of binder additive (although

TABLE 3-1. Effect of Water Content on the Slip Conditions and the Properties of Test Specimens

	Water content %		
Slip composition[1]	15.0	17.0	19.0
Metal powder[2]	84.70	82.70	80.70
Deflocculant (superloid)	0.30	0.30	0.30
Water/metal ratio	0.1771	0.2056	0.2354
Specific gravity, g/cc	3.87	3.57	3.37
Specimen conditions			
Density, g/cc, as cast	3.03	4.96	4.88
Density, g/cc, as dried[3]	4.77	4.70	4.62
Density, g/cc, as sintered[4]	7.18	7.08	6.94
Green strength, psi (as dried)	910	804	743

[1] Adjusted to pH = 10.
[2] 316 type SS 80%, −325 mesh, 20% −100 + 150 mesh.
[3] for 2 hr at 50°C in air.
[4] for 2 hr at 1300°C in dried hydrogen.

(from H. H. Hausner, Proc. MPIF, vol. 14, 1958, pp. 79–90)

the green strength increases as the amount of binder increases, the green and sintered densities decrease); (c) the proper design and materials of the mold; (d) careful consideration of both the magnitude and uniformity of shrinkage due to sintering; (e) proper drying methods to remove all moisture prior to sintering. This technique if often considered for materials that are relatively incompressible by conventional pressure die compaction.

Gravity compaction simply refers to filling a die with the loose powder and sintering the powder in this die (often referred to as "pressureless molding," "gravity sintering," or "loose sintering"). The obvious factor to concern one is the chemical inertness of the die with respect to the powder at the high sintering temperatures. For metals various ceramics, such as oxides and carbides, and graphite may be used as the die material. The process is not used to any great extent on a commercial basis except for the production of P/M filters. This is due not only to the above noted problem but also because of such factors as: (a) difficulty of part removal after sintering; (b) adequate die filling especially for complex shapes; (c) high amounts of shrinkage due to sintering; (d) necessity of large amounts of molds for high production rates; (e) sensitivity of powder to vibrations.

Continuous pressureless compaction is often used to produce porous sheet. The process (sometimes referred to as "slurry coating") usually consists of preparing a slurry of the metal powder, a liquid and various chemical additives that act as pore formers or viscosity conditioners and perhaps as binders. The slurry can then be coated on to a metal screen or solid metal sheet. It may then be passed through a set of rolls that applies virtually no pressure to the mass but controls the thickness of the slurry on the base support. Heating to dry the material may precede actual sintering of the sheet in a continuous manner. Very high porosity sheet (up to 90 volume % porosity) has been made in this manner for use as electrodes in nickel-cadmium rechargeable batteries and fuel cells. Porous coatings of various metals have been applied to conventional ferrous sheet stock to produce unusual composites.

3.3 BEHAVIOR OF POWDER DURING COMPACTION

What happens to the powder during compaction is one of the most fundamental phenomena in powder metallurgy. (Unless otherwise noted this and subsequent discussions are concerned with conventional die compaction techniques.) Surprisingly, relatively little direct experimental work has been carried out in this area.

Two basic processes occur during compaction under pressure:

(1) bulk movement of particles
(2) deformation and fracture of particles.

Bulk movement and rearrangement of particles will result in a more efficient packing of the powder; that is, densification. Such movement is limited by the frictional forces developed between neighboring particles and between particles and die, punch and core rod surfaces. The relative ease of such motion increases with decreasing apparent density of the powder. That is, with low apparent densities there is less particle-to-particle contact and more free space into which particles may move. It would also be expected that small particles could move relatively greater distances because of their ability to pass through the small channels among the particles. Although the bulk of the motion will be in the direction of the pressure application, in the case of die compaction, there will be some lateral motion due to the restraining action of blocking particles and the availability of free spaces. Naturally all powder characteristics that increase the frictional forces will reduce the extent of bulk particle movement. The movement of particles within the powder mass tends to take place at relatively low pressures and accounts for the early densification of the material. Additionally, the rate of pressure application would be expected to influence this bulk movement. High rates of pressure application will tend to cause premature immobilization of particles due to high compressive stresses being developed on the particles which will tend to block open passages.

Deformation of individual particles can also reduce the amount of porosity in the compact. Certainly with regard to the production of high density parts it is the major mechanism of densification. Both elastic and plastic deformation may occur. Most elastic deformation of course will be recovered when the stress is removed from the compact; this may take place before, during and after ejection from the die cavity. It is for this reason that compacts usually have dimensions slightly greater than the die dimensions. The extent of elastic deformation will increase with decreasing elastic modulus values and increasing values of particle stress relative to the yield stress or elastic limit of the material.

The actual stresses in individual particles remains as one of the undetermined factors concerning compaction. It is safe to say that these actual stresses may be radically different, both in magnitude and nature (tensile, compressive or shear), than the stress on the compact simply obtained by dividing the compaction load by the cross-sectional area of the compact. Then too, there is surely a wide variation of stresses throughout the compact.

Except for porous types of parts, plastic deformation of individual particles usually represents the most important mechanism of densification during compaction. Although there are some cases where evidence has been presented which indicates that no plastic deformation has occurred. The quantitative measurement of the extent of plasticity during compaction is far from comprehensive. It is evident that the greater the actual pressures on the particles, the greater the degree of plastic deformation. Rapid rates of pressure application may affect this process, but exactly how is not certain. Most materials work harden significantly, so that it becomes increasingly more difficult to improve densification by increasing the pressure on the compact. On this basis the effectiveness of the external pressure is greatest at low pressures where plastic deformation occurs relatively easily, and becomes progressively less effective with increasing pressure. There are several other factors which will determine the degree of plastic strain; in general the weakest materials are the most desirable to optimize this process. This means that it is best to use single phase materials, pure metals rather than alloys, and well annealed materials. A fine grain size is also desirable. Again, it should be realized that there will be a nonuniform stress distribution throughout the compact and, hence, varying degrees of plastic strain. Also, stress transfer between adjacent particles will depend on particle surface topography and particle size and shape. It is likely that there may be more surface deformation of particles than true volume strain.

One method of demonstrating the extent and importance of plastic deformation during compaction is to measure the increases in the microhardness of individual particles after varying amounts of compaction. The increase in hardness is a direct result of the work hardening due to plastic deformation. Such increases may then be correlated with similar increases induced through controlled deformation of the same metal. Such an approach was used to obtain the data in Figure 3-16 relating percent deforma-

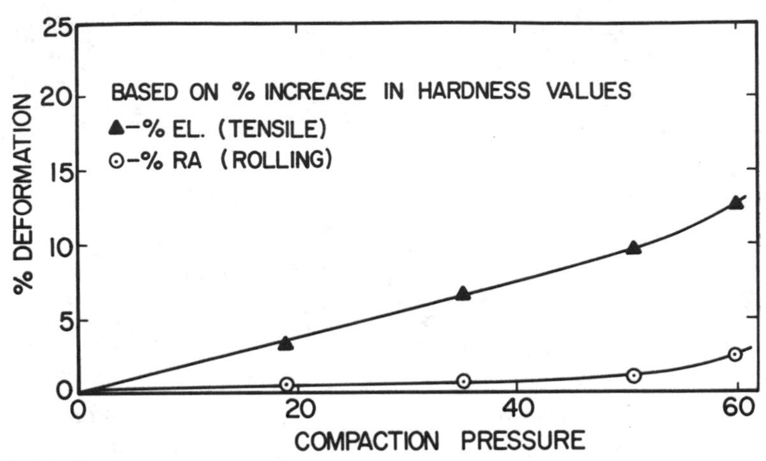

FIGURE 3-16.

The dependence of plastic deformation in individual particles on compaction pressure (tsi) for an atomized iron powder. (from J. S. Hirschhorn and M. W. Garey, Int. J. Powder Met., Vol. 5, no. 1, pp. 35–44, 1969)

tion to compaction pressure for a high compressibility atomized iron powder. It can be seen that in terms of tensile elongation there is a very considerable amount of plastic strain even at relatively low compaction pressures.

Naturally, it is possible that the stresses in individual particles become so high that the fracture stress of the particular material is exceeded. This would lead to fragmentation of particles during compaction. Materials with limited plasticity or ductility compacted at relatively high pressures will tend to exhibit this behavior. Also porous types of powders often undergo such fracturing because of the small cross-sections of the solid metal and the concomitant high localized stresses. This process of fracturing generally leads to densification also. The small fractured pieces can easily move into adjacent pores.

It should be noted that the processes of particle movement and deformation occur to a greater extent and in a much more uniform manner for isostatic type compacts. In this case the application of pressure on all surfaces of the compact induces a more intensive and uniform stress distribution within the compact. And in HERF techniques the extremely high pressures used cause an extremely high amount of plastic deformation and particle fracture often leading to complete densification. On the other hand, vibratory compaction would tend to promote densification by optimizing particle motion and rearrangement rather than deformation and fracture. The compaction techniques involving rolling, forging and extrusion of powders generally promote deformation and fracture of particles.

Porosity in green compacts is an important consideration and very much related to the above noted processes. Densification by particle movement, deformation and fracture implies that free space filled with air is replaced with solid material. This can take place as long as the air can exit from the powder mass; however, during compaction and densification one of the basic changes that takes place is the closing off of porosity so as to form isolated pores. Once pores become isolated it is extremely difficult to have solid material fill in that space. This entrapped air may have importance with respect to subsequent processing of the compact. Some data on entrapped air in die compacted electrolytic iron compacts are given in Table 3-2. In general the greater the green

TABLE 3-2. Data on Entrapped Air in Electrolytic Iron Compacts

Compaction Press. (tsi)[a]	Green Density (gm/cc)	Porosity (%)	Entrapped Air %[b]	Entrapped Air Pressure (atm)[c]	Release Time for entrapped air (hr)[d]
12	5.3	32.7	75	2.5	<0.5
22	6.0	23.8	82	4.0	1–2
40	6.35	19.3	86	5.0	17
80	7.35	6.6	78	15.5	21

(a) single end compacted at room temperature; thin cylindrical compacts
(b) percent of gas present in powder voids before compacting (in the loose powder)
(c) assuming an average of 80% of original gas entrapped
(d) for the bulk of the entrapped gas, at atmospheric pressure

(from J. Williams, "Trapping of Gases in Cold-Compacted Powders," J. Iron and Steel Inst., Sept. 1952, pp. 19–24) density the greater the amount of entrapped air and the absolute pressure of it within the compact, and the longer it takes for such

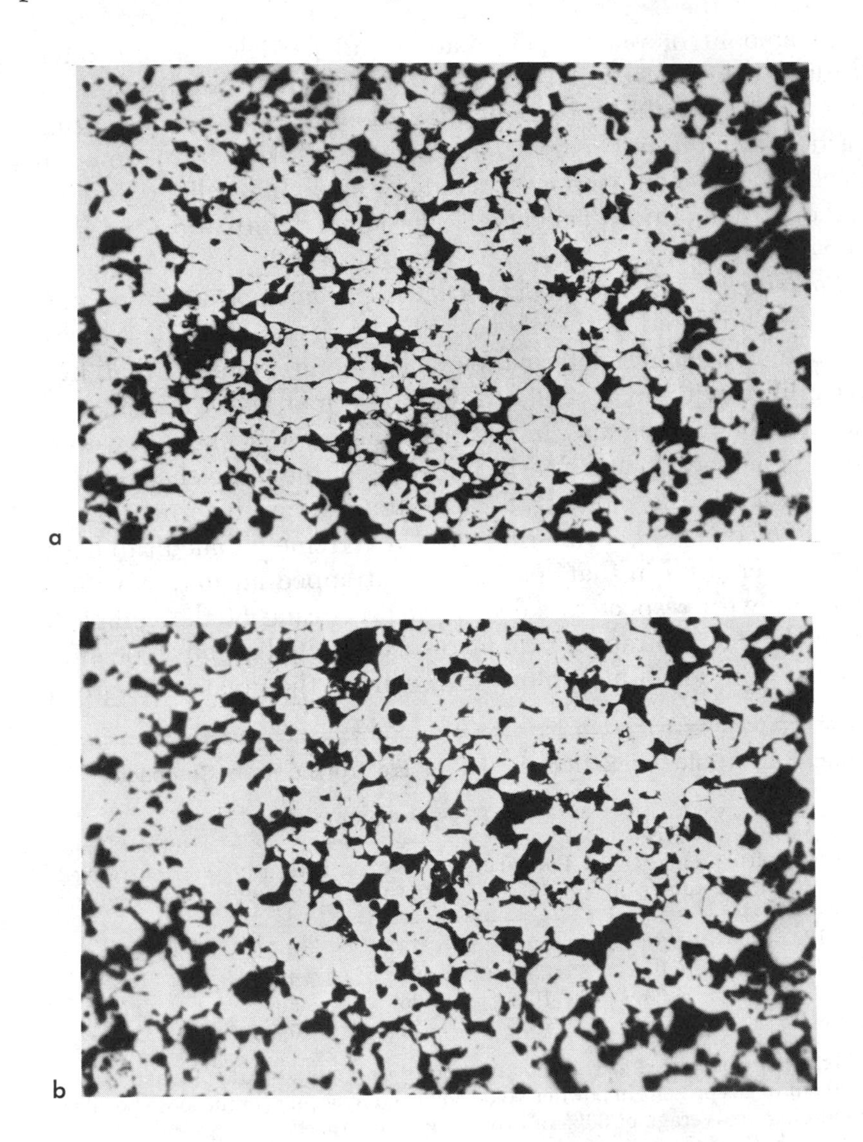

FIGURE 3-17.

Photomicrographs of cross sections of 316 stainless steel green compacts pressed at 50 tsi: (a) section parallel to pressing direction (100 ×); (b) section perpendicular to pressing direction (100 ×). (from G. J. Pearson, M.S. Thesis, Univ. of Wisconsin, 1967)

air to leave the compact under normal atmospheric conditions. Reducing the original particle size and using porous particles would promote such air entrapment.

Another basic change is the effect of increasing densification resulting from particle deformation on the shape of the porosity in the green compact. Although it is rather difficult to prepare green compacts metallographically so as to study the porosity, it is possible to show that in conventional die compaction there is a strong tendency to flatten the pores. The flattening comes about because of the greater deformation in the direction parallel to the compaction direction. Thus, if one examines a cross-section of a simple compact in planes parallel and perpendicular to the pressing direction, then this difference in pore shape may be observed. Such photomicrographs for a stainless steel compact are given in Figure 3-17. Careful examination of these will reveal the difference in pore shape; in the plane perpendicular to the pressing direction the pores are more equiaxed. Actual quantitative measurements on such photomicrographs can be made to further illustrate this effect. The width (the vertical dimension) and the length (the horizontal dimension) of the pores can be measured and these distributions obtained for the planes parallel and perpendicular to the pressing direction. In the former case the width corresponds to the dimension parallel to the pressing direction and the length perpendicular to it. If pore flattening has occurred, then the distributions are similar to the ones of Figure 3-18. The width and length distributions are virtually identical for the plane perpendicular to the pressing direction, while for the other one the width distribution is shifted to smaller values.

A series of photomicrographs of the cross-sections of isostatically prepared iron compacts over a broad compaction pressure range are given in Figure 3-19. It should be noted that as the compaction pressure increases from about 3 tsi to over 60 tsi the total amount of porosity decreases. But of greater interest is the transition from a high degree of interconnected porosity to greater amounts of isolated pores. It is this effect which allows highly porous P/M parts to be made for which the interconnected porosity can serve some useful function, such as oil or plastic impregnation or metal infiltration.

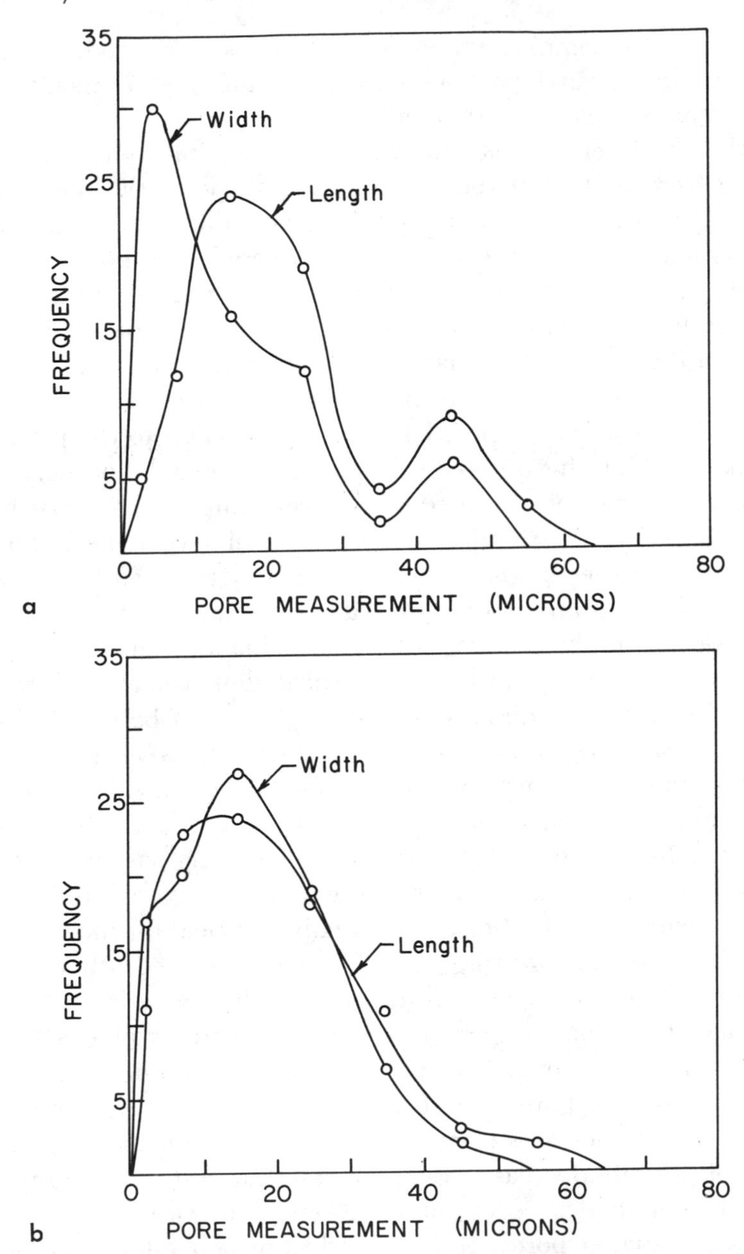

FIGURE 3-18.

Pore width and length distributions in 316 stainless steel green compacts pressed at 50 tsi: (a) in a plane parallel to pressing direction; (b) in a plane perpendicular to pressing direction. (from G. J. Pearson, M.S. Thesis, Univ. of Wisconsin, 1967)

3.4 GREEN COMPACT DENSITY

One of the most useful properties in powder metallurgy is the density of the as-compacted material or green compact. It is not only a measure of the effectiveness of compaction with regard to densification but also determines the behavior of the material during subsequent sintering. The general dependence of green density on several prime variables is shown schematically in Figure 3-20. *It is generally found that green density increases with:*

(1) *increasing compaction pressure,*
(2) *increasing particle size (or increasing apparent density),*
(3) *decreasing hardness and strength of the particles,*
(4) *decreasing compaction speed.*

Considering the discussion in the previous section the following basic explanations for the above are: (1) increasing the compaction pressure promotes particle movement, deformation and fracture; (2) increasing the particle size, which also leads to an increase in apparent density (as well as other particle characteristics leading to this), promotes particle movement and a more desirable distribution of stresses within the powder mass leading to greater deformation; (3) decreasing the hardness and strength of the particles simply promotes deformation; (4) decreasing the compaction speed promotes particle movement (it should be noted that for HERF type compaction although the speed is great there is also a very high pressure, and the latter is much more effective than the former). Some actual data illustrating the dependence of green density on particle size are given in Table 3-3, and on apparent density in Figure 3-21. Changing an actual somewhat complex size distribution in such a way that an increase in apparent density results normally leads to an increase in green density for a given material.

Although it is customary to deal with single values of green density for compacts it must be realized that in most compacts

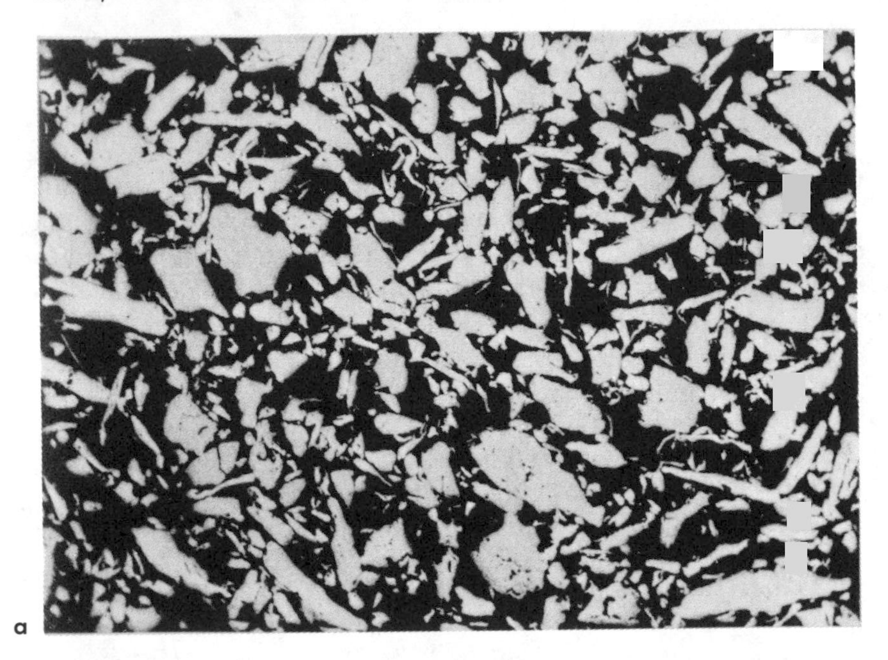

a

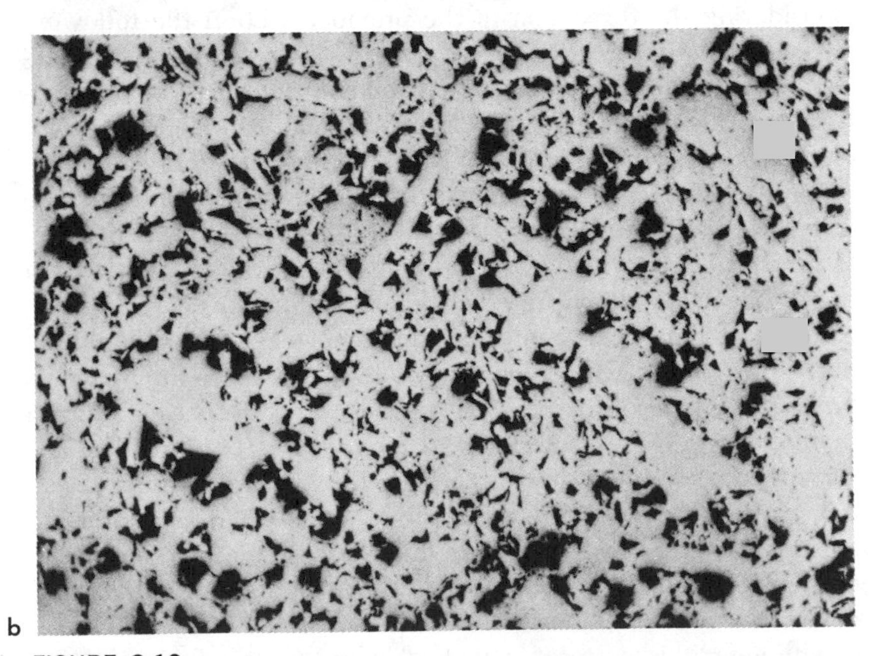

b

FIGURE 3-19.

Photomicrographs of sections of green iron isostatic compacts pressed at (a) 3.2 tsi, (b) 19.4 tsi, (c) 38.7 tsi and (d) 60.5 tsi, (100 ×). (from G.

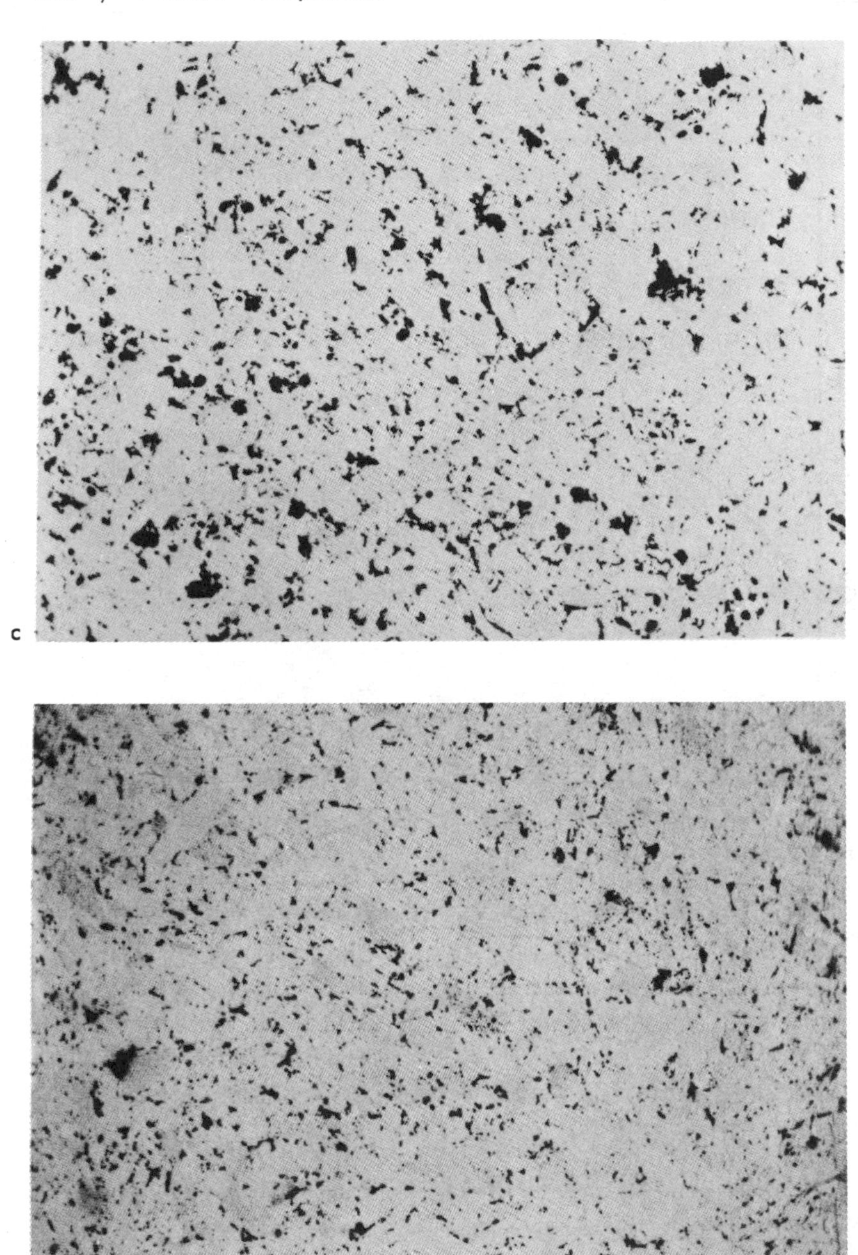

Bockstiegel, in Modern Developments in Powder Metallurgy, vol. 1, H. H. Hausner, editor, Plenum, N.Y., 1966, pp. 155–187)

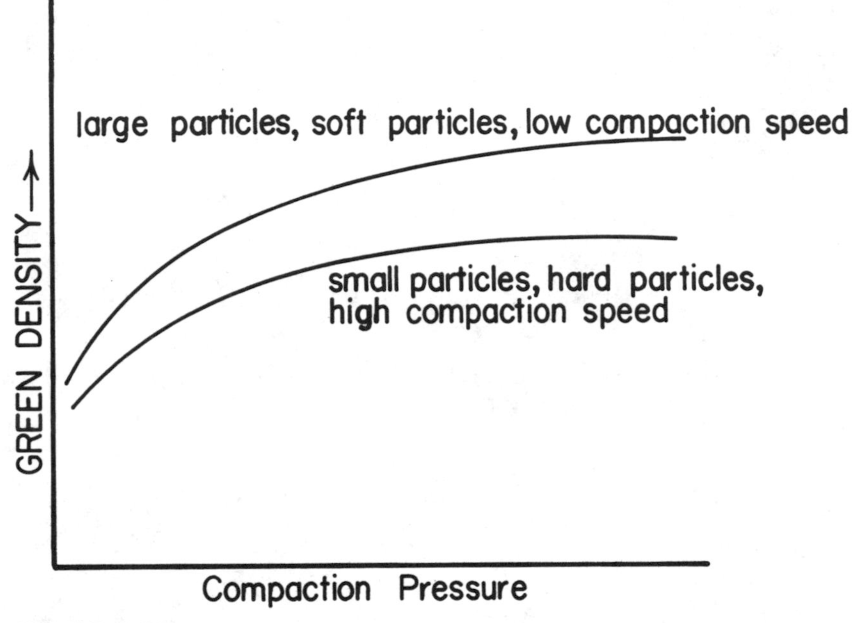

FIGURE 3-20.

Schematic illustration of dependence of green density on compaction pressure, particle size, particle hardness and compaction speed.

TABLE 3-3. Effect of Particle Size on Green Density

Material	Particle Size	Compaction Pressure (tsi)	Green Density (gm/cc)
Copper[a]	2 microns	30	6.94
	44–74 microns	30	7.65
Iron[b]	100% −325 mesh	30	6.15
	22% −325 mesh	30	6.54
316 stainless steel	100% +325 mesh	50	6.32
	100% −325 mesh	50	6.42

(a) from H. H. Hausner, Powder Metallurgy, Chemical Publishing, 1947, p. 66

(b) from C. E. Van Buren and H. H. Hirsch, in Powder Metallurgy, W. Leszynski, editor, Interscience, New York, 1960, pp. 403–440

there is a density distribution. These density distributions result from stress distributions within the compact, and the latter result chiefly from frictional forces developed at the die wall. Such stress distributions affect both particle movement and deformation. Al-

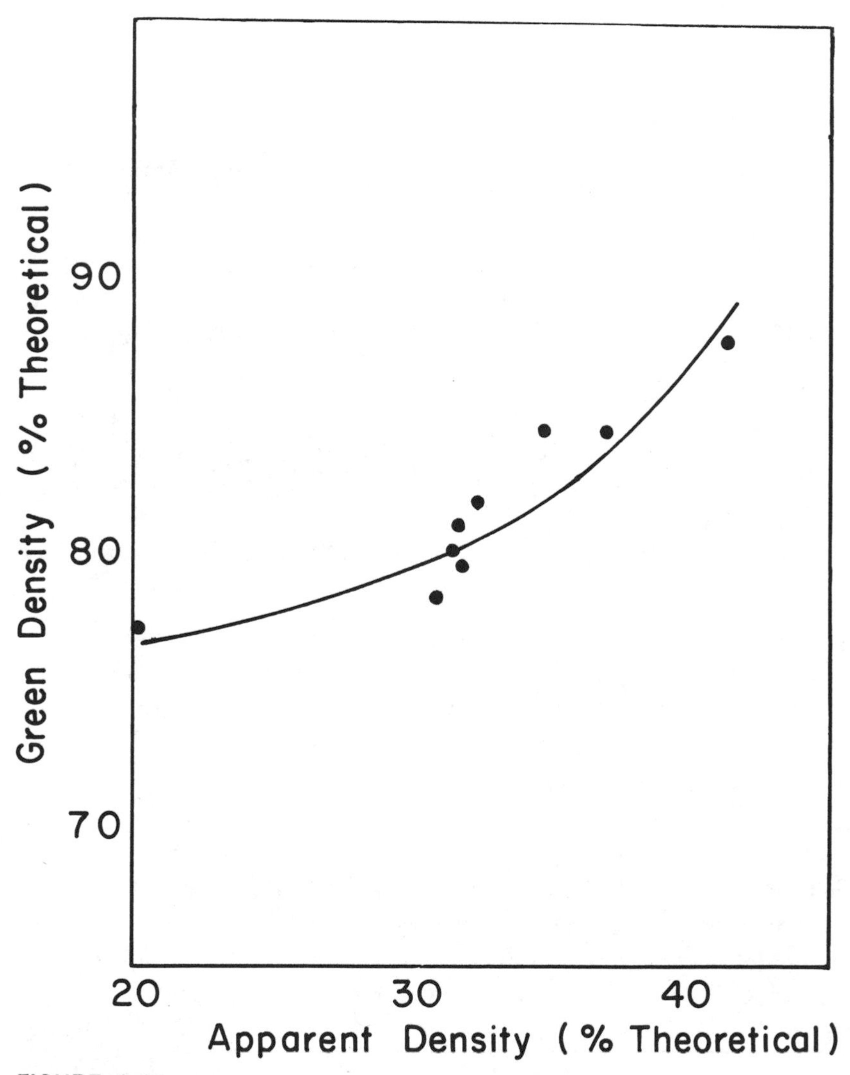

FIGURE 3-21.

Dependence of green density (at 30 tsi) on apparent density for different iron powders.

though a certain load is applied to the powder in the die, some fraction of this load is transferred to the die wall because of the friction developed there; that is, particles are moving in the direction of the moving punch, but are being inhibited by the die sur-

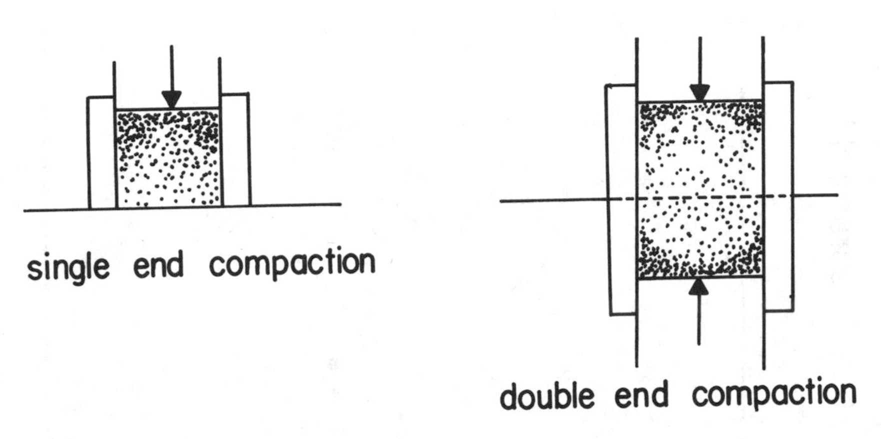

FIGURE 3-22.
Schematic illustration of basic green density distribution for single and double end die compaction.

face and other particles. Particles near the punch surface first move rather easily during the initial stages of compaction. This is particularly true in the central region, away from the die wall. This results in high densities and increased particle-die wall contact and frictional forces in the outer regions (near the die wall) of the powder mass near the moving punch. As compaction continues the particles furthest away from the punch move smaller distances and more porosity is retained in those regions. The extent of plastic deformation will increase with increasing particle-to-particle contact, which results from particle movement. Consequently, there will be less deformation at large distances from the moving punch. There is sometimes greater deformation and high density in a region some distance away from the punch, and in the center of the compact, because of the greater particle motion in the upper central region noted above. Understanding density distribution in a green compact becomes extremely important in developing properties and avoiding laminations in the finished P/M part. Here proper tooling design is most critical, as will be discussed later.

Actual density distributions may be obtained by sectioning techniques or by hardness measurements. The kinds of basic density distributions observed experimentally for simple cylindrical compacts and either single or double action compaction are shown schematically in Figure 3-22. Applying pressure from both ends simply results in the formation of the mirror image of the density distribution in the bottom half of the compact. An actual density distribution for a single end compacted nickel specimen is given in Figure 3-23.

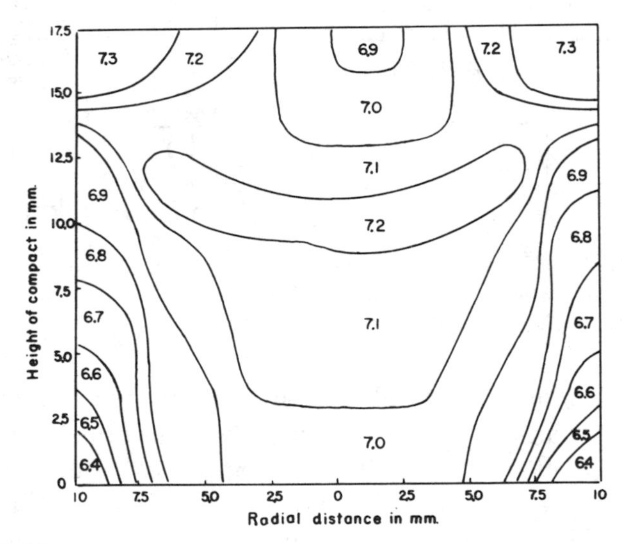

FIGURE 3-23.

Actual green density (in gm/cc) distribution for pure nickel, compacted at 46 tsi in single action press, L/D = 0.87. (from G. C. Kuczynski and I. Zaplatynskyj, Trans. AIME, vol. 206, p. 215, 1956)

A green density distribution is very much dependent on the length to diameter (L/D) ratio of the compact. This effect is shown schematically in Figure 3-24. If the L/D ratio is reduced, then the density distribution is minimized. This comes about simply because by decreasing the ratio the volume of the compact furthest away from the source of pressure is reduced. Pressing from both ends is very effective in reducing the density distribution, but unless the L/D ratio is quite low there will be a low

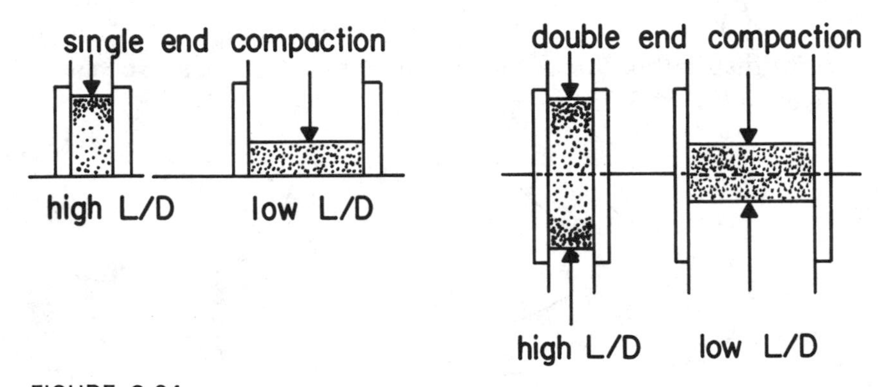

FIGURE 3-24.

Schematic illustration of green density distributions for high and low L/D ratios, both for single and double end compaction.

density region in the central portion of the compact. Some actual density distributions (given in terms of regions of equal pressure) for compacts of varying L/D ratios compacted from one end are given in Figure 3-25. With a ratio of less than onehalf there is a very good distribution; that is, relatively little variation in density from top to bottom, and from inside to outside. However, with ratios of about 0.8 and 1.7 there is an extreme variation in density; in particular the bottom of the compacts represents a very low density region. It is this decrease in density with increasing length that limits the thickness of compacts made with simple single action compaction systems, and even with double action compaction there is a limitation to the L/D ratio that can be made. Isostatic pressing essentially eliminates these problems; at the most there is a slight decrease in density going from the outside to the inside of the compacts.

The importance of the L/D ratio in die compaction can also be

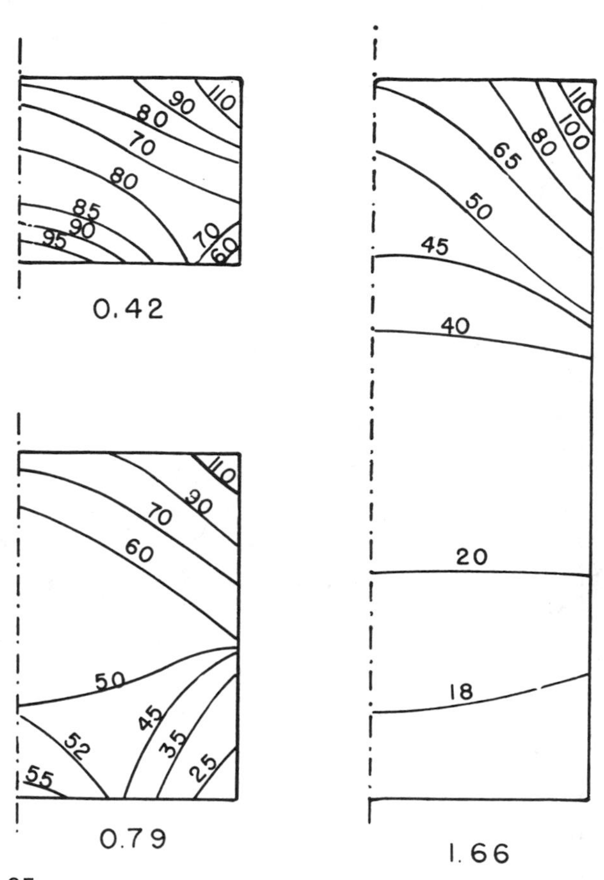

FIGURE 3-25.

Actual green density distributions (in terms of regions of equal pressure) for copper compacts, pressed at 50 tsi in a single action press, of varying L/D ratios. (from P. Duwez and L. Zwell, Trans. AIME, vol. 185, pp. 137–144, 1949)

assessed by considering the ratio of the real pressure acting on the lower stationary punch (single end compaction) to the nominal pressure applied to the upper punch. Some data illustrating this effect are given in Figure 3-26. This type of analysis dramatically shows that as the L/D ratio increases there is a greater loss of pressure (or energy) to the die walls so that there is less pressure

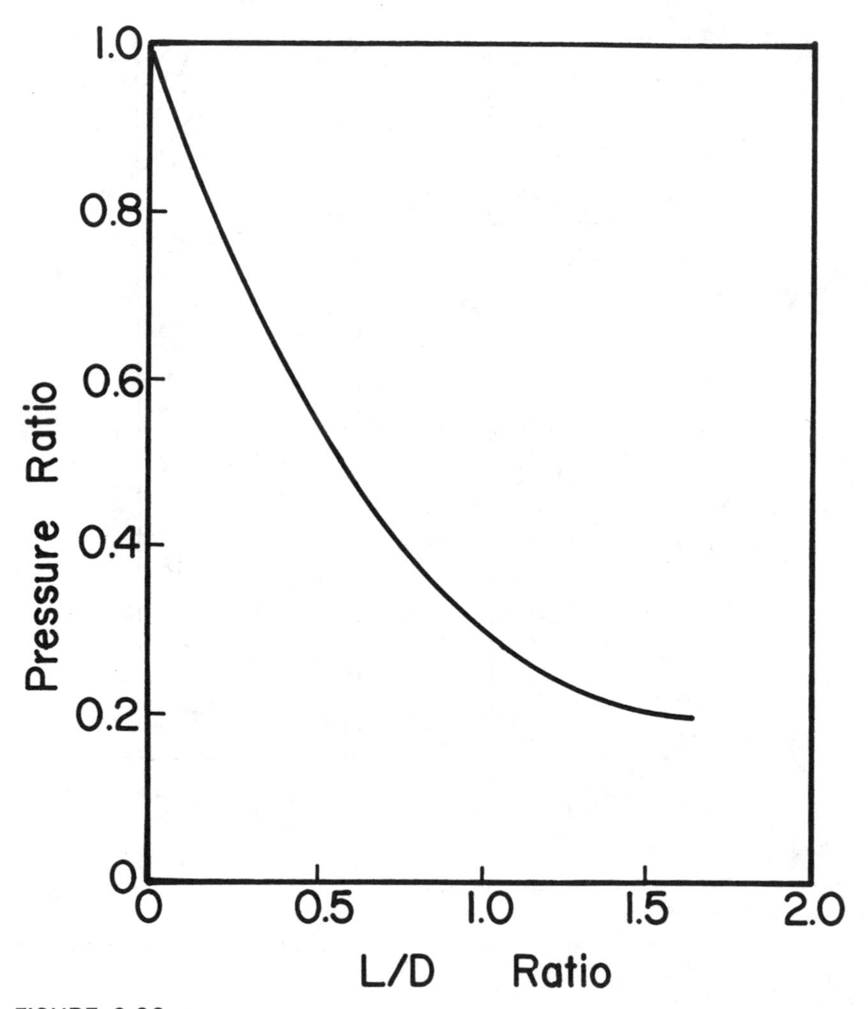

FIGURE 3-26.

Dependence of pressure ratio (real pressure on lower punch to applied pressure on upper punch) on L/D ratio for copper compacts, pressed at 50 tsi in a single action press. (from P. Duwez and L. Zwell, Trans. AIME, vol. 185, pp. 137–144, 1949)

developed in the powder compact. Such a curve as that in Figure 3-26 would be shifted up for a given material by promoting those factors that lead to greater densification (i.e. large particle size, soft particles, and the others noted earlier) and by reducing the friction at the die wall-powder interface.

The use of moving or floating dies reduces the frictional forces and loss of load to the die by allowing the particles to move the die during compaction rather than moving relative to the die. Once the die is moving it aids the movement of particles furthest away from the moving upper punch. Very often floating dies are used to reduce the variation in green density normally resulting in a single action compaction system. The actual distribution approaches that of a double end compacted part.

Summarizing, variations in green density distribution within a given compact can be minimized or eliminated by the use of the following procedures, for a given powder:

(a) using lubricants to reduce die wall friction,
(b) using high pressures,
(c) using low L/D ratios,
(d) using the floating die principle,
(e) using double action compaction,
(f) using precompaction for some portion of the compact.

Actual commercial practice for making high density structural P/M parts of relatively large dimensions usually makes use of several of these approaches. Naturally, if it is possible to change the powder, then this could also be used to improve densification without increasing the compacting pressure or size of press.

Various theories and mathematical analyses have been proposed to describe quantitatively the compaction process in terms of the dependence of green density on compaction pressure, and possibly some other factors. Such analyses really neglect the density distribution problem; however, experimental values of density can be meaningful if some procedures have been used to minimize or eliminate the problem. No one equation has been formulated which has universal application. This is not unexpected since the behavior of the powder during compaction can be highly complex and will be influenced by many factors, including properties of the powdered material and geometrical and process parameters. In general there can be two well defined parts of the density-pressure curves. An early low pressure stage where plastic deformation is relatively unimportant and particle movement dominates the densification process, and a second stage where deformation, and possibly fracture, is the critical mechanism. An equation that appears to be very useful has been developed by Heckel and has the form:

$$\log \frac{1}{(1-D)} = A + KP \qquad (3\text{-}1)$$

where P = compaction pressure
D = relative compact density (ratio of compact density to theoretical solid density)
K = constant related to the yield strength of the material and is about $(1/3S)$, where S = yield strength of the particulate material
A = constant for the material and the compaction method.

The term KP represents the plastic deformation contribution towards densification. The A term can be given as

$$A = \log \frac{1}{(1 - D_o)} + B \qquad (3\text{-}2)$$

where D_o is the relative apparent density and B a constant which decreases with decreasing particle size and increasing sphericity ($B = 0$ for spherical particles). The B term is supposed to take into account the early predeformation densification. A final equation may be written as

$$\log (1 - D) = [\log (1 - D_o) - B] - (P/3S) \qquad (3\text{-}3)$$

This shows that a convenient way of analyzing data for many materials is to plot the log of $(1 - D)$ versus the ratio of $P/3S$. It can be seen that the green density will increase with increasing pressure, apparent density and B, and with decreasing yield strength of the particle material; this is in agreement with previous comments.

3.5 MECHANICAL STRENGTH AND QUALITY OF GREEN COMPACTS

The strength of green compacts results chiefly from mechanical interlocking of the irregularities on the particle surfaces. This is promoted by plastic deformation during compaction, particularly surface deformation. *Green strength is promoted by:*

(1) *increasing particle surface roughness:* this simply provides more sites for mechanical interlocking;
(2) *increasing the powder surface area:* this is equivalent to increasing the irregularity and reducing the size of the particles; these provide more areas for interlocking;
(3) *decreasing the powder apparent density:* this is simply a consequence of the first two factors;
(4) *decreasing particle surface oxidation and contamination:* "dirty" surfaces prevent optimum mechanical interlocking;
(5) *increasing green density (or compaction pressure):* greater particle movement and deformation are the very basis for achieving interlocking;
(6) *decreasing the amount of certain interfering additives:* the addition of some alloying elements, such as soft graphite to iron, and lubricants prevents proper mechanical interlocking.

Some actual data for commercial iron powders illustrate the dependence of green strength on apparent density in Figure 3-27. It can be seen that the green strength can be changed by more than a factor of four simply by selecting different apparent density iron powders. Also shown in this figure is the corresponding curve for the dependence on green density for these same powders. It would appear that the green strength decreases with increasing green density—but this is a consequence of the dependence of green density on apparent density. In actual fact if we consider data for a particular type of iron powder, then we observe the type of dependence shown in Figure 3-28. Additional data are presented in Table 3-4; it may be seen that the green strength increases with decreasing apparent density and increasing green density. Also some data for isostatically prepared material are presented; these show that for a given apparent density or green density isostatic compaction yields considerably high green strengths as compared to conventional die compaction. This is a conse-

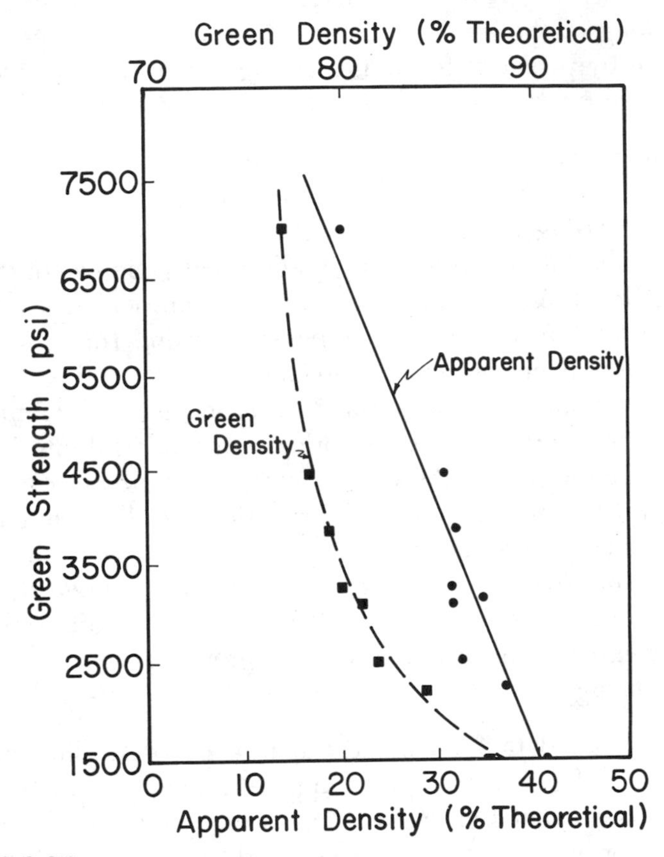

FIGURE 3-27.

Dependence of green strength on apparent and green density for various iron powders.

quence of the improved stress distribution resulting in greater particle movement and deformation. This is one of the reasons why isostatic compaction is used; some powdered materials would not have sufficient green strength for production by conventional die compaction techniques.

It should also be noted that spherical powders provide the lowest degree of mechanical strength because of initial point contact between adjacent particles and a low surface-to-volume ratio. Compaction of such powders, even at very high pressures, will normally result in powder being ejected from the die. Isostatic

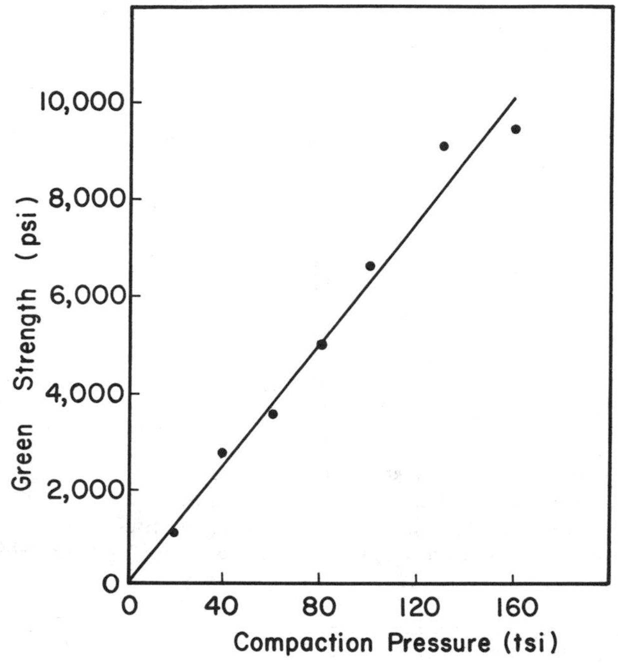

FIGURE 3-28.

Dependence of green strength on compaction pressure for electrolytic iron powder. (from H. H. Hausner, Powder Metallurgy, Chemical Publishing, N.Y., 1947)

compaction would not normally alleviate the problem sufficiently.

The fundamental factor is that the strength of a green compact is determined by the weakest structural feature; this is the interparticle surface and not the strength of the actual solid material. There is no substantial chemical bonding across the interface. There are some additives that provide a degree of adhesiveness between the particles; these are known as "binders" and are often used in those cases where very low compaction pressures are used (for the production of porous materials) and for pressureless compaction techniques. A normal green compact will not exhibit any

TABLE 3-4. Green Density and Green Strength for Various Types of Iron Powders

Powder	Apparent Density (gm/cc)	Compaction Pressure (tsi)	Green Density (gm/cc)	Green Strength (psi)
Sponge[a]	2.4	30	6.2	2100
		40	6.6	3200
		50	6.8	4100
Atomized sponge[b]	2.5	30	6.55	1900
		40	6.8	2700
		50	7.0	—
Reduced[a]	2.5	30	6.5	2300
		40	6.7	3000
		50	6.9	3500
Sponge[a]	2.6	30	6.6	2700
		40	6.8	3600
		50	7.0	3900
Electro.[c]	2.6	30	6.3	4600
		40	6.7	6200
		50	6.95	7800

[a] powders contained 1% zinc stearate blended in
[b] powder contained 0.75% zinc stearate blended in
[c] unlike the other powders this one was isostatically pressed
(from C. E. Van Buren and H. H. Hirsch, in Powder Metallurgy, Interscience, New York, pp. 403–440)

plastic behavior but will simply fracture; that is, it is brittle. This is particularly true in tension where interparticle surfaces are easily pulled apart. In compression some plastic behavior may be observed because compressive stresses push particles together, but lateral motions (sliding) quickly break the mechanical bonds.

The strength of green compacts is usually determined by transverse rupture testing of rectangular specimens. A load is applied to a flat surface of the compact midway between two supports on the opposite side of the material. The load at breaking is used to calculate the green strength. This test lends itself to materials which act in a brittle fashion and eliminates such problems as alignment and difficult specimen preparation associated with tensile testing. The precise procedures to be used in this testing are described in MPIF 15-62 and ASTM B 312-64 standards.

Elastic recovery upon ejection is harmful because it subjects the compact to tensile forces and tends to cause separation of the interparticle surfaces. Very hard materials with high elastic moduli are very difficult to compact to reasonable strengths because a high percentage of the deformation during compaction is elastic rather than plastic. If there is significant plastic deformation during compaction leading to some mechanical interlocking, then the material may not be able to entirely recover its elastic strains. This means that there is a residual stress (tensile) in the compact which leads to a sensitivity to external stresses. Additionally, the compact may "swell" in time because of the gradual breaking of the mechanical bonds and the recovery of the elastic strains.

It is important to have adequate green strength to permit handling of the part for quality control measurements and transport to the sintering furnace. This is particularly important for thin parts, for thin components of large parts, for low density parts and for the edges of parts. Poor green strength can result in fracture (possibly during ejection) or spalling of the part. Atomized prealloyed powders which have rounded shapes, smooth surfaces and high strengths are especially difficult to use because of the low green strengths they yield. Also, variations in green density in any type of compact mean that there are also differences in strength, and this can make a compact susceptible to fracture or spalling.

Defects in green compacts can seriously decrease the mechanical strength but, more importantly, can cause rejection of the compact or remain in the part after sintering and affect the final sintered properties and performance. The most severe problem is the formation of *laminations* or planar cracks within the green compact. Usually these are perpendicular to the pressing direction; they may be very visible to the naked eye (in some cases there is actually an explosive fracturing of the compact) or very fine and extremely difficult to detect. The major reasons for this lamination formation are:

(1) elastic recovery stresses which tend to pull interfaces apart; stresses parallel to the compaction direction act on flattened porosity (act on less interfaces) and tend to extend pores (actually the pores are cracks to begin with);

(2) stresses induced during ejection; the material is held back at die wall surfaces while the material within the compact has less restraint; this sets up bending stresses and tensile stresses which cause fracture along interfaces, especially for stress components acting perpendicular to flattened pores;

(3) stresses induced within the compact while it is still in the die but the load has been removed; these can come about due to improper die design that results in elastic expansion of the die during pressure application and recovery when the pressure is removed; the latter tends to put stresses on the outer regions of the compact and can lead to gross fracture;

(4) interfaces which represent changes in green density; often laminations appear in the center of a part because this is where the density changes abruptly and the amount of porosity increases; this means that loads are transmitted through small necks or bridges and easily exceed the strength of the interfaces;

(5) high compaction pressures may lead to increased flattened type of porosity and possibly induce fracture of particles themselves that lead to crack-pore combinations on a large scale which are very susceptible to stresses induced by ejection or elastic recovery;

(6) excessive lubricant additions which prevent interparticle contact and allow cracks to form easily;

(7) entrapped air in isolated pores under high pressure may cause fracturing.

Methods that may be used to minimize or eliminate laminations include:

(1) use of a powder with a higher green strength;

(2) reduction of ejection stresses by reducing compaction pressure to minimize die wall friction, improving the die wall lubrication and maintenance of a compressive pressure on the compact during ejection;

(3) use of a powder with better compressibility requiring lower pressure to achieve the desired density;

(4) change the kind or amount of lubricant mixed with the powder;
(5) change the die design to allow some degree of radial relaxation (elastic expansion) during ejection such as by having a taper to the upper portion of the die or by using a split die;
(6) change the die design so as to eliminate any significant amount of elastic expansion during compaction.

Another type of defect is a surface bulge. This usually comes about because of inadequate removal of air during the compaction and the formation of pockets of entrapped air, possibly under high pressure.

3.6 LUBRICATION FOR COMPACTION AND EJECTION

It has already been noted that a major loss of compaction energy takes place because of the friction between the powder and the die wall; other sources of friction also are present, such as between adjacent particles, between the powder and the punches and core rods and between the punches and the die wall. Minimizing or eliminating these sources of friction allows greater pressure to be applied to the powder for a given loading. Of equal importance is the friction between the green compact and the die wall during the ejection of the compact from the die. Actual compaction may be relatively easy compared to the difficulty often encountered in ejecting the compact without damaging it. For all these reasons it is necessary to have an effective system of lubrication both for compaction as well as ejection and without interfering with the sintering process.

The traditional approach, for conventional die compaction, has been to mix a powdered lubricant with the metal powder; such an admixed lubricant is present throughout the powder. Some of it will be at the die wall; in some cases this is probably aided by the compaction process which forces some of the lubricant through the porous mass to the die wall. An argument against this approach is that much of the lubricant stays within the powder mass and is relatively ineffective. Also, the admixed lubricant may seriously affect the properties of the loose powder in an adverse manner. The alternative to admixed lubrication is to use a system involving die wall lubrication only. This puts the lubricant where it is really needed and eliminates the effect of the lubricant on the loose powder. In both methods of lubrication the lubricants most frequently used are low melting point organic materials such as metal stearates, stearic acid and waxes. It should be noted that such materials have very low densities and, hence, a small weight percent addition actually corresponds to a relatively large volume fraction.

Admixed lubrication may be achieved in two ways; either the metal powder may be purchased with a certain amount of lubricant mixed in already or the parts manufacturer may mix the lubricant with the metal powder in his plant. In any case it should be realized that the extent of mixing is quite important. Enough mixing must be done to insure a uniform distribution of the lubricant; however, excessive mixing can cause enough heating of the mix to make the lubricant somewhat gummy. The latter can lead to segregation and agglomeration within the mix. Reducing the particle size of the lubricant is also an effective way to promote distribution and may actually reduce the amount necessary for a particular application.

First, we may consider the effect of admixed lubricants on the apparent density and flow time of the loose powder; such data are given in Table 3-5. For many systems there is first an initial increase in apparent density and then a decrease as the amount of lubricant is increased. It is possible to achieve a higher apparent density than the unlubricated powder if one stays below a critical concentration of the lubricant. Apparently a small amount of admixed lubricant aids packing of the powder particles. In some cases the flow time can be reduced by a small addition of lubricant, while in others any amount leads to an increase in flow time.

A truly effective admixed lubricant should increase the green density for a particular compaction pressure as compared to the unlubricated powder. Again one usually observes an initial increase followed by a decrease in the green density with increasing amounts of lubricant. Some data on this effect are given in Table

TABLE 3-5. Effect of Admixed Lubricants on the Apparent Density and Flow Time of Iron Powder

Powder	Lubricant Type	Wt. %	Apparent Density (gm/cc)	Flow Time (sec)
sponge[a]	zinc stear.	0.5	2.75	33
		1.0	2.73	36
		1.5	2.63	52
	stearic acid	0.5	—	24
	(10 min. mixing)	1.0	—	27
		1.5	—	31
	stearic acid	0.5	2.91	24
	(30 min. mixing)	1.0	2.83	28
		1.5	2.69	34
	lithium stearate	0.75	—	31
		1.0	—	34
		1.25	—	38
reduced[b]	zinc stearate	0.5	2.57	—
		1.0	2.57	—
		1.5	2.51	—
	stearic acid	0.5	2.42	—
		1.0	2.40	—
		1.5	2.26	—
	lithium stearate	0.5	2.47	—
		1.0	2.41	—
		1.5	2.40	—
	acrawax c	0.5	2.43	—
		1.0	2.40	—
		1.5	2.37	—

[a] apparent density and flow time of unlubricated powder were 2.40 gm/cc and 28 sec., respectively; from E. J. Geijer and R. S. Jamison, in Powder Metallurgy, W. Leszynski, editor, Interscience, New York, 1961, pp. 585–610.
[b] apparent density of unlubricated powder was 2.36 gm/cc; from H. H. Hausner, Proc. Metal Powder Assn., 1954, pp. 6–27.

3-6. There is a critical concentration of lubricant for a particular system below which the green density is greater than the unlubricated powder, and above which it may become lower.

Similarly, an effective lubricant should reduce the pressure necessary to eject the compact from the die (often termed the "stripping" pressure). This is usually the case, with increasing amounts of lubricant reducing the ejection pressure still further. Some data illustrating this potent effect are given in Table 3-7. The higher the compaction pressure and, hence, the green density the greater

TABLE 3-6. Effect of Admixed Lubricants on Green Density

Powder	Lubricant Type	Wt. %	Green Density (gm/cc)
Copper[a]	none	—	6.59
	stearic acid	0.5	6.68
		1.0	6.48
		2.0	6.37
	zinc stearate	0.5	6.84
		1.0	7.15
		2.0	7.02
Iron[b]	none	—	5.41
	zinc stearate	0.25	5.92
	(fine)	0.5	6.06
		1.0	6.12
		2.0	6.18
	zinc stearate	0.25	5.85
	(coarse)	0.5	6.05
		1.0	6.07
		2.0	6.17
	lithium stearate	0.25	5.74
		0.5	6.08
		1.0	6.15
		2.0	6.11
Iron[c]	none	—	6.09
	acrawax c	0.5	6.06
		1.0	6.17
		1.5	6.09
	stearic acid	0.5	6.09
		1.0	6.13
		1.5	6.09

[a] −100 +325 mesh electrolytic powder pressed at 25 tsi
[b] electrolytic powder pressed at 30 tsi
[c] reduced powder pressed at 30 tsi

(from H. H. Hausner, Proc. Metal Powder Assn., 1954, pp. 6–27)

the ejection pressure at any level of lubrication. The die material, its composition, hardness and surface condition, also has an influence on the ejection pressure. As can be seen in Table 3-7 for the same powder, compaction pressure and lubricant addition a carbide die reduced the ejection pressure as compared to a steel die. Ejection pressures can also be influenced by the exact nature of a powder; for example, a small particle size often increases the ejection pressure. This may come about because small particles may become trapped in the clearances between the tooling.

Finally, we may consider the effect of the admixed lubricant on strength. In a great many cases an admixed lubricant reduces the green strength of the compact. This comes about because the lubricant interferes with mechanical interlocking among the particles. However, there are some lubricants that have an adhesive quality and may in fact improve the green strength. The effect on sintered strength is usually deleterious. The lubricant is eventually burned off in a pre-sintering operation and this means that some porosity will be introduced into the compact. Additionally, there may be residues that interfere with the sintering process. The net result is that the sintered strength is usually lowered as shown by the data in Table 3-8. It should also be noted that the burning off of the lubricant is a rather costly operation.

TABLE 3-7. Effect of Admixed Lubricants on the Ejection Pressure for Sponge Iron Compacts

Die Material	Compaction Pressure (tsi)	Lubricant Type	Wt. %	Ejection Pressure (psi)
Steel	20	zinc stearate	0.5	1800
			1.0	900
			1.5	800
	48	zinc stearate	0.5	4100
			1.0	2000
			1.5	1500
Carbide	48	zinc stearate	0.5	3400
			1.0	1900
			1.5	1300
Steel	20	lithium stearate	0.75	2100
			1.0	2000
			1.25	1750
	48	lithium stearate	0.75	4400
			1.0	2800
			1.25	2100

(from E. J. Geijer and R. S. Jamison, in Powder Metallurgy, W. Leszynski, editor, Interscience, New York, 1961, pp. 585–610)

One may now appreciate the problem of selecting the most desirable amount and kind of admixed lubricant for a particular operation so that the benefits of improved green density and/or reduced ejection pressure can be achieved without sacrificing too

TABLE 3-8. Effect of Admixed Lubricants on Sintered Strength of Sponge Iron[a]

Lubricant	Green Density (gm/cc)	Transverse Rupture Strength (psi)	
		No Lubricant	1 wt. % Lub.
Stearic acid	6.6	70,000	55,000
Lithium stear.	6.2	54,000	48,000
	6.6	70,000	59,000
			1.25 wt. % Lub.
Zinc stearate	6.6	70,000	62,000
	6.8	79,000	70,000
Calcium stear.	6.2	54,000	40,000
	6.6	70,000	46,000

[a] compacts sintered 40 min. at 2050°F in purified exogas, 1200°F preheat for burnoff of lubricant

(from E. J. Geijer and R. S. Jamison, in Powder Metallurgy, W. Leszynski, editor, Interscience, New York, 1961, pp. 585–610)

much of a decrease in apparent density, flow time, green strength or sintered strength.

Die wall lubrication has long been used on a laboratory basis but has not achieved significant commercial status. There are some operations in which hand spraying of a lubricant on to the die wall is done. Automated die wall lubrication is required for large scale commercial practice. One such system involves the use of a lubricant suspended in a liquid which is drawn by capillary action between the tooling during the ejection part of the cycle and thereby coats the die wall with a thin film of lubricant. Although such a system offers several economic and technical advantages it takes some time to bring about such a major change in commercial practice.

3.7 BLENDING AND MIXING OF POWDERS

Although this topic is somewhat out of sequence, it does pertain to the compaction operation and deserves some consideration.

The term "blending" strictly should be applied to a one component operation and the term "mixing" to an operation involving more than one type of powder; however, the former is often used for both cases. Both types of operations precede compaction and are carried out in the same type of equipment. Usually double-cone mixers (also known as "V" or "Y" mixers) are used for metal powders. A single type of metal powder may be blended by itself in order to insure a uniform powder for compaction; that is, that there be no segregation with respect to particle size or shape. Such an operation may also be done in order to change the apparent density or flow time of the powder, and perhaps some other characteristic, by causing some degree of fracturing of the particles (size reduction) or by rounding of the particle shape and perhaps smoothing of the surfaces. Excessive blending may even result in significant plastic deformation of the particles; this could introduce an undesirable degree of cold work and reduce compressibility.

Mixing is usually carried out in order to introduce a lubricant into the powder and to achieve various types of alloys. The basic purpose is to achieve a uniform mixture of the various components. At the present time it is extremely difficult to determine whether a satisfactory degree of mixing has taken place, except by going through the entire sequence of operations and evaluating the various steps as well as the final product. In most cases the mixing operation is probably carried out for too long a time in order to insure a good mix. Excessive mixing is undesirable because: (a) it is a rather costly operation in terms of manpower used and equipment costs; (b) it may result in demixing and gross segregation of some component (for example, due to differences in density); (c) it may result in some undesirable change in the powders; (d) one component may become coated with a softer one with an undesirable result on properties; (e) softening of the lubricant may lead to a gummy and agglomerated powder.

Although the blending or mixing operation is an extremely important part of the powder metallurgy process it is relatively unstudied. There have been many theoretical analyses of the operation, but it is extremely difficult to apply the results to practical applications. It may be noted here that there are three generally accepted mechanisms operating in a mixing machine (of which there are many different designs); they are:

(1) the transfer of groups of adjacent particles from one location to another; this is termed "convective mixing";
(2) the movement or distribution of particles over a newly developed surface (or surface layer); this is usually termed "diffusive mixing";
(3) the formation of slipping planes within the powder mass; this is termed "shear mixing."

The extent of any one of these will depend on the exact design of the mixing machine.

REFERENCES FOR FURTHER READING

3-1. Powder Metallurgy Equipment Manual, MPIF, N.Y., 1968. Part I on Compacting Presses and Tooling contains much useful and practical information.

3-2. H. H. Hausner, K. H. Roll and P. K. Johnson, editors, New Methods for the Consolidation of Metal Powders, Plenum, N.Y., 1967. Contains many papers dealing with the newer methods of compaction, including rolling, forging, extrusion, slip casting, isostatic and vibratory compaction of powders.

3-3. M. H. D. Blore, V. Silins, S. Romanchuk, T. W. Benz and V. N. Mackiw, Pure Nickel Strip by Powder Rolling, ASM Metals Engr. Quarterly, vol. 6, no. 2, pp. 54–60, 1966. A good paper containing details on practical powder rolling.

3-4. M. C. Noland, H. M. Gadberry, J. B. Loser and E. C. Sneegas, High-Velocity Metalworking, NASA SP-5062, 1967. Contains an excellent review of HERF type compaction techniques and many references.

3-5. H. H. Hausner, K. H. Roll and P. K. Johnson, Vibratory Compacting—Principles and Methods, Plenum, N.Y., 1967. Contains a number of papers, on a more advanced level.

3-6. H. H. Hausner, editor, Modern Developments in Powder Metallurgy, Plenum, N.Y., 1966. Volume I contains several good papers on compaction, including isostatic compaction, slip casting, extrusion and rolling of powders and porosity in green compacts.

3-7. W. D. Jones, Fundamental Principles of Powder Metallurgy, Arnold, London, 1960. Chapter II on pressing has much useful information and references.
3-8. P. Duwez and L. Zwell, Pressure Distribution in Compacting Metal Powders, Trans. AIME, vol. 185, pp. 137–144, 1949. One of the best papers on density distributions in green compacts.
3-9. E. J. Geijer and R. S. Jamison, Lubricants for Powder Metallurgy Parts Manufacturing and Their Influence on Properties, in Powder Metallurgy, W. Leszynski, editor, Interscience, N.Y., 1960. A good paper dealing with admixed lubrication with much useful data.
3-10. R. Stewart Haeckl, Automatic Lubrication of Powder Compacting Punches and Dies, Int. J. Powder Met., vol. 4, no. 1, pp. 13–23, 1968. An excellent paper dealing with a die wall lubrication method.
3-11. P. R. Marshall, The Production of Powder Metallurgy Parts, Metallurgical Reviews, vol. 13, pp. 53–72, 1968. A good modern review containing a good discussion of compaction, has many references.
3-12. R. W. Heckel, A New Approach to the Study of Powder Compaction, Progress in Powder Met., vol. 17, pp. 66–81, 1961. As noted in the text this is a useful analytical approach to compaction. (See also Trans. AIME, vol. 224, pp. 1073–1074, 1962.)
3-13. C. Orr, Jr., Particulate Technology, Macmillan, N.Y., 1966. Some very good discussions and data on blending and mixing of powders.

PROBLEMS

(3-1) Discuss the relative merits of using double action die compaction, isostatic compaction or slip casting with respect to producing extremely large, both laterally and in thickness, structural P/M parts.

(3-2) Does the fact that a spherical powder is associated with virtually no green strength signify that such a powder does not actually densify during pressure compaction? Explain.

(3-3) Are there any basic differences in the nature of the porosity in green compacts prepared by die compaction, isostatic compaction and slip casting? Explain.

(3-4) Explain why it is relatively simple to achieve virtually theoretical density in green sheet made by powder rolling.

(3-5) Does vibratory compaction have greater potential for the production of small or large P/M parts? Explain.

(3-6) Explain how you might improve the green strength of a low carbon steel part whose green density is fixed.

(3-7) Why are canned powders often evacuated in powder extrusion and forging techniques?

(3-8) For a given metal would you expect any difference in the green density distribution in compacts, of identical size and density, prepared by using admixed and die wall lubrication? Explain.

(3-9) Consider using a multiple motion die compaction system for producing complex multilevel parts of uniform density. Explain why the punches for different levels must move different distances.

(3-10) In most commercial operations the green density of a part is maintained by carefully controlling the volume of loose powder put into the die and by compacting to fixed dimensions (rather than to a pressure). Explain the possible effects of having variations in the apparent density of the powder and random type vibrations of the press.

CHAPTER

FOUR

SINTERING

4.1 INTRODUCTION

The sintering of green compacts or loose powder is a very complex process. Much of the difficulty in defining and analyzing sintering is based on the many changes within the material that may take place either simultaneously or consecutively. Some of these changes may be unique to the heating of a porous material, while others are typical of the effects of elevated temperatures on any polycrystalline material. Economic use of the powder metallurgy process is critically dependent on the structural and dimensional changes produced during sintering. The subject of sintering is best approached from the viewpoint that any green compact or mass of loose powder is at the very least a two phase material–porosity and solid material. Each has its own morphology; that is, size, shape, distribution and amount.

It is appropriate at this time to attempt to give a simple and straightforward definition of sintering as it pertains to powder metallurgy. *Sintering may be considered the process by which an assembly of particles, compacted under pressure or simply confined in a container, chemically bond themselves into a coherent body under the influence of an elevated temperature.* The sintered material is analogous to conventional forms of solid materials, such as castings, forgings and wrought shapes. In addition to the bonding of the particles sintering may be used to accomplish other functions; these include: alloying, heat treatment, joining and densification. Densification or shrinkage of the sintered material is very often associated with all forms of sintering. However, sintering can take place without any shrinkage resulting; expansion or no net dimensional change are quite possible. In fact, in the vast majority of commercial applications it is preferable to avoid very large amounts of dimensional changes. Having a slight shrinkage to compensate for the elastic expansion of the green compact upon ejection from the die, leading to no net dimensional change with respect to the die dimensions, is an extremely advantageous approach.

In addition to the conventional form of sintering, consisting of heating the original powder mass or compact to a rather high temperature but below its melting point in a protective atmosphere, there are two major variations. *Hot pressing* refers to an application of both an elevated temperature and an external pressure to the powder mass or compact; here too the temperature is below the melting point of the material. This technique has been widely used for ceramic materials and refractory metals, but not for the conventional ferrous and nonferrous materials. Sintering is usually considered a solid state process; that is, no molten or liquid phase is present. *Liquid phase sintering* refers to those cases for which the sintering temperature is high enough that one or more components of the material is present as a liquid during all or part of the sintering process. Included in this category is the case of liquid infiltration combined with sintering; that is, a mass of a lower melting point metal is allowed to melt and flow into the porosity of the green compact. Both types of liquid phase sintering lead to the attainment of high sintered densities, and this is often why they are used. However, the infiltration technique achieves densification without necessarily causing any shrinkage of the original green compact; that is, the porosity is simply filled up by the infiltrant. In most other cases densification signifies shrinkage resulting from the elimination of the porosity.

There has been a great deal of experimental and theoretical work on the fundamental aspects of sintering. However, today there is much about the process that is not understood and one universally applicable theory of sintering has not been achieved. Most of this work has been concerned with the "why" and "how" of sintering. The "why" refers to the driving forces for the process; the reasons for the changes taking place during sintering. And the "how" is related to the mechanisms of material transport within the sinter mass that bring about the changes. The changes themselves are usually referred to as the "stages of sintering"; these changes are detected by careful examination of the material during or after various degrees of sintering. There is relatively good acceptance of the driving forces for sintering but a great deal of controversy exists about the material transport mechanisms. One of the basic difficulties is that sintering is so complex that for any given material and set of sintering conditions there are likely to be several stages, driving forces and material transport mechanisms associated with the process.

Most sintering theories have dealt with the material transport problem associated with a particular stage of sintering. Mathematical descriptions of the sintering process, in terms of the time dependence of some change in the material related to the particular stage of sintering being considered, are formulated for rather ideal systems. By ideal we mean for example that the sintering of two spheres together, or a sphere on a flat plate, or an assembly of uniformly packed spherical particles is considered. Consequently, the results of most of these theories are extremely difficult to apply to real materials consisting of irregular arrays of very irregular particles. Many of these theories have been proved correct by rather indirect methods. Very often experimental data, reflecting the time dependence of some change in an ideal system, are shown to "fit" a particular equation. However, various theories yield almost identical time dependencies for some changes, and it is extremely difficult to demonstrate that the data fit one equation better than another. Direct physical observation of some critical aspect of the material transport process is more desirable for unequivocal proof of a theory. Then too, it has become clear that for real materials there is likely to be more than one specific material transport mechanism operating for a particular stage of sintering. Some recent theoretical approaches have attempted to describe sintering in terms of several of these mechanisms, and this is a very fruitful approach.

Because of the problems of validity and applicability associated with the many theoretical treatments of sintering, particularly the mathematical details, we will not attempt to treat them in a very detailed manner in this chapter. Instead, the most important physical concepts and their limits of usefulness will be emphasized. It is particularly important for a mature evaluation of sintering theories that the actual stages of sintering, based on sound experimental observations, be fully recognized and that any particular theory be compatible with them. A true understanding of commercial sintering practice and potential advancements can be greatly aided by an objective evaluation of the fundamental and theoretical aspects of the process.

In the next three sections dealing with the stages, driving forces and material transport mechanisms of sintering we will consider the simplest type of sinter mass—a simple solid undergoing no structural changes or transformations and porosity. The basic sintering process is then related to the bonding of the particles and the changes in the nature of the porosity. In later sections some of the more important changes that may occur within the solid will be considered; these are very likely to take place simultaneously with the more basic stages of sintering. The unique aspects of liquid phase sintering and hot pressing will be discussed later in this chapter.

4.2 STAGES OF SINTERING

One of the basic aspects of sintering is that it usually takes place at a constant temperature (or at least a major part of it) and the time is varied to achieve certain results. Consequently, it becomes useful to attempt to describe the stages of sintering in terms of their relative order with respect to time. However, this can only be done in a very qualitative manner because of the simultaneous rather than sequential occurrence of some of them much of the time. There is also some latitude with respect to the exact definition of the stages, and there is much variation in this area. We will consider sintering to be well defined in terms of the following six stages:

(1) initial bonding among particles
(2) neck growth

(3) pore channel closure
(4) pore rounding
(5) densification or pore shrinkage
(6) pore coarsening.

Naturally there can be substantial differences among the initial materials. Green compacts may have very large amounts of porosity, in which cases the porosity will be essentially all interconnected, or they may be very close to theoretical density with the residual porosity in an isolated form. Porosity within the original powder particles promotes the isolated type of porosity within the compact. We will consider the six stages given above to pertain to the sintering of a compact or loose powder containing most of its porosity in an interconnected form. For green compacts containing essentially all isolated porosity stages 2 and 3 would be minimized or entirely absent. The six stages will now be considered individually in some detail.

Bonding takes place very early in the sintering process as the material heats up. The bonding process involves diffusion of atoms leading to the development of grain boundaries. This takes place at those sites where there is intimate physical contact between adjacent particles. There are, of course, many such locations within a pressure formed compact, but even in a mass of loose powder there is contact between particles sufficient in magnitude to allow bonding. Much of this bonding process may take place while the sinter mass is being heated to a specific sintering temperature and during the early time at the constant temperature. This stage of sintering does not lead to any dimensional change of the material. However, it does represent an extremely important change in the material. It is this bonding that imparts a high degree of coherency and integrity to the material; this is evidenced by rather large increases in strength and hardness even after relatively short exposures to an elevated temperature. Naturally, the greater the original density of the material, the greater the amount of contact area and potential grain boundary area. It should be realized that in many powder metallurgy operations, particularly in the production of high porosity materials, the sintering process may only lead to this one stage of sintering. Additionally, one may note that having substances in the original material that interfere with intimate physical contact also make this bonding process very difficult to take place, and consequently the strength of the final sintered material may be lowered.

Neck growth is the second stage of sintering and is related very much to the first stage of initial bonding. The newly formed bond areas are termed necks; in the second stage these necks grow in size. This signifies a greater degree of bonding within the sinter mass. The neck growth requires the transport of material within the sinter mass but does not imply any decrease in the amount of porosity; that is, no shrinkage of the material. It does not affect the continuity of the porosity either. If we picture the original porosity in the sinter mass as somewhat irregular channels of an interconnected nature, then neck growth leads to a smoothing of these channels. Although neck growth is generally accepted to take place rather rapidly and early in the sintering process, it may in fact continue for some time and overlap some later stages. This is promoted by the formation of new necks during sintering associated with stages three and five. It has become commonplace to use and consider spherical particles in fundamental sintering

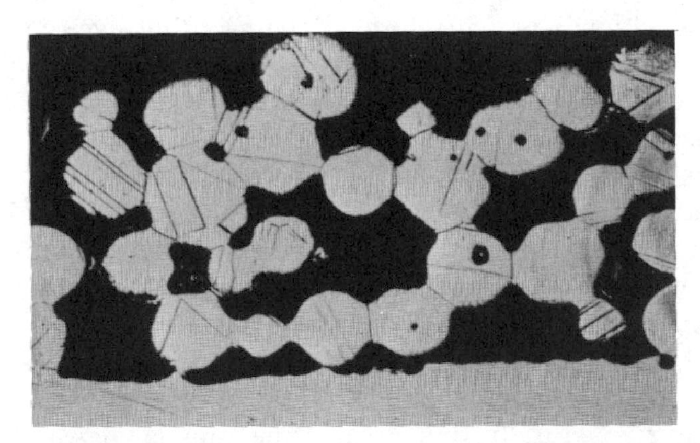

FIGURE 4-1.

Photomicrograph of cross section through some loose sintered spherical copper powder, sintered at 1472°F for 6 hr, illustrating neck growth and formation of grain boundaries in the original neck areas (about 260 ×). (from G. C. Kuczynski, in Powder Metallurgy, W. Leszynski, editor, Interscience, N.Y., 1961, pp. 11–30)

work and although we too shall make use of this simplification, it should be recognized that real powder systems are much more complex. A photomicrograph of some loose sintered spherical copper powder is given in Figure 4-1. The original contacts among the particles were merely point ones; after some sintering resulting

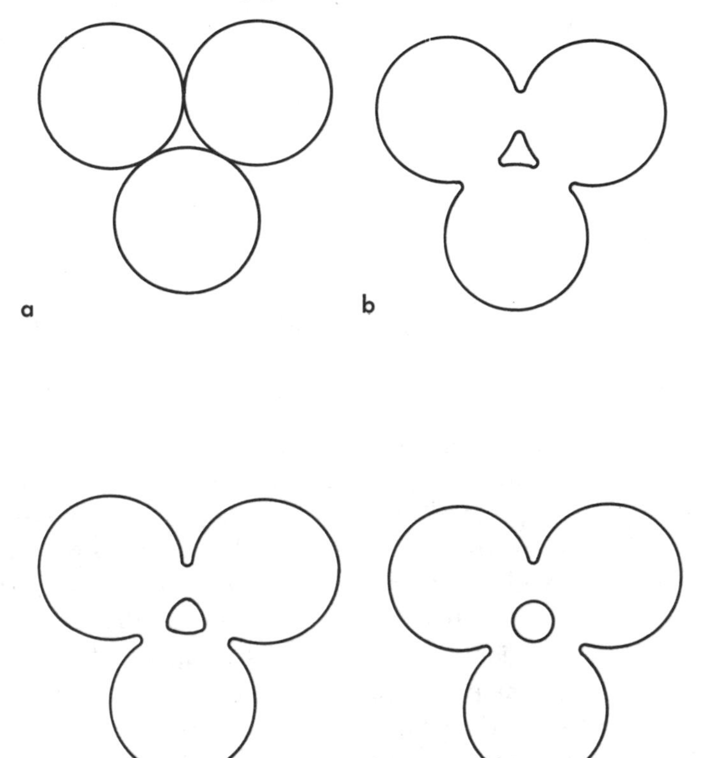

FIGURE 4-2.

Schematic illustration of three sphere sintering model: (a) original point contacts, (b) neck growth, (c) and (d) pore rounding.

in neck growth these contacts become more planar in nature. One may note in this figure that the neck growth also results in growth of the initial grain boundary associated with stage one. Neck growth is also illustrated schematically in terms of a three sphere model in Figure 4-2.

Pore channel closure represents a rather major change in the nature of the porosity in the sinter mass. Closing off of the tortuous and interconnected pore channels leads to the development of isolated or closed porosity. This is a particularly important change with respect to the usage of interconnected porosity for fluid carrying purposes, such as in filters and self-lubricating bearings. One of the causes of pore channel closure is neck growth; this is illustrated schematically in Figure 4-3. However, pore shrinkage

FIGURE 4-3.

Illustration of pore channel closure resulting from neck growth among spherical particles. (from F. N. Rhines, in Plansee Proc. 1958, F. Benesovsky, editor, Metallwerk Plansee, Reutte/Tyrol, Austria, 1959, pp. 38–54)

(stage five) can also lead to channel closure by causing new contacts to be formed among pore surfaces. Hence, the pore channel closure stage may proceed for some time and overlap stages four and five. The change from interconnected to isolated porosity can usually be observed microscopically; an example of this change is given in Figure 4-4. It must be remembered that such figures represent cross sections of the material and, therefore, even in the case of interconnected porosity the pore network will not appear perfectly continuous. The actual distribution of the total porosity into the interconnected and closed types may be determined experimentally by several methods (usually involving measuring the density of the porous solid and also filling the interconnected porosity with a fluid); some such data for copper compacts are given in Figure 4-5. Although there is not an abundance of such data for a great many materials and processing conditions, it does appear that these data are qualitatively correct for most sintered materials. In particular it is noted that: (a) with porosities greater than about 10% most of the porosity is in an interconnected form; (b) with porosities less than about 5 to 10% most of the porosity is of the closed or isolated type.

Pore rounding may be considered a natural consequence of

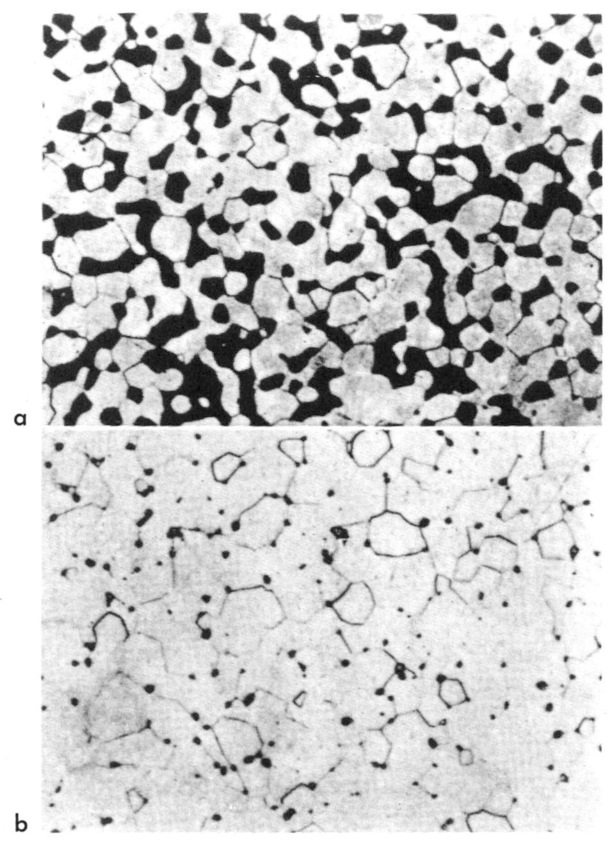

FIGURE 4-4.

Photomicrographs of sintered Al_2O_3: (a) early stage with interconnected porosity; (b) later stage with closed porosity (about 125 ×). (from R. L. Coble, J. Appl. Phys., vol. 32, pp. 787–792, 1961)

neck growth. When material is transported to the neck regions from the pore surfaces the pores themselves become more rounded. This process is also illustrated in Figure 4-2 for the three sphere model. No pore shrinkage is necessary for pore rounding, although it too may be taking place during the same time. The rounding process pertains both to isolated and interconnected porosity; however, it usually is considered with respect to the former. With sufficient time at temperature it is possible to achieve almost perfectly spherical pores. A photomicrograph of a well sintered metal with a rounded type of residual porosity is given

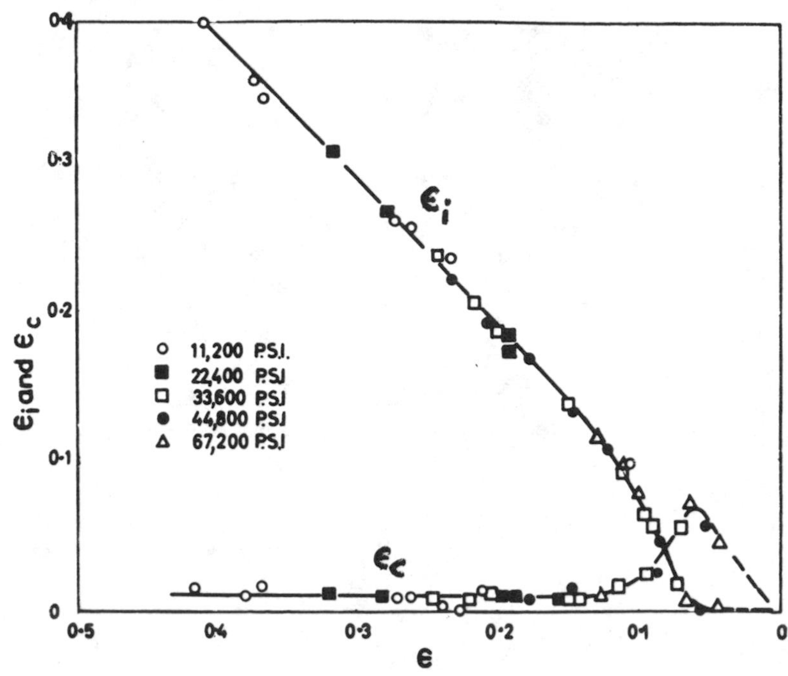

FIGURE 4-5.

Variation of interconnected and closed porosities with total porosity for copper compacts (pressed at various pressures as shown and sintered at 1832°F). (from G. Arthur, J. Inst. Metals, vol. 83, pp. 329–336, 1954–55)

in Figure 4-6. It should be noted that pore rounding is promoted by high sintering temperatures. This stage of sintering is particularly important with respect to the influence of porosity on the mechanical properties of sintered materials. It is possible to carry out sintering for a given material without this stage taking place to any significant degree.

Pore shrinkage and eventual elimination is often considered the most important stage of sintering. Although it is a fundamental aspect of sintering, it does not have to occur. Only with sufficient time at temperature may it evidence itself by densification of the sinter mass. For single one component systems densification may be equivalent to pore shrinkage, but in more complex materials other processes can lead to both shrinkage and expansion. They may mask any densification due to pore shrinkage. It is important to realize that the process of pore shrinkage, leading to a decrease

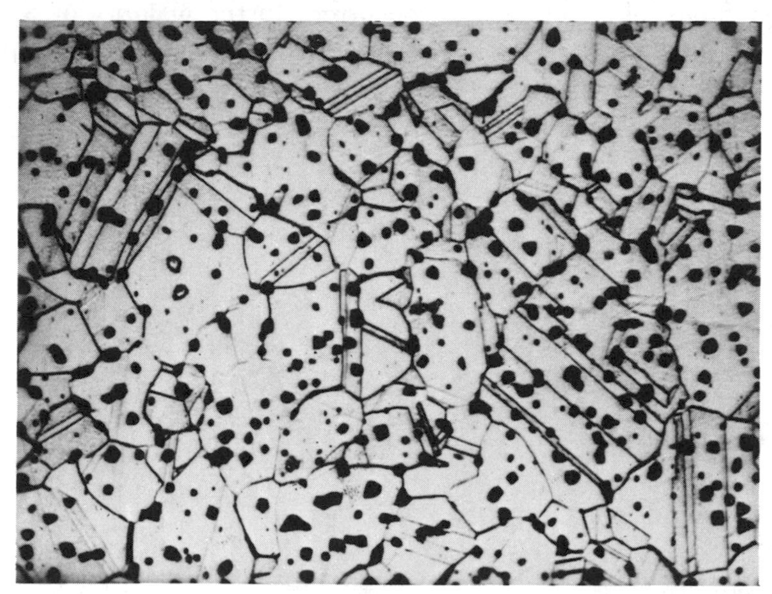

FIGURE 4-6.

Photomicrograph of sintered carbonyl nickel (compacted at 50 tsi and sintered at 1900°F for 2 hr) with about 17% rounded porosity (the black areas are isolated pores) (400 ×). (from E. M. Daver, M.S. Thesis, Univ. of Wisconsin, 1967)

in the volume of the sinter mass, must involve movement of the solid into the porosity and movement of any gas in the porosity to the external surfaces. Although the measurement of density increases is often used to follow the progress of sintering, it does not reflect the changes in the material resulting from the other stages of sintering. Pore shrinkage becomes less important as a stage of sintering with increasing density of the green compact. The elimination of all porosity in a powder metallurgy material, often a highly desirable objective, is very rarely based on the operation of this stage of sintering. It is simply too impractical in terms of the temperatures and times necessary. A photomicrograph of carbonyl iron sintered for a very long time at a rather high temperature is given in Figure 4-7; there is still a small amount of fine, isolated and virtually spherical porosity remaining in the material.

Pore coarsening usually takes place, if at all, after most of the other stages of sintering have occurred. In the majority of commercial operations it is of no consequence. The process simply consists of the shrinkage and elimination of small isolated (and usually quite spherical at this stage) pores and the growth of

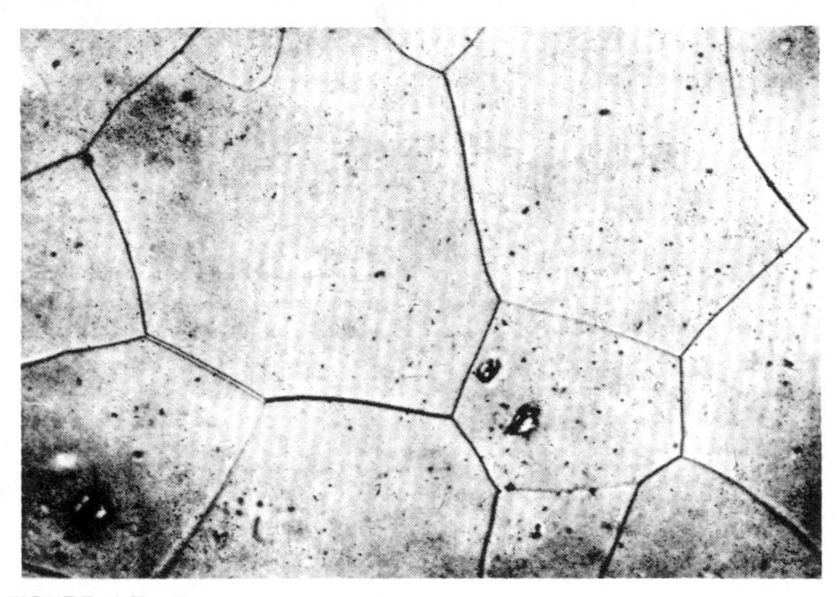

FIGURE 4-7.

Photomicrograph of carbonyl iron sintered in hydrogen for 765 hours at 1634°F illustrating very small amount of residual porosity (about 640 ×). (from G. Ciceron and P. Lacombe, Compt. Rend., vol. 240, p. 427, 1955 as given by F. Thummler and W. Thomma, Metal. Rev., vol. 12, pp. 69–108, 1967)

larger ones. The total amount of porosity associated with all these pores remains the same, but the number of pores decreases and the average size increases. Hence, no densification of the material is associated with this stage. Very careful metallographic examinations are required to verify the operation of this stage.

One of the important modern developments related to the stages of sintering is the approach developed by Rhines and his co-workers (see references at the end of this chapter) that is still being refined and further expanded. A highly sophisticated mathematical procedure for describing the evolution of structure of the sinter mass during all stages of sintering is utilized. This "topological" approach allows a quantitative characterization of sintering without the necessity of considering particle shape or size, or the many variables associated with compaction or sintering. It is based on very basic concepts and is applicable to all systems, and it does not invoke any particular mechanisms of sintering. Additionally, experimental techniques have been developed within the realm of quantitative metallography to reduce the theoretical considerations to practical utilization. A complete review of this approach is beyond the scope of this text, however several of the important points will now be noted.

The generalized geometric description of sintering in the topological approach is based on the use of several parameters: the number of particles in the given mass of powder P, the volume of the specific mass V, the surface area per unit volume of the mass S_v, the number of separate surfaces required to define the shape of the material at any stage in the process N, the number of points at which the powder particles make contact C, and the topological genus of all the surface in the sinter mass G. The genus is given by

$$G = C - P + 1 \tag{4-1}$$

The term genus describes the connectivity of the two-dimensional surface of the sinter body. Its use is restricted to the surface and not to the three-dimensional volume enclosed or excluded by it. The volume enclosed by this surface is the sinter body, and the volume excluded is the porosity. The genus has a physical meaning also. It represents the number of contacts that would have to be cut (self re-entrant cuts) to reduce the connectivity of the sinter mass to that of a single chain of particles (one connected surface). The genus concept is illustrated for simple bodies in Figure 4-8, and for sphere combinations in Figure 4-9.

The genus and the other parameters may be utilized to describe sintering in both a qualitative and quantitative manner from the viewpoint of the structural changes taking place or the kinetics of the process. For example, three stages of sintering have been described within the context of this approach. An initial stage corresponding to no substantial change in the topological parameters; this involves neck growth and smoothing of surface irregularities (no change in G, N or V). A second stage in which there are substantial changes in the parameters, in particular: the approach of the genus to zero related to pore channel closure and pore shrinkage and elimination, the decrease in V (densification) due to pore shrinkage and elimination, and the decrease in S_v related to the

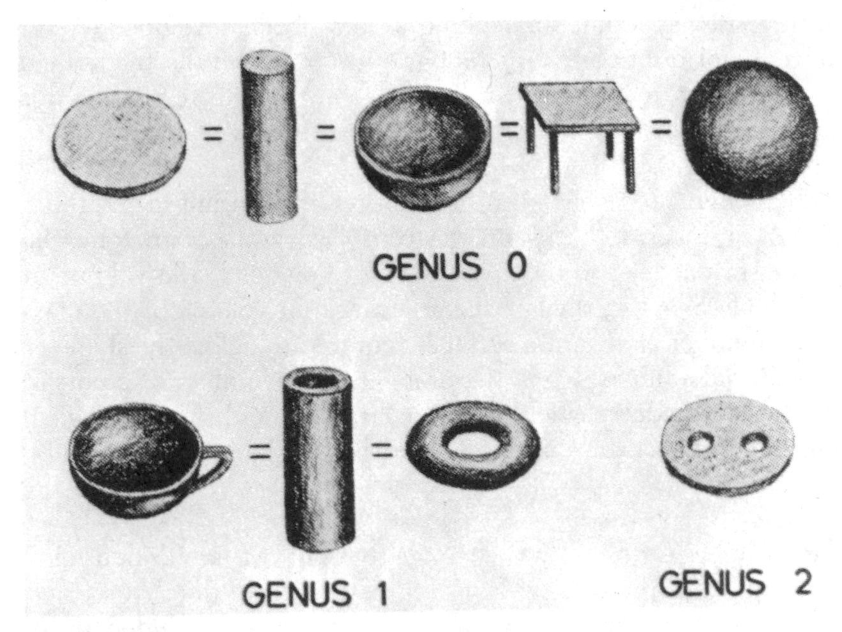

FIGURE 4-8.

Typical bodies bounded by surface of genus zero, one and two. (from F. N. Rhines, in Plansee Proc. 1958, F. Benesovsky, editor, Metallwerk Plansee, Reutte/Tyrol, Austria, 1959, pp. 38–54)

decrease in V (the analysis of plots of experimental values of S_v versus V or density has been particularly enlightening). The third stage is related to a zero or residual genus that is constant; shrinkage of isolated pores and pore coarsening may take place.

4.3 DRIVING FORCES FOR SINTERING

It is clear from the preceding section that a mass of loose powder or a green compact is basically an unstable material at elevated temperatures; that is, it is prone to substantial changes in its in-

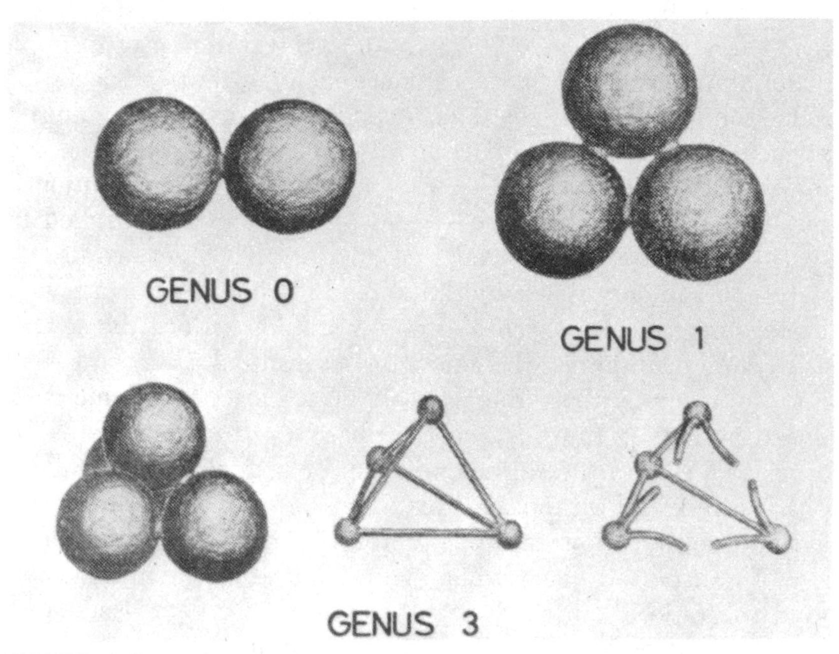

FIGURE 4-9.

Sphere combinations illustrating particle aggregates with genus zero, one and three; the case of the four particle assembly is analyzed by the use of skeletal models. (from F. N. Rhines, in Plansee Proc. 1958, F. Benesovsky, editor, Metallwerk Plansee, Reutte/Tyrol, Austria, 1959, pp. 38–54)

ternal structure. The subject of "driving forces" attempts to explain why these changes take place in terms of quite fundamental concepts. Although there are several major driving forces used to explain various aspects of sintering, it is most important to recognize that the major distinction between the sinter mass and other forms of materials is the presence of internal surface area associated with the pore-solid interface. And also that this surface is quite nonuniform in terms of type and magnitude of curvature.

The thermodynamic approach may be used to arrive at what many people believe to be the most significant driving force for sintering. The transition from an unsintered porous mass to a sintered material may be considered to be analogous to a chemical reaction. Consequently, we may apply the concepts discussed in Chapter Two and equation (2-2) regarding free energy changes.

There must be a reduction in the free energy of the system if the reaction is to take place. If we consider the sintering of a simple material undergoing no compositional changes, then the necessary reduction in free energy is associated with the decrease in internal surface area in the sinter mass. A decrease in surface area corresponds to a decrease in the surface free energy contribution to the total free energy of the system (that is, area multiplied by specific surface or interfacial free energy). In other words, the sinter mass undergoes changes that tend to eliminate surface area. For example, neck growth and pore rounding reduce the surface area while maintaining the amount of porosity at a constant level. For any discrete phase the ratio of surface area to volume is reduced by having the shape of the phase approach a sphere. But even for a sphere the surface area can be reduced by having the phase shrink and disappear—this is analogous to the pore shrinkage and densification stage of sintering. By increasing the average size of a dispersed phase while maintaining the total volume constant the ratio of surface area to volume is also decreased—pore coarsening does just this. Pore channel closure may also accomplish the latter.

Hence, the greater the amount of surface area in the original material, the greater the driving force for sintering. Not just densification—but all the stages of sintering. Even the initial stage of bonding reduces the amount of surface energy. The grain boundary energy will be less than the energy associated with the two unbonded surfaces (because of the greater degree of chemical bonding across the grain boundary interface). It should be remembered that the specific surface energy of the solid will be a function of the gaseous substance in contact with it and of the precise crystallographic orientation of the solid.

Another approach also based on thermodynamic considerations leads to more of a "mechanical" driving force for sintering. At high homologous temperatures of a solid the surface energy may be assumed equal to the surface tension; high atomic mobility is necessary for this equivalence. The surface tension is the force acting to minimize the surface area and, hence, surface energy. The classical thermodynamic equations of capillarity relating surface tension, curvature and internal pressure can be applied to sintering. The mechanical equilibrium existing at the pore-solid interface is considered.

To illustrate this driving force one must consider an actual model. For example, for neck growth we may use an idealized two sphere model as shown in Figure 4-10. The neck area is defined in

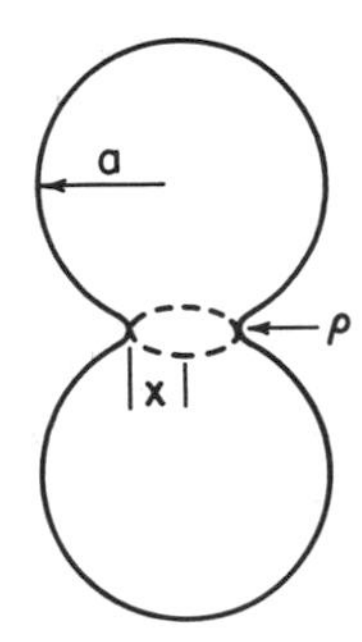

FIGURE 4-10.

Schematic illustration of two spherical particles sintering together and defining geometry of neck growth.

terms of two radii of curvature: ρ in the plane of the paper, and x in the plane at right angles to it. x is often termed the half neck width. The shape of the neck is analogous to the inside of a torus. Mechanical equilibrium at the outer (circular) edge of the neck is described by

$$p_s = p_v - \gamma[(1/\rho) - (1/x)] \tag{4-2}$$

where p_s = the pressure or stress in the solid
p_v = the pressure in the porosity
γ = the surface tension value of the solid

In most cases the size of the neck is very small, and x is much less than the particle radius a; and ρ is much less than x. For this case we may simplify equation (4-2) to

$$p_s = p_v - (\gamma/\rho) \tag{4-3}$$

In the above equation the (γ/ρ) term signifies the stress attempting to expand the neck region—promote sintering. The p_v term opposes this, and the greater the pressure of the gas in the porosity, the greater the opposition to this stage of sintering. If the (γ/ρ) term dominates, then p_s is negative and neck growth is possible. The stress acting on the surface of the solid may be thought of as being tensile in nature and pulling the outer edge of the neck into the porosity. The negative p_s term is the driving force. In most cases the porosity in the sinter mass during the neck growth stage is interconnected to a large extent; therefore, the value of p_v equals the pressure of the sintering atmosphere and this is usually one atmosphere (14.7 psi). Values of (γ/ρ) have been calculated for various realistic values of γ and ρ; these are given in Table 4-1. In

TABLE 4-1. The Dependence of (γ/ρ) on Surface Tension γ and Neck Radius ρ

	(γ/ρ) psi			
ρ (microns) γ =	500	1000	2000	dynes/cm
0.001	72,500.0	145,000.0	290,000.0	
0.01	7,250.0	14,500.0	29,000.0	
0.1	725.0	1,450.0	2,900.0	
1.0	72.5	145.0	290.0	
10.0	7.3	14.5	29.0	
20.0	3.7	7.3	14.5	

most cases the value of ρ would be sufficiently small so that a large driving force (negative p_s) exists. The driving force increases with increasing surface tension and decreasing size of the neck. As neck growth proceeds the driving force becomes smaller because of the increasing value in ρ.

A second geometrical situation to consider is the shrinkage of an isolated spherical pore of radius r. Mechanical equilibrium for this case is described by

$$p_s = p_v - (2\gamma/r) \qquad (4\text{-}4)$$

The promotion of sintering is given by the $(2\gamma/r)$ term; this represents the stress acting to reduce the pore surface by reduction of the pore size. Pore shrinkage is possible if this stress is greater than the pressure of the gas in the pore. Again the negative p_s terms is the driving force for this stage of sintering; it may be thought of as a compressive stress in the solid surrounding the pore. Values of $(2\gamma/r)$ have also been calculated for realistic values of γ and r; these are given in Table 4-2. Although it is not

TABLE 4-2. The Dependence of $(2\gamma/r)$ on Surface Tension γ and Pore Radius r

r (microns)	$(2\gamma/r)$ psi, $\gamma =$ 500	1000	2000 dynes/cm
0.1	1,450.0	2,900.0	5,800.0
1.0	145.0	290.0	580.0
10.0	14.5	29.0	58.0
20.0	7.3	14.5	29.0
50.0	2.9	5.8	11.6
100.0	1.5	2.9	5.8

possible to assume a particular value for p_v (it may be less or greater than one atmosphere), very large stresses are possible for the solid and the driving force would increase with increasing surface tension and decreasing pore size. The latter indicates that in this case as sintering (pore shrinkage) proceeds the driving force increases.

The difference in pressure within the solid as compared to that of the pore gas, driven by the surface tension and related to the surface curvature as considered above may be used to show the existence of two additional driving forces for sintering. First, it has been shown that the vapor pressure of a solid can be related to surface tension and curvature for the neck geometry given in Figure 4-10 by the following

$$\frac{p - p_o}{p_o} = \frac{\gamma V_o}{RT}\left[\frac{1}{\rho} - \frac{1}{x}\right] \qquad (4\text{-}5)$$

where $p =$ the vapor pressure over the curved surface
$p_o =$ the vapor pressure over a flat surface of the solid
$V_o =$ the molar volume of the solid
$R =$ the gas constant
$T =$ the absolute temperature

If, as discussed earlier, one neglects the $1/x$ term (signifying that the neck is considered concave in nature), then the above equation simplifies to

$$\frac{p - p_o}{p_o} = \frac{-\gamma V_o}{RT} \qquad (4\text{-}6)$$

Because all the individual terms in the above equation are positive the conclusion is that the vapor pressure in the neck region is less than that over a flat surface. Some distance away from the neck region on the convex surface of the solid the appropriate equation is

$$\frac{p - p_o}{p_o} = \frac{2\gamma V_o}{RTa} \tag{4-7}$$

Similarly, this equation signifies that the vapor pressure on this convex surface is greater than that above a flat surface. Hence, the vapor pressure above the convex surface is greater than that above the concave neck region. This difference in vapor pressure constitutes a driving force for a particular material transport mechanism leading to neck growth and pore rounding. The driving force increases with increasing surface tension and increasing curvature (in an opposite sense) of the two surfaces.

Lastly, it is possible to demonstrate that there is a dependence of vacancy concentration on surface curvature. A vacancy is a point defect in a crystalline solid corresponding to a lattice site at which the normal atom is missing. There is an equilibrium concentration of vacancies in any crystalline solid, in regions not associated with internal or external surfaces or interfaces, that is determined by the absolute temperature (increasing sharply with increasing temperature) and a thermodynamic factor characteristic of the particular material. Again considering the neck region as shown in Figure 4-10 and neglecting the $1/x$ term the vacancy concentration is given by

$$\frac{c - c_o}{c_o} = \frac{\gamma V_o}{RT\rho}$$

where c = the vacancy concentration in the solid near the neck region

c_o = the vacancy concentration in the interior of the solid

The conclusion is that the vacancy concentration in the neck region of the solid is greater than the normal equilibrium value and increases with increasing surface tension and increasing curvature (concave).

Some distance away from the neck region on the convex surface the concentration is given by

$$\frac{c - c_o}{c_o} = \frac{-2\gamma V_o}{RTa} \tag{4-9}$$

Thus, the vacancy concentration on this convex surface is less than the normal equilibrium value. It is seen then that there is a difference in vacancy concentration between either type of surface location and the interior of the solid, and between the two surfaces themselves. These concentration differences constitute driving forces for particular material transport mechanisms that can lead to neck growth, pore rounding and pore shrinkage.

One may also consider the situation of an isolated spherical pore; for the solid near this surface the vacancy concentration is given by

$$\frac{c - c_o}{c_o} = \frac{2\gamma V_o}{RTr} \tag{4-10}$$

In the solid near such pores there is a higher than equilibrium value of the concentration; and the concentration increases with decreasing pore size (increasing concavity). Hence, there is a difference in vacancy concentration between the interior and the region near the pore, and others between pores of differing sizes. These concentration differences represent driving forces for particular material transport mechanisms for pore shrinkage and pore coarsening.

Lastly, we may note that the vacancy concentration in the lattice near a grain boundary under a stress can be significantly different than the equilibrium value. The concentration is given by

$$c = c_o \exp(SV/RT) \tag{4-11}$$

where S = the stress acting on the boundary (positive if tensile and negative if compressive)
V = the volume an atom or vacancy occupies

Hence, it is seen that there is a higher vacancy concentration near boundaries under a tensile stress as compared to ones under a compressive stress. Such concentration differences within individual grains may constitute a driving force for a unique material transport mechanism.

4.4 MATERIAL TRANSPORT MECHANISMS

Evaporation and Condensation Because of the higher vapor pressure over convex surfaces as compared to neck regions, it is possible in some systems for material to be transported as vapor to the neck region. Neck growth, pore rounding and pore channel closure can be accomplished by this mechanism. As long as significant differences in curvature remain in somewhat localized regions of the sinter mass, this mechanism may operate. However, material is merely rearranged within the sinter mass and no reduction in pore volume (densification) takes place.

This mechanism would only be important for a material whose vapor pressure is relatively high so that significant amounts of material are transported. Most metals have too low a vapor pressure, with the possible exceptions of zinc and cadmium. Experimental evidence has been presented to support the operation of this mechanism for some nonmetallic materials such as NaCl, TiO_2, ZnO_2 and ice. A quantitative description of the kinetics of neck growth for spherical particles resulting from evaporation and condensation of the vapor in the neck region is given by

$$x^3/a = (9\pi/2MRT)^{1/2} V_o \gamma p_o t \tag{4-12}$$

where $M =$ the molecular weight of the material
$t =$ the time of sintering

The equilibrium vapor pressure p_o increases exponentially with increasing temperature. Hence, it is seen that neck growth by this mechanism would increase with increasing temperature, increasing intrinsic vapor pressure of the solid and increasing surface tension.

Volume (Lattice) Diffusion This general method of material transport is widely accepted for the sintering of metallic materials; however, there are a number of precise mechanisms invoking volume diffusion. Volume or lattice diffusion refers to the movement of atoms within the solid crystalline material. The most prevalent specific type of atomic motion is the "vacancy exchange" mechanism. This means that atoms move into vacant lattice sites—vacancies. If there is a directionality associated with a substantial amount of such atomic motion, then there is a net transport of material in a specific direction. The magnitude of this mass transport is described by the diffusivity D of the particular atomic species within a given crystalline solid; and this is given by

$$D = D_o \exp(-Q/RT) \tag{4-13}$$

where D_o = the pre-exponential material constant
Q = the activation energy for diffusion
R = the gas constant
T = the absolute temperature

The activation energy is associated with the energy needed to create and move a vacancy in the lattice; it may also be thought of as a measure of the temperature dependence of D (a plot of the logarithm of D versus $1/RT$ yields a straight line whose slope is Q). The diffusivity D may refer to the diffusion of atoms in a pure metal, referred to as self-diffusivity, or the movement of an impurity or alloying element in a particular solid. The above equation signifies that diffusion increases very rapidly with increasing temperature. It also increases with increasing D_o and decreasing Q, it is analogous to equation (2-11).

Diffusion of atoms from one location to another (rather than a random motion that takes place at all times) is a consequence of chemical potential gradients existing within the solid. This transport of atoms in one direction signifies that vacancies must be moving in the opposite direction. One way in which material transport by volume diffusion takes place consists of the existence of vacancy concentration potentials (differences) in the solid, and the movement of vacancies from regions of high concentrations to regions of lower ones. The atoms then move in the opposite directions. Consequently, diffusional mass transport is discussed in terms of vacancy motion. Hence, the relevance of the discussion in the previous section on vacancy concentration differences as driving forces for sintering. For a particular diffusional mechanism explaining one or more stages of sintering we are particularly interested in the regions of excessive vacancy concentrations (sources) and those where vacancies are deposited or absorbed (sinks). A mechanism involving the movement of vacancies through the crystalline lattice from the source to the sink qualifies it for inclusion in this section.

The major variations of the volume diffusion mechanism are summarized in Table 4-3. Each of these will be briefly described:

TABLE 4-3. Volume Diffusion Paths and Their Sintering Effects

Case	Vacancies from this source	moving to this sink	lead to these stages
(1)	concave neck surfaces	convex particle surfaces	neck growth pore rounding
(2)	concave neck surfaces	grain boundaries	neck growth pore rounding pore shrinkage
(3)	concave neck surfaces	dislocations	neck growth pore rounding pore shrinkage
(4)	small rounded pores	larger pores	pore coarsening
(5)	small rounded pores	grain boundaries	pore shrinkage pore coarsening
(6)	small rounded pores	dislocations	pore shrinkage pore coarsening
(7)	dislocations	grain boundaries	pore shrinkage pore coarsening
(8)	dislocations	particle surfaces	neck growth pore rounding
(9)	grain boundaries	grain boundaries	neck growth pore shrinkage

Case (1) Vacancies more from the high concentration region near the concave neck surface to the lower concentration region near the convex particle surface. This movement through the lattice is accompanied by a movement of atoms in the opposite direction. Material is thus transferred from the particle surfaces some distance away from the neck to the latter. Neck growth and eventually pore rounding can take place. No pore shrinkage or compact densification results from this process.

Case (2) Vacancies move through the lattice from the neck region to grain boundaries existing within the interior of the particle where there is a lower concentration of vacancies. The vacancies may move along the grain boundary network in the sinter mass and reach an external surface of the material. Atoms moving in the opposite direction can reach the neck surface leading to neck growth and pore rounding. Because the atoms may have come from distant regions of the sinter mass, particularly near external surfaces, pore shrinkage may result. The movement of the atoms along grain boundaries is also considered to be a diffusion process; however, it cannot be thought of in terms of a vacancy exchange mechanism because of the noncrystalline structure of the grain boundaries. Equation (4-13) still applies for the case of grain boundary diffusion. For a given material and temperature the grain boundary diffusivity is usually greater than the volume diffusivity. However, for sintering to occur by this mechanism the atoms must move through the lattice by volume diffusion (the two steps are in "series") and the kinetics of the process would be controlled by this slower second step.

Case (3) In a similar manner as the above case, but believed to be less important, is the movement of vacancies from the neck region to dislocations (the line defects consisting of somewhat distorted regions of the crystalline lattice) within the interior of the solid. Vacancies and atoms may move along these dislocations; diffusivity along dislocations is also more rapid than volume diffusivity. As in the previous case, neck growth, pore rounding and pore shrinkage are possible.

Case (4) Considering the presence of isolated spherical pores, vacancies may move from the regions around small pores to those associated with larger ones. Hence, material is removed from the surfaces of the larger pores and deposited on the ones of smaller pores. The result is pore coarsening without a change in pore volume.

Case (5) Vacancies may move from regions associated with relatively small isolated pores through the lattice to grain boundaries in the interior of the solid. Movement of the vacancies and atoms along the grain boundaries can lead to pore shrinkage. If the grain boundaries should lead to larger pores rather than to external surfaces, then atoms may come from these pores and reach the smaller ones leading to pore coarsening.

Case (6) The results obtained in the previous case may also come about because of the presence of a dislocation network in the solid; this is not believed as likely.

Case (7) It is possible for dislocations to be a source of vacancies. The vacancies may move from the dislocations through the lattice to grain boundaries. From the latter they could go to several places, but the most likely would be external surfaces or large pores. The reverse flow of atoms would lead to pore shrinkage or coarsening. This case is an unlikely one.

Case (8) Dislocations might provide vacancies that travel through the lattice to particle surfaces, particularly convex surfaces (because of their low vacancy concentration). Atoms leaving the latter would cause pore rounding and might eventually reach neck regions leading to neck growth. This too is an unlikely case.

Case (9) As noted in the previous section grain boundaries may act as either sources or sinks for vacancies because of the stress acting on them. The Nabarro-Herring viscous creep theory of deformation is based on this effect and may be applied to sintering. Deformation is a consequence of the higher vacancy concentration at boundaries under a tensile stress as compared to ones under a compressive stress, and the diffusion of atoms through the lattice in the opposite direction. The situation is illustrated in Figure 4-11. For a sinter mass with a substantial grain boundary network this mechanism might lead to neck growth and pore shrinkage. The stresses need not come from external loading of the material; they may be a consequence of gravitational forces acting on the system, residual stresses resulting from compaction or stress fields associated with the pore surfaces (as discussed in the previous section in terms of p_s values). It has been found that this mechanism of plastic deformation (a particularly unique one) tends to be operative at very low stresses and high temperatures; these can be consistent with sintering conditions. However, this case is not considered a prevalent one.

Whether any, one or several of the above variations of volume diffusion material transport takes place in a given material under specific conditions will depend on the magnitude of the driving forces present and alternative mechanisms operating. Direct experimental proof for the validity of these cases is not abundant. There has been some very good metallographic evidence, supporting cases (2) and (5), for the necessity of grain boundaries for pore shrinkage and elimination. An example of such an observation

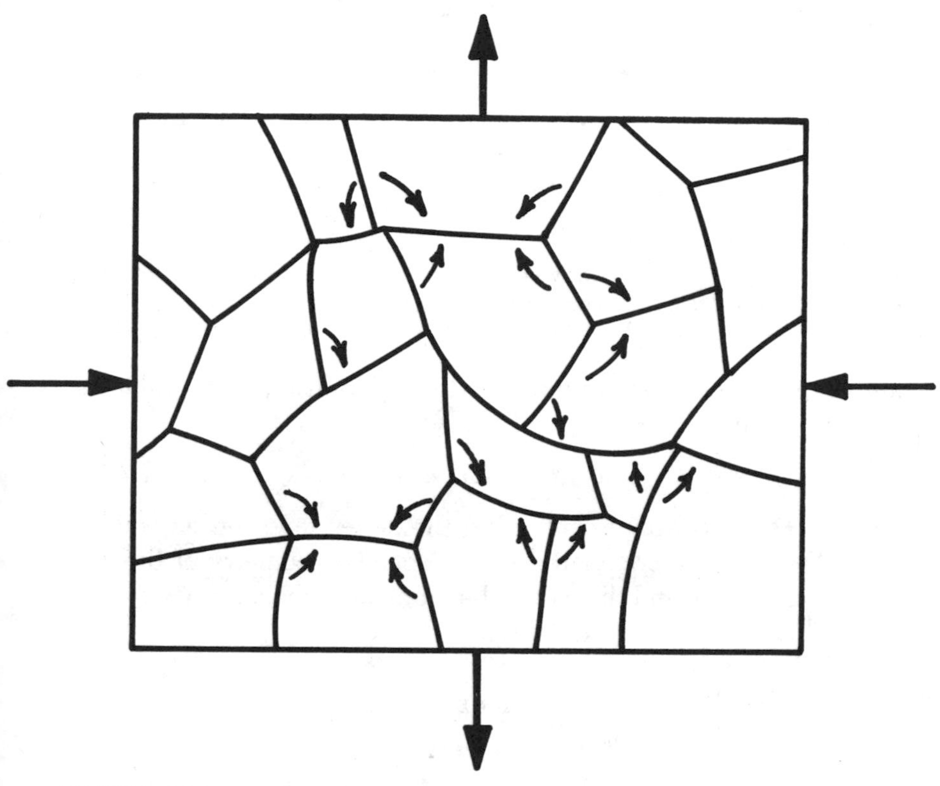

FIGURE 4-11.

Illustration of paths of atom movement (opposite to that of vacancies) between grain boundaries in polycrystalline body under tensile (vertical) and compressive (horizontal) stresses.

is given in Figure 4-12. However, there have also been a great many cases for which no dependence on the presence of grain boundaries is found. Indirect confirmation of volume diffusion being the rate controlling mechanism for sintering has been obtained by measuring the time dependence of neck growth or shrinkage and noting the agreement with theoretical predictions. For ex-

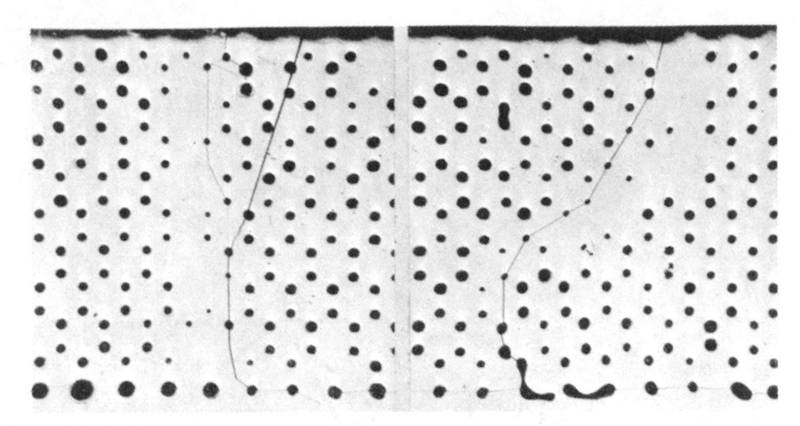

FIGURE 4-12.

Preferential elimination of voids near grain boundaries in copper (an array of wires used instead of powder) sintered 408 hr at 1967°F (49 ×). (from B. H. Alexander and R. W. Balluffi, Acta Met., vol. 5, pp. 666–667, 1957)

ample, a general type of mathematical relationship describing the rate of neck growth is

$$x^n/a^m = KD\gamma t/RT \tag{4-14}$$

where K = a constant containing the dependence on several parameters related to the specific geometry of the system and the particular transport mechanism
D = the volume diffusivity
t = time
n = the half neck width exponent
m = the particle radius exponent

For volume diffusion controlled neck growth it is generally accepted that $n = 5$ and $m = 2$ (except for case (9) for which $n = 2$ and $m = 1$). For most cases then, one expects to observe for neck growth controlled by volume diffusion a dependence on time to the one-fifth power. Shrinkage of a compact dependent on volume diffusion would follow a $t^{2/5}$ dependence. It should of course be noted that neck growth or shrinkage would be directly proportional to surface tension and diffusivity.

Finally, it might be noted that for all the cases of volume diffusion controlled material transport cited the most probable or accepted ones are cases (1), (2), (4) and (5).

Grain Boundary Diffusion It has been suggested that vacancies may move *directly* on to grain boundaries in contact with the neck surface and other pore surfaces. The grain boundary usually formed between adjacent particles in the original sinter mass would be particularly likely. The vacancies might move along the grain boundaries to external surfaces or perhaps in some way become accommodated at locations along the boundaries within the solid. Atoms from external surfaces or from locations along the boundaries would diffuse down the grain boundaries to cause neck growth, pore rounding or pore shrinkage. The shrinking of pores would most likely require movement of atoms from external surfaces, even if in a very indirect manner.

The evidence noted earlier for the necessity of grain boundaries for pore shrinkage would also be applicable to the grain boundary diffusion controlled material transport not involving volume diffusion at all.

Naturally, in most sinter masses both volume and grain boundary diffusion paths are possible. An analysis of diffusion data indicates, however, that grain boundary diffusion would become more important or effective with decreasing sintering temperature. This is a consequence of two factors: (a) at all times there is much more lattice than grain boundary volume available for diffusion; (b) because the activation energy for grain boundary diffusion is usually considerably less than that for volume diffusion (often about onehalf as great), the difference between the higher grain boundary diffusivity and the smaller volume diffusivity increases with decreasing temperature. Only a small amount of experimental evidence has been presented to support the grain boundary mechanism. Accepted mathematical formulations for neck growth or shrinkage are lacking also.

Surface Diffusion Atom movement in the solid state can also come about by the process known as surface diffusion: this signifies the motion of atoms on external surfaces (or more correctly solid-vapor interfaces). There are a number of ways for atoms to move along such surfaces; however, analogous to volume diffusion the exchange between surface atoms and surface vacancies is probably most significant with regard to sintering. Because atoms are much more loosely bonded on surfaces, the surface diffusivity is often much greater than volume or grain boundary diffusion. But surface diffusivity, also given in terms of equation (4-13), can be greatly affected by adsorption of atoms from the gaseous environment. It must be remembered that although the surface diffusivity itself can be very high, there must be a relatively large amount of surface area available as compared to the lattice itself if a significant amount of material transport is to take place by this mechanism.

Neck growth is a very likely process for surface diffusion controlled material transport. Atoms would move to the neck region from the convex particle surfaces because of the inherent difference in curvature and the vacancy concentration gradient. This early stage of sintering corresponds to the greatest amount of surface area in the sinter mass. A number of recent experimental results have demonstrated the validity of this mechanism for neck growth. Small particles, maximizing the ratio of surface area to volume in the initial sinter mass, would be expected to promote the dominance of this mechanism. Equation (4-14) for neck growth can also be applied to the surface diffusion mechanism, replacing the volume diffusivity with the appropriate surface diffusivity. Early work indicated that for this case $n = 7$ and $m = 3$, but more recent studies support values of $n = 6$ and $m = 2$. Pore rounding and pore channel closure may also be dependent on this mechanism in some cases. However, it is generally accepted that surface diffusion cannot account for pore shrinkage and elimination. This is a consequence of the lack of a driving force for long range surface diffusion of atoms, particularly from the outer to the inner regions of the sinter mass. Interestingly enough there are several experimental studies that indicate that surface diffusion does indeed affect compact shrinkage—apparently in some indirect manner still not delineated. The major role of surface diffusion in sintering is quite important because of the potential use of manipulation of the sintering atmosphere to promote sintering.

Creep Deformation by Slip Plastic deformation that takes place at an elevated temperature, under constant load or stress conditions, and increases with increasing time is termed "creep deformation." There are several fundamental mechanisms of such deformation, but the one most applicable to metallic materials is the "slip" one. Slip refers to the movement of dislocations within the crystalline structure on particular crystallographic planes (the slip planes) and in certain crystallographic directions (the slip directions). Several widely accepted creep models also require dislocation climb for creep to occur. Cimb refers to the movement of edge dislocations perpendicular to the plane originally containing them. This movement is a direct result of volume diffusion involving the atoms making up the dislocation (the edge dislocation may be thought of as a row of atoms making up the edge of a plane of atoms, situated between two other planes but not extending completely through the crystal, often termed an "extra" plane). The edge dislocation and climb process are illustrated in Figure 4-13. Atoms leaving or added to the dislocation cause it

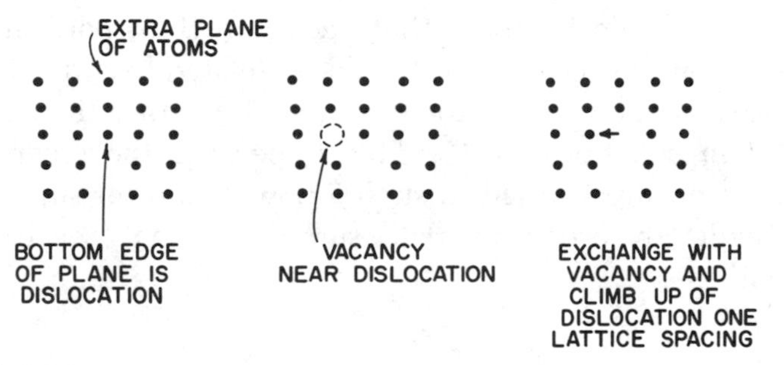

FIGURE 4-13.

Illustration of edge dislocation and climb process associated with creep deformation.

to move up or down, respectively. The climb process in itself does not cause plastic deformation but only a rearrangement of dislocations.

The actual creep process consists of two steps: (1) generation of dislocations from some type of source in the material activated by a shear stress followed by their movement on the slip plane (creating plastic deformation) and their eventual cessation at some obstacle in the lattice; (2) climb of the lead dislocation in the pile-up of dislocations against the obstacle off of the slip plane, thus allowing a new dislocation to be generated at the source.

Creep deformation is a consequence of the repeated operation of these two steps. The rate controlling step is the diffusion dependent climb. There is a stress concentration at the head of the dislocation pile-up which can lead to the production or annihilation of vacancies. The driving force for this material transport mechanism is the presence of shear stresses in the solid.

Stresses in the neck region and around isolated pores, discussed in the previous section in terms of p_s, can induce deformation leading to neck growth, pore rounding, pore channel closure and pore shrinkage. At high temperatures the stresses necessary for dislocation generation and movement are relatively small, and there has been some evidence presented for operation of this transport mechanism in sintering. Those factors that promote stresses in the solid, such as a large curvature in the neck, small pore radius and high surface tension, would tend to increase the probability of having this mechanism be the dominant one for sintering. It should be noted that neck growth or pore shrinkage dependent on this mechanism would be related to surface tension raised to some power (4.5 for pure metals) rather than to just γ as given in equation (4-14). This is because the creep rate is dependent on stress raised to such a power, and for sintering the stress is directly proportional to surface tension (see equations (4-3) and (4-4)).

4.5 TRANSFORMATIONS DURING SINTERING

At this point we shall consider those changes or transformations that may take place in the solid portion of the sinter mass. Virtually any structural or compositional change that may take place in a solid at an elevated temperature can also take place during sintering. The emphasis in this section will be on those transformations having some degree of uniqueness with respect to sintering. Any transformations related to the sintering atmosphere will be discussed in section 4.8.

Grain Growth The heating or annealing of cold worked metals generally leads to three distinct structural changes, assuming there is sufficient time at a high enough temperature: recovery, recrystallization and grain growth. The first change is related to the recovery of internal elastic strains (also often referred to as strain or stress relief) and minor structural changes that do not affect the properties of the material very extensively. This process would not likely be affected by the presence of porosity in the sinter mass; naturally, some type of compaction involving deformation of the powder particles would be a prerequisite for this to occur. For most cases recovery would tend to take place during the heating of the sinter mass to the sintering temperature.

Recrystallization refers to the evolution of new strain (dislocation) free grains from the original cold worked structure; a fairly large degree of plastic deformation during compaction would be necessary for this to be a significant change in the sinter mass. The driving forces for both recovery and recrystallization are associated with free energy reductions resulting from defect (mostly dislocations) rearrangement and removal.

Grain growth is the process that normally follows recrystallization; it is the most important one for sintering and can easily be the only one taking place. The driving force for grain growth is quite similar to the fundamental one considered earlier for sintering. Grain boundaries represent a positive contribution to the free energy of the material; for a particular solid and type of grain boundary (there are several) there is a specific grain boundary energy. Removal of grain boundaries is simply another method to reach the lowest energy state (highest degree of stability) of the material. Grain growth does just this. In a normal sinter mass there is a very large amount of grain boundary area. This comes about because of the rather small particle sizes used originally, the formation of grain boundaries at the original contact areas, and the presence of grains within individual particles. Hence, there is normally a large driving force for grain growth. And in most cases there is a substantial amount of grain growth during sintering.

Grain growth in a sinter mass can be somewhat different than the conventional cases. The motion of grain boundaries necessary for grain growth (these arguments would also apply to recrystallization for which grain boundary motion is also required, but to a lesser extent) may be impeded by the presence of second phases within the solid. The term "second phases" usually refers to actual particles of a material different than the matrix. However, it also characterizes pores. And although second phase particles may indeed exist within the sinter mass (such as impurity oxide inclusions in reduced powders or dispersed particles in composite materials), the effect of porosity is of greater interest. If we consider a portion of a grain boundary in the solid associated with a pore, as shown in Figure 4-14, and its disassociation

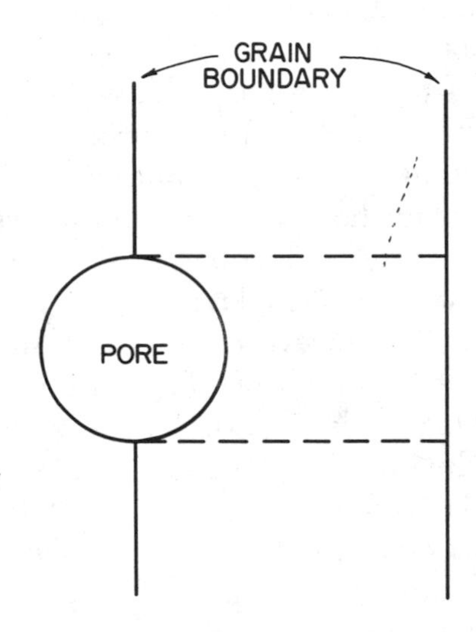

FIGURE 4-14.

Presence of pore on a grain boundary signifies a reduction in length (or area) and energy associated with the boundary.

from it, then the basis of the effect is realized. Removal of the grain boundary from the pore signifies an increase in the length of the boundary and, hence, an increase in free energy. Once grain boundaries become associated with pores, either as a result of their original formation (neck boundaries) or of their movement through the solid, they become anchored to some extent and further motion is restricted.

The effect of second phases on grain growth has been treated quantitatively and is given by the Zener relationship, assuming spherical phases or pores, as follows

$$R = 4r/3f \tag{4-15}$$

where R = the radius of curvature of the average grain (grain growth would correspond to an increasing R)
r = the pore or phase radius (probably an average value)
f = the volume fraction of porosity or second phase

It is seen that *the smaller the dispersed phase or pore, and the greater the amount of them, the more restricted is grain growth.* Porosity in green compacts and in the developing sinter mass represents a very effective hindrance to grain growth. One usually observes a rather great number of pores associated with grain boundaries in sintered materials, as may be seen in Figure 4-6 for example.

Very often particles may become coated with a foreign substance during the initial blending and preparation of the powder mix. For example, alloys containing soft graphite powder or mixes containing lubricant powders. Even small amounts of such substances may drastically hinder bonding between adjacent particles and the formation of grain boundaries. As a result of this interference there could be virtually no grain growth during sintering. To illustrate this effect Figure 4-15 should be compared to Figure 4-6. The only significant difference between the two materials illustrated in these figures was the introduction of a small amount of graphite powder in the latter. The coating of the nickel powder with the graphite has inhibited all grain growth; the grain size in this case is analogous to the original nickel particle size.

Yet another factor may restrict grain growth. In a polycrystalline material some grain boundaries will intersect external surfaces. When such a material is heated to an elevated temperature "grain boundary grooves" can be formed. The groove on the surface is formed because of the balance of surface tension forces, of the surface and the boundary, at the line of intersection. This effect is illustrated in Figure 4-16. The dihedral angle of the groove is given by

$$\cos(\theta/2) = \gamma_b/2\gamma_s \tag{4-16}$$

where θ = the groove dihedral angle
γ_b = the grain boundary tension (analogous to the energy)
γ_s = the surface or interfacial tension

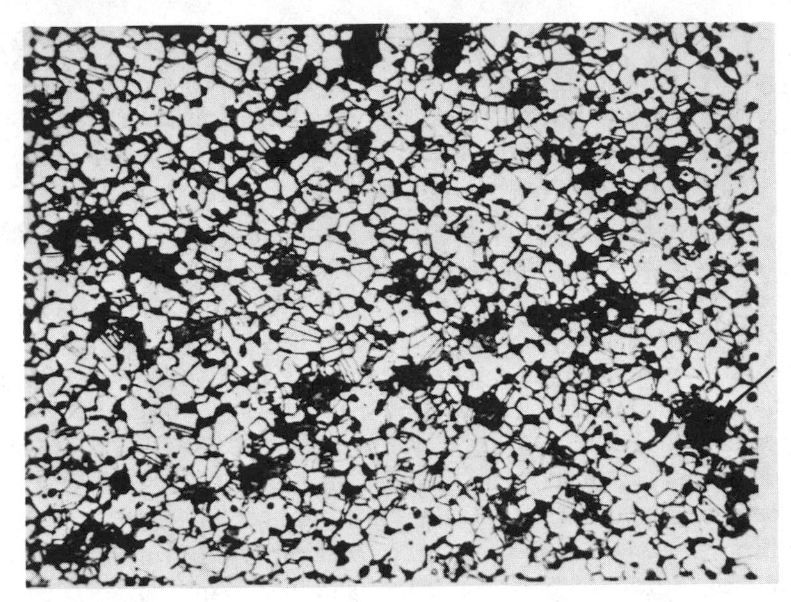

FIGURE 4-15.

Photomicrograph of nickel—10 vol. % graphite (compacted at 50 tsi and sintered at 1900°F for 2 hr) illustrating inhibiting effect of particle coatings on grain growth during sintering; arrow in lower right corner shows a typical graphite grain (400 ×). (from E. Daver, M.S. Thesis, Univ. of Wisconsin, 1967)

For a grain boundary associated with a groove to move there would be an increase in the grain boundary area and, hence, free energy of the material. This is shown in Figure 4-17. Grain

FIGURE 4-16.

Illustration of balance of surface and grain boundary tension forces leading to formation of grain boundary groove on surface.

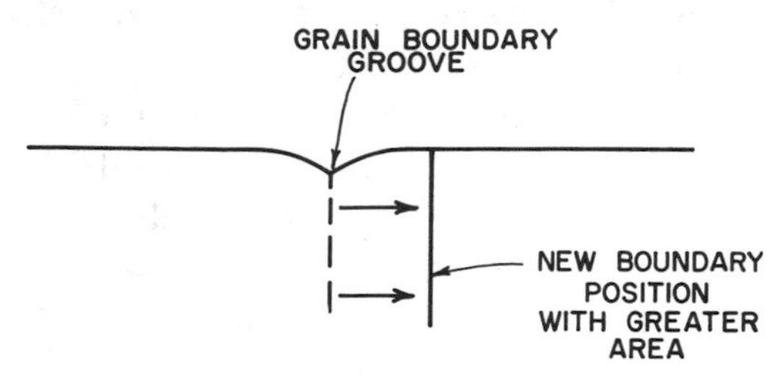

FIGURE 4-17.

Movement of grain boundary away from its groove would lead to an increase in grain boundary area and energy.

boundary grooves tend to inhibit grain growth. Ordinarily this effect would be insignificant. In a bulk material the ratio of surface area-to-volume is quite small and the number of grain boundaries anchored by grooves would be small in proportion to all the boundaries unaffected. However, for powder particles and a sinter mass just the reverse case exists. This is particularly true if we are dealing with particles having a small internal grain size that have undergone some annealing treatment as part of their original manufacture. The latter would facilitate the formation of grain boundary grooves, although they could of course form during the early period of sintering.

The above three effects help explain why grain growth during sintering may happen (or purposefully manipulated) to be less than the amount expected to result on the basis of the fine grain structure in the original material.

One last factor that should be noted concerns the orientation of the resulting grain structure. Very often grain growth preceded by recrystallization leads to the development of a preferred crystallographic orientation to the grains. However, in sintered materials there is usually a random orientation of the new grain structure because of the absence of a strongly directional type of plastic deformation in the original material.

Alloying Very often the sintering operation is used to produce a homogeneous alloy from the original mechanical mixture of two or more elemental powders; for example, the blending of graphite with iron to produce steel. The evolution of a homogeneous alloy structure for a completely solid state sintering system comes about by the process of diffusion. Although much of the available experimental data indicates that volume (lattice) diffusion is the predominant mechanism for alloying, both grain boundary and surface diffusion may be operative and possibly dominant. The latter would be particularly likely at relatively low temperatures. What mechanism is important for a particular case will decide whether some key structural features will be advantageous or not. If volume diffusion is rate controlling, then porosity acts as an obstacle to the diffusing atoms and reduces the rate of alloying or homogenization. However, if surface diffusion is dominant, then having a great amount of pore surface area could facilitate the process. Similarly, a fine grain structure in the original particles and minimum grain growth during sintering would be desirable if grain boundary diffusion is critical. As in the case of material transport for straightforward sintering there is likely to be some combination of diffusional processes leading to alloying for any specific system; the relative importance of each may change substantially during sintering as the structure changes.

Alloying during sintering is also so complex because of the potential structures that can develop. By blending different powders together one obtains an average composition for the material. The structure for such a material, in terms of the kinds, amounts and compositions of the individual phases, at a particular elevated temperature and corresponding to the equilibrium (the lowest energy state, usually associated with long time exposures) condition is given by the appropriate phase diagram. The greater the number of chemical components (elements) the greater the complexity of the phase diagram. Most often people attempt to work with or analyze simple two component systems so as to make use of binary phase diagrams. But even for binary compositions there are a variety of structures that may develop upon complete alloying. The simplest case, and luckily extremely prevalent for practical powder metallurgy systems, is the formation of solid solutions of one or more elements in another. Diffusion can allow one element to become dissolved in another, such as graphite becoming dissolved in iron. Or each of the two elements in a binary mix may dissolve each other to produce a uniform solid solution.

The fundamental fact to appreciate is that there must be a substantial amount of uniform material transport, requiring sufficient time at temperature, to achieve complete alloying during sintering. A number of mathematical analyses of alloying during sintering have been formulated. The complexity of real materials is so great, however, that the many assumptions made in these analyses and theories severely limit their application. At best they yield useful qualitative results that may aid our understanding and control of the process. One of the most realistic and useful models for alloying during sintering, for simple binary mixtures and the formation of single phase solid solutions, is the "concentric-sphere" one. Like all others it does not include the presence of porosity. The model is illustrated in Figure 4-18 (a). The diffusional mass

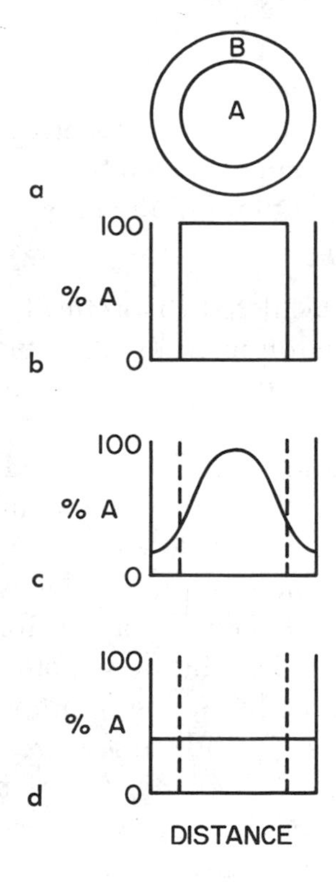

FIGURE 4-18.

Alloying during sintering: (a) concentric-sphere model, and concentration-distance profiles for (b) time = 0, (c) intermediate time and (d) time = infinity.

transport for a very simple configuration is considered to be valid for the entire sinter mass. It is seen that one of the components in spherical form is assumed to be completely surrounded by a spherical shell of the other element.

Also given in Figure 4-18 are the concentration-distance profiles corresponding to the beginning, some intermediate time, and the end of alloying for the concentric-sphere geometry. If we consider high density pressure formed compacts, then this model is reasonably accurate. Indeed, many of the theoretical predictions based on it have been found to be in relatively good agreement with experimental data. One of the techniques used in both the theoretical and experimental work to describe the progress of alloying is to make use of a "degree of homogenization" or "degree of interdiffusion" factor F, defined by

$$F = m_t/m_\infty \tag{4-17}$$

where m_t = the mass of material transferred across the boundary between components in time t

m_∞ = as above, but for infinite time (the maximum amount possible)

Values for F may be calculated theoretically or determined from x-ray diffraction or electron microprobe data. The limits of F are zero, at the beginning of the process, and one corresponding to complete diffusion.

Alloying during sintering may be evaluated in terms of F values and their dependence on the major process and material variables. Some actual data, given in Table 4-4, for a simple binary alloy forming a single phase solid solution will be used to illustrate some of the most important and generally applicable effects:

(1) *temperature:* This has the most potent affect on alloying; the process depends directly on the appropriate diffusivities (as defined by equation (4-13)) and these increase very sharply with increasing temperature. Hence, *the degree of alloying increases greatly with relatively small increases in sintering temperature.* The data in Table 4-4 indicate increases of from 20 to 40% in F for only about a 10% increase in sintering temperature.

(2) *time:* Naturally, *with increasing time more material is trans-*

TABLE 4-4. Effects of Material and Process Variables on Alloying in Copper-Nickel Powder Mixtures During Sintering

Powder Mix[a]	Powder Size	Comp. Press. (tsi)	Temp. (°F)	Time (hr)	F
elemental Cu and Ni	−100 + 140 mesh	50	1562	100	0.64
			1742	1	0.29
				50	0.71
			1922	1	0.42
				54	0.87
	−270 + 325	50	1562	100	0.84
			1742	1	0.57
				50	0.87
			1922	1	0.69
				54	0.91
	−270 + 325	2.5	1742	1	0.41
prealloyed cupronickel[b] and elemental Ni	−100 + 140	50	1742	1	0.52
				50	0.71
elem. Cu and prealloyed Monel[c]	−270 + 325	50	1742	1	0.65
elem. Cu and composite Monel[d]	−270 + 325	50	1742	1	0.80

[a] all specimens with a mean concentration of 52 atomic % nickel
[b] a 70 Cu-30 Ni alloy
[c] a 70 Ni-30 Cu alloy
[d] nickel coated copper powder

(from R. W. Heckel, Trans. ASM, vol. 57, pp. 443–463, 1964)

ported and the degree of alloying increases. However, the rate of change is not as great as with increasing temperature. As shown in Table 4-4 increases of from 50 to 100% in *F* require time increases of about 50,000%!

(3) *particle size: The degree of alloying increases with decreasing particle size.* All other factors being equal, particularly the amount of each component, a reduction in particle size of both or either of the constituent powders signifies: an increase in the amount of interfacial area between the two phases providing more paths for material transport; and a decrease in the "diffusion distance" over which the atoms must move to affect the desired

change. The size differences in Table 4-4 are not especially great (−325 mesh powders are often used to promote alloying) but increases of 100% in F were possible.

(4) *porosity:* In most cases *decreasing the amount of porosity in the sinter mass, as indicated by increasing green density or compaction pressure values, increases the degree of alloying.* Greater physical contact and more paths for diffusion account for this effect. The effect, although quite significant, is proportionately minor; as seen in Table 4-4 an increase in compaction pressure of about 2,000% produced an increase of 40% in F. This effect also explains the possible acceleration of alloying during sintering of a material that is also undergoing a substantial amount of densification due to pore shrinkage and elimination.

(5) *form of the powder:* By form of the powder we mean the nature with respect to the potential alloying process; for example, one may use elemental, prealloyed or composite (usually signifying coated) type powders either singly or in conjunction with each other. Naturally, using all prealloyed powder with the desired composition eliminates the need for alloying during sintering altogether. However, *using some amount of prealloyed or composite powder in conjunction with elemental powder to achieve a desired composition usually promotes alloying as compared to using just elemental powders.* This is a consequence of reductions in the diffusion distance and/or the amount of material required to be transported. The data of Table 4-4 illustrate this effect; its magnitude is not comparable to the temperature and particle size effects.

A number of other factors affecting alloying could also be thought of; these are usually minor in their effect and very obvious in cause. For example, the interfering effect of lubricant particles in the sinter mass, the advantageous increase in interparticle contact with nonspherical shapes and the interfering effect of particle surface contamination.

Phase Transformations Many types of phase transformations may occur in the solid state during sintering at a constant temperature or during the cooling of the material from the sintering temperature. In some cases such transformations would follow sufficient alloying, as discussed in the previous section, or in others for which prealloyed powder was used they could take place immediately. Any conventional type of phase transformation, either isothermal or athermal, can be associated with sintering. The only unique aspects concern the influence of porosity and a fine grain structure on the transformation. For example, many solid state transformations in which some new phase is formed are nucleated at internal surfaces or interfaces; hence, the large amount of grain boundary and pore surface area can lead to greater than normal heterogeneous nucleation. The usual result is a fine size to the new grains or phases that are formed. This fineness of metallurgical structure can also be promoted by the effect of grain boundaries and pore surfaces on the movement of new phase boundaries. Consequently, it is commonplace to see unusually fine structures in sintered materials that have undergone some type of phase transformation.

Probably the best example of a phase transformation associated with sintering is the production of sintered steels. Plain carbon steels would be made by mixing graphite and iron powder; during sintering the iron and graphite would alloy to form the high temperature austenite phase (a solid solution of carbon in face-centered-cubic iron). The temperature of sintering is selected so that austenite with the desired carbon content can be obtained in a reasonable time. The solutioning of the carbon in the iron is the prime reason why a relatively high sintering temperature (usually 2050°F) is used. Once the austenite is formed, then the desired pearlitic structure can be obtained upon cooling. Naturally, any nonuniform alloying during sintering leads to an inhomogeneous structure after the transformation. The importance of sintering temperature for this particular type of transformation is illustrated in Figure 4-19. At low temperatures there is virtually no alloying of the carbon in the iron and, hence, no increase in the sintered strength. However, after a critical temperature of almost 1900°F is reached alloying is attained. The further increases with increasing temperature are related to the conventional stages of sintering.

A photomicrograph of a sintered steel, with a rather high carbon content (hypereutectoid because there is greater than 0.8% carbon) is given in Figure 4-20. The black areas are pores while the

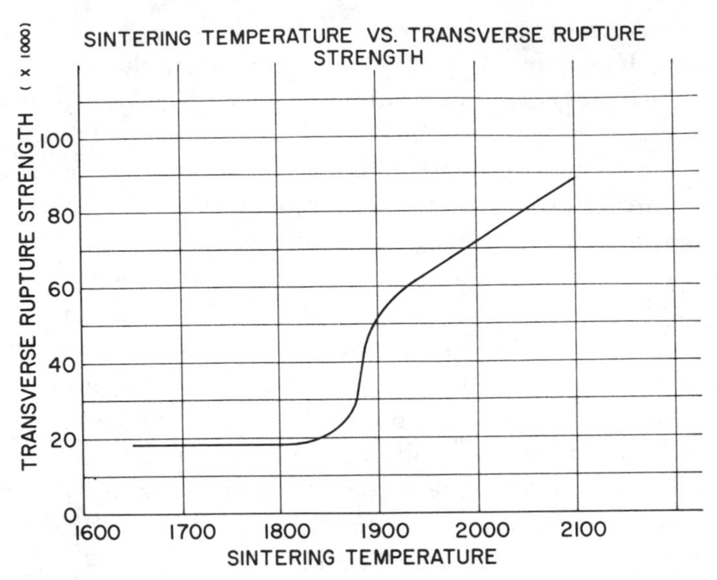

FIGURE 4-19.

Dependence of sintered transverse rupture strength on sintering temperature for iron-1.25% graphite materials (time constant at 30 minutes). (from A. Stosuy, Metallography of Sintered Steel, Hoeganaes Corp., Riverton, N.J.)

remainder of the structure contains conventional phases for the iron-carbon system. Proeutectoid cementite (iron carbide) is present on the pore surfaces and pearlite and ferrite are in the interior of the solid.

As for conventional materials the cooling rate can have a strong effect. The faster the cooling rate the finer is the structure; that is, for pearlite the spacing between the cementite and ferrite plates is decreased. The same effect is found for sintered materials as shown by the data in Table 4-5. It should be noted, however, that sintered materials are unique in one respect with regard to transformations taking place upon cooling. The presence of porosity reduces the thermal conductivity of the mass. This means for a given external set of cooling conditions the actual cooling rate throughout a sintered material is considerably less than for a conventional solid one. For some types of transformation particularly dependent on cooling rate, such as the martensitic one in the iron-carbon system, this can be a very significant factor.

Precipitation from solid solutions is also a very common type of

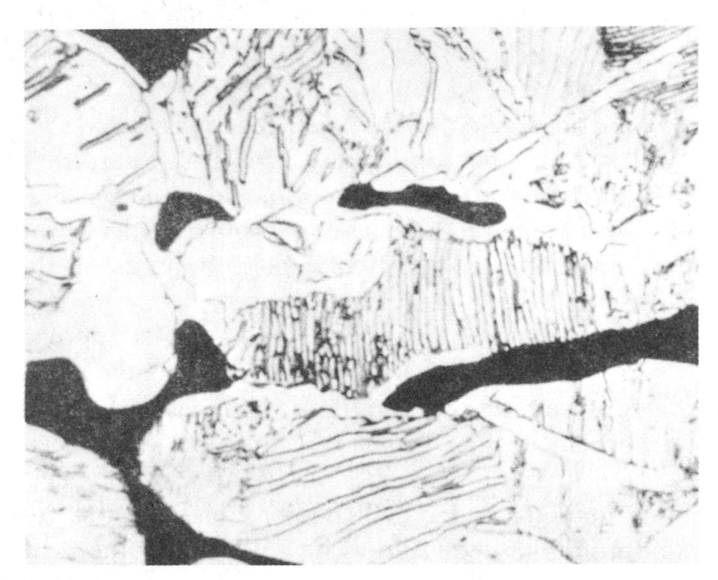

FIGURE 4-20.

Photomicrograph of sintered steel (1.2% carbon) sintered at 2050°F for 30 min; density about 6.3 gm/cc (about 2000 ×). (from A. Stosuy, Metallography of Sintered Steel, Hoeganaes Corp., Riverton, N.J.)

transformation associated with sintering. For some powders of the prealloyed type precipitation may take place during sintering. In other cases, once the alloy is formed during sintering the decreasing solid solubility of one element in another with decreasing

TABLE 4-5. Effect of Cooling Rate on Pearlitic Steel

Cooling Rate (°F/min)	Transverse Rupture Strength (psi)	Hardness R_B	Pearlite Spacing
3.5	67,000	37	very coarse
115	82,000	50	medium
225	87,000	57	very fine

Material with 0.7% carbon sintered at 2050°F for 30 min; slowest cooling rate obtained by furnace cooling in hot zone after power turned off; fastest rate obtained by shoving compacts immediately into cooling chamber.

(from A. Stosuy, Metallography of Sintered Steel, Hoeganes Corp., Riverton, N.J.)

temperature causes precipitation during cooling; this is the case for some alloyed steels.

Chemical Reactions Actual chemical reactions may take place during sintering, either intentionally for a useful purpose or unavoidably with possible undesirable effects. A good example for the latter case is related to the use of graphite powder mixed with iron powder in the production of steels. In most of the iron powders used there is a significant amount of oxygen, either in solid solution or as metal oxide, whose amount is approximated by the hydrogen loss value (as discussed in section 2.3) of the powder. During sintering the graphite can react with this oxygen to form carbon monoxide. From one viewpoint this is beneficial because it helps to purify the material, however it also means that some of the graphite added will be consumed by this reaction. An amount of graphite equal to as much as 75% of the amount of oxygen present can be lost in this manner; hence, for this reason and another one to be considered in a later section more than the desired amount of graphite is added initially. Another undesirable effect of this reaction concerns dimensional changes, this will be discussed in the next section. It might be noted that the amount of carbon in the form of iron carbide is termed the "combined carbon"; any unreacted and unalloyed carbon remaining is the "free graphite."

4.6 EFFECTS OF MATERIAL AND PROCESS VARIABLES

In this section we shall review the effects of the major material and process variables on sintering. Some of this information may be somewhat repetitive; however, its practical importance is so great and the subject so complex that any repetition is justified.

Particle Size In terms of the basic stages of sintering *decreasing particle size leads to increased sintering.* All other factors being equal, particularly green density, a decreasing particle sign signifies a greater driving force for sintering that is, there is more pore-solid interfacial area in the sinter mass. Arguments supporting this effect can also be made in terms of material transport. For example, with a smaller particle size there would be greater interparticle contact (number of necks) and, hence, more paths for volume diffusion. Or a small particle size may correspond to a smaller internal grain size, promoting grain boundary diffusion transport. And the greater surface area might be interpreted to mean more paths for surface diffusion transport. Some data illustrating this size dependence are given in Table 4-6. Both the rate

TABLE 4-6. Effect of Particle Size on Sintering

Material	Particle Size	Green Density	Measure of Sintering
Copper	$-270 + 325$ mesh	6.7 gm/cc	3×10^{-5} [a]
	-325 mesh	6.7 gm/cc	10×10^{-5} [a]
Alumina [b]	0.8 –1.0 micron	— [c]	7 [d]
	0.2 –0.3 micron	— [c]	10 [d]
	0.08–0.1 micron	— [c]	30 [d]
Tungsten [e]	14–16 microns	63.4%	71 [f]
	3– 4 microns	64.1%	72 [f]
	0.5 micron	62.6%	73 [f]

[a] shrinkage rate in min^{-1}
[b] from N. C. Kothari, J. Nuclear Materials, Vol. 17, pp. 43–53, 1965.
[c] compacted at 20 tsi
[d] percent linear shrinkage at 100 min.
[e] from N. C. Kothari, Powder Met., Vol. 7, no. 14, pp. 251–260, 1964.
[f] percent theoretical density at 100 min.

of sintering and the magnitude of any change due to sintering are increased by reducing the particle size. We have already indicated that particle size can greatly affect transformations accompanying sintering, such as the promotion of alloying and the hindrance of grain growth (there would be more pore boundary interactions and more surface grooves).

Particle Shape and Topography *Those changes that lead to greater intimate physical contact among particles in the sinter mass and increased internal surface area promote sintering.* Such changes would include decreasing sphericity, increasing micro and macro-surface roughness. As above the reasons are enhancement of the driving force or of a particular material transport mechanism.

Particle Structure A fine grain structure within the original particles can promote sintering because of its favorable effect on several material transport mechanisms. The presence of a greater than normal amount of lattice imperfections, such as dislocations, usually resulting from plastic deformation can promote sintering because such defects enhance diffusional processes. Some data illustrating this effect are given in Table 4-7. Internal particle

TABLE 4-7. Effect of Plastic Deformation on the Sintering of 316L Stainless Steel Powder

	Measure of Sintering[a]	
Temperature (°F)[b]	Strained[c]	Unstrained[d]
1950	0.14	0.10
2050	0.17	0.12
2150	0.19	0.14

[a] given in terms of a densification parameter defined by

$$\frac{\text{sintered density} - \text{green density}}{\text{theoretical dens.} - \text{green dens.}}$$

[b] loose sintered in ceramic containers for 4 hrs in vacuum
[c] ball milled for 16 hrs; over 20% deformation indicated by x-ray diffraction analysis
[d] ball milled powder annealed in hydrogen at 1950°F for one hr

(from C. C. Fatino and J. S. Hirschhorn, Trans. AIME, vol. 239, pp. 1499–1504, 1967)

porosity can promote sintering by increasing the driving force; this can be a consequence of simply greater surface area or, because such porosity is often extremely fine, greater stresses in the solid promoting neck growth, pore rounding and pore shrinkage. Fine pores may also inhibit grain boundary movement and grain growth and, thus, promote material transport along grain boundaries. The latter effect may also be promoted by dispersed phases within the particles. Modifications in crystal structure can also affect sintering because of the dependence of diffusivities on this, even though the chemical composition is unchanged. For example, some pure metals and alloys have allotropic transformations; that is, they can exist with different crystal structures in different temperature ranges (some structures can be maintained outside of their normal temperature range). The diffusivity tends to increase as the crystal structure becomes less dense (easier for atoms to move around). Consequently, diffusion is faster in body-centered-cubic (ferrite) iron than in face-centered-cubic (austenite) iron, and sintering often mirrors this change.

Particle Composition The driving force for sintering may be affected by alloying additions or impurities in a metal, either increased or decreased. Surface contamination, such as oxidation, normally reduces the surface energy of the base metal, because of this and its interference with material transport it is usually undesirable. Diffusional mass transport may also be affected by the presence of alloying or impurity atoms in the lattice. Dispersed phases within the matrix may promote sintering by inhibiting grain boundary motion. Reactions between impurities and either the base metal or alloying additions at the relatively high sintering temperature may be undesirable.

Green Density One may argue that the use of compaction pressure is equivalent to green density; however, compaction pressure is a process or operational variable not associated directly with sintering. Green density is a material variable that is directly related to sintering and is more desirable. Much of the time these data are not available and compaction pressure must be used instead. All the material factors that affect green density should be kept in mind. For sintering a decreasing green density signifies an increasing amount of internal surface area and, consequently, a greater driving force. *Both the rate of sintering and the magnitude of any change resulting from it increase with decreasing green density.* Sintered density is probably the most widely used parameter to follow the progress of sintering, and the variation of density-time curves with green density is shown schematically in Figure 4-21. Although the rate, at any time, and the percent change in density increase with decreasing green density, the absolute value of the sintered density remains highest for the higher green density material. Some data illustrating the latter effect are given in Table 4-8. Variations in green density in the

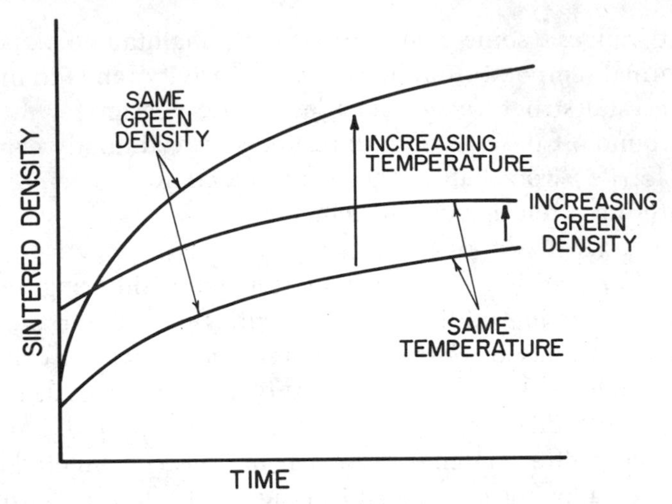

FIGURE 4-21.

Sintered density-time curves illustrating effects of increasing green density and sintering temperature on the process of densification.

original material lead to different degrees of sintering in the sinter mass, and this may produce quite undesirable effects. It must be emphasized that densification is not a requirement for sintering. High green density materials may exhibit very small

TABLE 4-8. Effect of Green Density and Sintering Temperature on Sintered Density

Material	Compaction Pressure (tsi)	Green Density (gm/cc)	Sintering Temp. (°F)	Sintered Density (gm/cc)
Cobalt	20	5.07	1292	5.16
	40	6.03	1292	6.05
	60	6.61	1292	6.62
	20	5.07	2012	8.34
	40	6.03	2012	8.36
	60	6.61	2012	8.38
Iron	30	6.72	2050	6.73
	50	7.23	2050	7.25
Molybdenum	36	—	2192	8.0
	50	—	2192	8.6
	36	—	3092	9.8
	50	—	3092	10.0

changes in certain properties, such as density, after sintering. Nevertheless, other stages of sintering, particularly bonding, are likely to have taken place to a substantial degree. Increasing the green density would increase alloying and probably grain growth during sintering.

Temperature The discussions on diffusional mass transport and alloying have already indicated that sintering is extremely dependent on temperature. *Increasing the sintering temperature greatly increases the rate and magnitude of any changes occurring.* Figure 4-21 illustrates the effect of increasing temperature for a constant green density, and Table 4-8 contains some actual data. Many of the experimental investigations on sintering have indicated that the precise material transport mechanism controlling the rate of sintering changes with varying temperature. And there is increasing evidence for the hypothesis that several mechanisms may be determining the kinetics of the process. Although an activation energy for sintering can often be obtained by analyzing the temperature dependence of the sintering rate or something directly dependent on it, it cannot be used to unequivocally determine the controlling transport mechanism.

Time Although *the degree of sintering increases with increasing time,* the effect is small in comparison to the temperature dependence. The rate of sintering decreases with increasing time (as shown by a dependence of any change on t^n where n is less than one). As shown in Figure 4-21 the largest change comes about in the earliest period of sintering. Tens or hundreds of hours are normally required to affect changes that could be brought about by an increase in sintering temperature of perhaps 100°F. The loss of driving force with increasing time at any temperature is one of the reasons why it is so very difficult to remove all porosity by sintering. Less important would be any possible reduction in material transport capability, such as that resulting from grain growth. Both time at temperature and the temperature itself are also important in the economics of the sintering process. Higher temperatures require more heat energy. Longer cycling time reduces the rate of production.

4.7 DIMENSIONAL AND DENSITY CHANGES

Changes in density and dimensions resulting from sintering represent an extremely important area in powder metallurgy, especially with respect to large scale production of parts with small dimensional tolerances. Talking about density and dimensional changes may appear to be redundant; this is not the case. There may be no dimensional changes (from a fundamental viewpoint changes in dimensions are based on the original green compact dimensions; however, it is commonplace to find dimensional changes referred to the original die dimensions in commercial operations) resulting from sintering, but the weight of the compact may change. Most common are weight losses resulting from reactions between the sinter mass and the atmosphere or within the sinter mass itself leading to the production of a gaseous compound. In such cases a density decrease can be measured, if there was no volume decrease to compensate for the weight loss.

Measurements of sintered density changes, either in the laboratory or plant, are used routinely to evaluate sintering. It should be noted, however, that when dealing with more than one compact using just sintered density values may be misleading. Slight changes in the green density of compacts are very difficult to avoid and will affect the sintered density values obtained. This is undesirable because usually the effect of more direct sintering processing variables are of interest. One method that can be used to avoid this problem is to make use of a densification parameter given as

$$\begin{array}{c}\text{densification parameter}\\ \text{for sintering}\end{array} = \frac{\text{sintered density} - \text{green dens.}}{\text{theoretical dens.} - \text{green dens.}} \tag{4-18}$$

Actual values will be between zero and one, and represent the fraction of the maximum amount of densification possible.

In many cases sintered density or parameter values are obtained as a function of time for a given temperature. A generalized equation, widely applicable, for sintering may be given as

$$\text{density} = Kt^n \tag{4-19}$$

where K = a system constant containing the temperature dependence among other things

t = time of sintering

n = the time exponent that can be related to the rate controlling transport mechanism

Plotting the logarithm of density, or the above parameter, versus the logarithm of time should yield a straight line whose slope yields n. A series of such lines for various temperatures is a convenient method of data presentation.

It is appropriate at this point to consider in some detail the various causes for dimensional changes resulting from sintering. It is best to think of the sinter mass volume and its components, such as the volume of the base metal, the volume of any alloying element powder, the volume of the porosity, and normally the volume of the admixed lubricant.

Pore Shrinkage and Elimination The fundamental process of sintering leads to a reduction in the volume of the sinter mass because of pore shrinkage and elimination. In virtually any system this process may be potentially significant. This effect is most important for relatively simple systems for which most of the other causes for dimensional changes do not have to be superimposed.

Entrapped Gases Closed porosity may be formed in the compaction operation. The air in these pores will expand when the compact is heated. Although the volume of the pore will increase due to thermal expansion, it is still possible for an appreciable pressure to be built up. This is particularly true for a rapid rate of heating to the sintering temperature which makes diffusion of some of the gaseous atoms into the solid of less significance. Counteracting the gas pressure is the surface tension force acting to minimize the pore volume. Equation (4-4) applies to this problem. Should the gas pressure p_v become greater than $2\gamma/r$, then there is a net stress acting on the surrounding solid to expand the pore. The values of $2\gamma/r$ given in Table 4-2 indicate the magnitude of the pressures required, and the fact that this mechanism of pore expansion is more difficult for small pores. An approximate value for p_v may be obtained by applying the ideal gas law to the original formation of the entrapped gas (room temperature and atmospheric pressure) and the sintering conditions. Assuming no change in the original pore volume one obtains

$$p_v = (T + 460)\,(14.7)/540 \qquad (4\text{-}20)$$

where T = the sintering temperature in °F

For example, for a sintering temperature of 2050°F the value of p_v is about 70 psi (note that p_v values are independent of pore size). In view of the data in Table 4-4, this would indicate that pores less than about 10 microns in radius would have no driving force for expansion. Larger pores would have a driving force for expansion; however, an operative mechanism for material transport would actually have to be present for this process to lead to compact expansion. The most likely mechanism would be plastic deformation of the surrounding solid. This might be possible for very high sintering temperatures corresponding to very low mechanical strength of the solid. A rigorous analysis of this mechanism of expansion would have to take into account the change in net stress once the original pore changed its size, either by shrinking or expanding. In most cases this mechanism is probably insignificant; at the most it might be a contributory factor for the very early period of sintering.

Chemical Reactions The reaction between graphite and oxygen discussed earlier can lead to compact expansion. The formation of the gaseous product within an isolated portion of the compact becomes analogous to the entrapped gas mechanism. Another possible reaction would be between hydrogen from the sintering atmosphere and oxygen in the sinter mass. Hydrogen is a common component of sintering atmospheres and can often diffuse through the metal to isolated portions of the compact where it reacts with oxygen to form water vapor. The pressure of the water vapor can lead to expansion of the entire mass. This explanation has been applied to expansion of copper compacts. The oxidation of a metal can come about in a poorly controlled atmosphere. The oxide formed on the pore surfaces can eventually fill the porosity and thereafter lead to expansion of the compact. It is also possible to have reactions that lead to the loss of some element from the sinter mass to the atmosphere, such as volatilization, and result in a shrinkage of the material.

Alloying The alloying that may take place between two or more elemental powders (or perhaps a prealloyed powder also), very often leads to expansion of a compact. When one element is dissolved in another to form a solid solution there may be either an expansion or contraction of the matrix (solvent) lattice. For substitutional type solid solutions expansion is related mostly to a larger atomic size of the alloy or solute atom as compared to the matrix, and this is usually the case for systems of practical interest. Interstitial type solid solutions are associated with lattice expansion also (the dissolving of gaseous atoms and carbon). In the original green compact there is a volume associated with both the metal (matrix) and the alloy (solute) powders. If, during sintering, the alloy powder becomes dissolved in the base metal powder and the pores created by the loss of the alloy particles remain unchanged, then the net dimensional change is dictated by the solid solution effect. This is usually an expansion of the lattice and, hence, the compact. Although this is very often the case, with increasing time at temperature the probability increases that these new pores will start to shrink due to "natural" sintering. Should the latter occur, the amount of expansion due to the alloying actually observed at room temperature after sintering would appear to decrease. Of course shrinkage of the original porosity in the compact would also offset any expansion due to alloying (as it would do for any type of expansion). Let us consider some actual data for the iron-graphite system as shown in Figure 4-22. At the lowest temperature of 1900°F the expansion first increases with increasing time and then begins to decrease rather slowly. This is due to the somewhat slow alloying of the graphite with the iron at this temperature. Once all the carbon is dissolved the shrinkage of pores causes the reduction in compact growth, however at this temperature the rate of pore shrinkage is slow. At the higher sintering temperatures solutioning of the carbon takes place very rapidly. Hence, pore shrinkage causes a steady reduction in the amount of growth, with the rate of change increasing with increasing temperature.

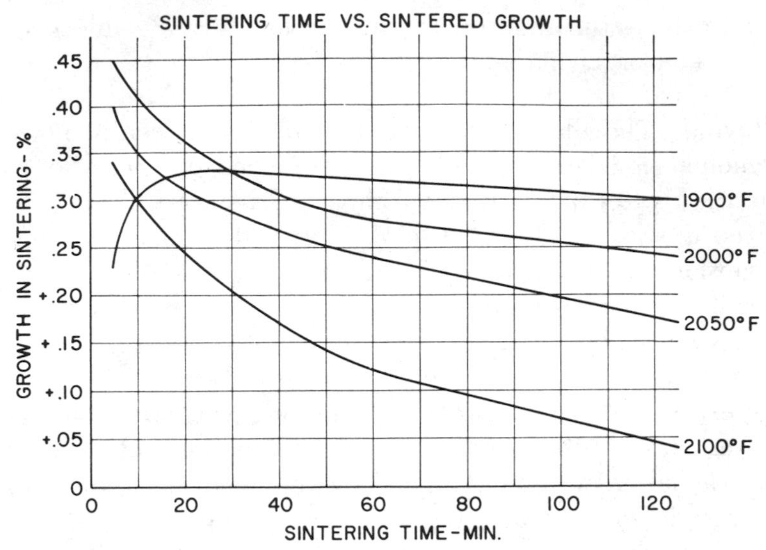

FIGURE 4-22.

Growth of iron-1.5% graphite compacts, green density 6.1 gm/cc, at various times and temperatures. (from A. Stosuy, Metallography of Sintered Steel, Hoeganaes Corp., Riverton, N.J.)

It should be understood that the dimensional behavior for a given metal varies from one type powder to another. For example, some iron powders containing substantial amounts of very fine particle porosity tend to exhibit strong shrinkage. Others, without such porosity, when compacted to high green densities exhibit some degree of expansion. Consequently, different iron powders may be blended together to yield a desired type of dimensional change. The same can be done with respect to using different alloying elements. For example, copper and graphite are often added in very controlled amounts to iron in order to achieve dimensional stability. Some data illustrating this effect are given in Table 4-9 for a particular type of iron powder. The goal of zero dimensional change with respect to die dimensions can be attained after some preliminary experiments are conducted for a particular alloy and set of processing conditions.

The practice of blending small amounts of copper with iron, and with iron and graphite, can be analyzed in terms of alloying effects. In most cases the sintering temperature is above the melting

TABLE 4-9. Effect of Copper and Graphite Additons to Iron on Dimensional Changes

Compaction Pressure (tsi)	% Copper	% Graphite Added	Dimensional Change, %
30	2.0	0.0	+0.3
		0.5	0.0
	4.0	0.7	+0.3
		1.2	0.0
	6.0	0.0	+1.2
		0.6	+0.6
		1.0	+0.3
		1.4	0.0
		2.0	−0.3
40	0.0	1.5	0.0
	1.0	0.8	0.0
	6.0	0.5	+0.9
		0.8	+0.6
		1.2	+0.3
		1.7	0.0
50	0.0	0.7	0.0
	9.0	1.6	0.0

Reduced iron also blended with 1% zinc stearate; sintered 30 min at 2040°F in endothermic atmosphere.

point of the copper; however, this is not a true case of liquid phase sintering. The molten copper soon gets dissolved in the iron. In a simple iron-copper system, this formation of a solid solution and the retention of the porosity created by the removal of the copper particles leads to an expansion of the compact. The expansion of the iron reaches a maximum with copper contents corresponding to the maximum solid solubility of copper in iron at the sintering temperature; this is about 8% at 2050–2100°F. The series of photomicrographs given in Figure 4-23 illustrate the dissolution of a copper particle and the resulting pore; the compact in question contained 7.5% Cu and exhibited marked expansion. The addition of relatively small amounts of graphite (as shown in Table 4-9) to an iron-copper alloy leads to the formation of a ternary eutectic and a greater amount of liquid phase. The latter promotes a mechanism of shrinkage associated with liquid phase sintering, to be discussed in a later section, and this can offset the expansion due to the solutioning of the copper in the iron.

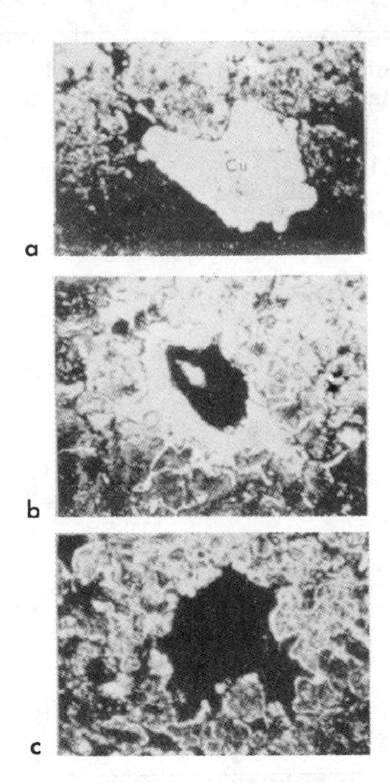

FIGURE 4-23.

Photomicrograph of portion of an Fe-7.5% Cu compact during heating to the sintering temperature (over 2000°F) illustrating: (a) original copper particle, (b) solutioning of copper into the surrounding iron and (c) pore remaining after complete diffusion of the copper into the iron (about 87 ×). (from G. Bockstiegel, Stahl u. Eisen, vol. 79, pp. 1187–1201, 1959)

There is yet another mechanism for dimensional changes associated with alloying during sintering. If we consider a simple binary mixture, then there is a very strong possibility that the rate of diffusion of each metal into the other is different. In other words, across the interface that separates the two metals there is a greater amount of mass transport in one direction. Consequently, the material into which the faster diffusing species moves will expand and the other will contract. Also, because there is an opposite flow of vacancies the side losing material (the faster diffusing species) will have an excess of vacancies. This can lead to pore formation. Stresses are also created. The side gaining material is put in compression, and the side losing material in tension. This preferential diffusion process is usually termed the "Kirkendall" effect. Experiments have indicated that the element with the lower melting point diffuses faster. Thus, in a mixture of copper and zinc powders the zinc diffuses faster, and for copper and nickel the copper diffuses faster. If in sintering the faster diffusing species should mostly be dissolved in the other, and the pores created by its removal remain, then the compact could expand. The stresses and pores created may affect sintering in complex ways.

Lubricants In a compact containing admixed lubricant and pressed to a high density there is the likelihood of having some lubricant particles imbedded within the metal, and remote from any interconnected porosity. As part of the sintering process this admixed lubricant is burned off at a relatively low temperature (several hundred degrees). However, if the gaseous substances produced upon decomposition cannot reach the external surfaces of the compact, then they may cause compact expansion.

It is important to realize that in a real sinter mass several of the above described causes of dimensional changes may be operating, either simultaneously or sequentially. Hence, full understanding and control of dimensional changes in complex alloy systems is often lacking. Some of the more sophisticated experimental techniques, such as hot stage microscopy and dilatometry, are required for truly meaningful work. Several other topics associated with dimensional changes, and of considerable importance in commercial practice, will now be discussed.

Shrinkage Ratios Most dimensional change figures are given in terms of a linear variation. For many systems, particularly simple ones without extensive alloying taking place during sintering, there is shrinkage in all directions. Thinking in terms of conventional die compaction it is convenient to speak of radial and axial dimesional changes. A useful parameter is the shrinkage ratio: the linear radial shrinkage divided by the linear axial shrinkage. It would be quite advantageous to have the shrinkage ratio R/A, equal to one; that is, uniform shrinkage in all directions in the compact. But this is usually not the case. The R/A may be considerably greater or less than one. First let us consider those structural or material features, or possibly conditions, that can cause a sintered material to exhibit a R/A greater than one:

(a) flattened porosity in the green compact would strongly interfere with material transport in the axial direction as compared to its influence on transport in the radial direction; this feature would be promoted by high compaction pressures, large amounts of plastic deformation during compaction, large pores in the loose powder which are promoted by large particle sizes, and flake-like particles;

(b) laminations in the green compact would also preferentially interfere with material transport in the axial direction; high compaction pressures, poor die design, low green strength, insufficient lubrication for ejection and improper ejection procedures can account for laminations;

(c) a flattened grain structure leading to a greater density of grain boundaries in the radial direction could promote material transport in this direction; large amounts of plastic deformation during compaction would promote this;

(d) low L/D ratio for the compact could signify more low density material in the radial direction as compared to the axial direction and, hence, a greater driving force leading to more shrinkage in the radial direction.

The following factors may explain a material exhibiting a R/A ratio less than one:

(a) stresses acting in the axial direction could promote material transport by enhancing physical contact among particles or by favoring a Nabarro-Herring type mechanism; such stresses may exist because of gravitational forces as has been demonstrated for loose sintering, or possibly because of residual stresses from the compaction operation;

(b) more effective physical contact among particles in the axial direction would enhance material transport in this direction; certain ejection procedures can lead to greater elastic expansion in the radial direction and possibly restraining it in the axial direction;

(c) high L/D ratio for the compact could signify more low density material in the axial direction and consequently greater shrinkage in this direction.

Much of the data in the literature on shrinkage ratios, particularly the effect of material and processing variables, appears quite inconsistent and contradictory. However, using the above concepts most of these results can be explained in a reasonable fashion. For example, sometimes increasing the compaction pressure increases the R/A and in other cases it does just the opposite. For a material having a tendency to exhibit flattened porosity, increasing the compaction pressure could induce greater pore flattening and, hence, promote radial shrinkage leading to an increasing R/A. However, for a material not prone to pore flattening (such as hard particles), or perhaps in a relatively low pressure range, increasing the pressure could induce greater particle movement and contact in the axial direction; and in this case the R/A would decrease. Results of different investigations on the same metal are often very difficult to compare because different powders or L/D ratios were used.

Shape Changes It is often convenient to forget about the existence of green density variations in particular directions in green compacts. However, because of the strong dependence of sintering, especially shrinkage, on green density such nonuniformities can lead to substantial changes in shape. Low green density regions will exhibit a greater amount of shrinkage during sintering. For example, a cylinder with a relatively high L/D ratio compacted by a single action technique would have a gradually decreasing green density from one end to the other. Such a cylinder would change during sintering into a truncated cone, as shown in Figure 4-24. And such a cylinder prepared by a double action technique would likely achieve an "hourglass" shape, as shown in Figure 4-24.

Joining The unique ability to prepare materials that will undergo a predetermined kind and amount of dimensional change during sintering provides the basis for a method of joining. Two or more green compacts can be fitted together or placed in intimate contact to produce what is termed a "green assembly" (one or more of the components could be a wrought, machined or cast part). By having some portions of the assembly shrink and others expand

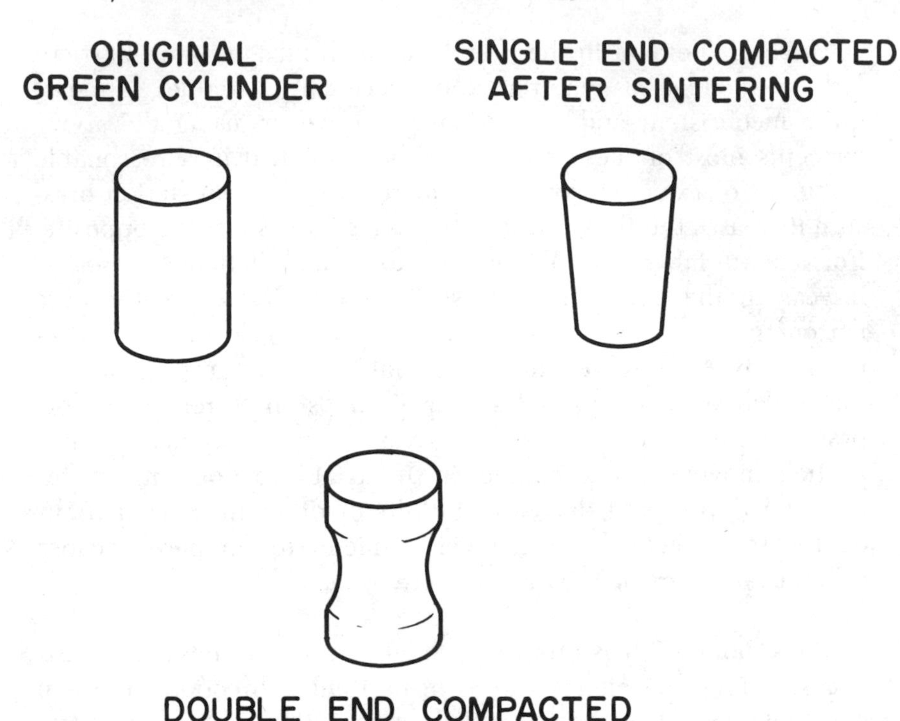

FIGURE 4-24.

Illustration of changes in shape of cylindrical compact due to sintering for single and double end compaction; also signifies nonuniform sintered densities.

during sintering very intimate contact can be established. The assembly can become joined together as a result of the stresses (analogous to a shrink fit) acting on various components or because of actual diffusion-bonding between the components.

4.8 SINTERING ATMOSPHERES

The proper production, use and control of sintering atmospheres is absolutely required for optimum use of the powder metallurgy process. In this section we shall deal with some of the more important aspects of the nature of atmospheres and their interaction with the material being sintered. The practical considerations of atmosphere production and control, especially in terms of equipment, will not be covered; there is considerable literature on these topics and some references are given at the end of this chapter.

Function of an Atmosphere For any case of sintering the atmosphere may have one or more of the following three functions:

(1) The prevention or minimization of any chemical reaction between the sinter mass and its environment which would inhibit or interfere with the sintering process. A good example is the prevention of oxidation of the metal.

(2) The cleaning and purification of the sinter mass involving the removal of adsorbed impurities, oxide films and impurity elements or compounds within the metal. This may occur not only on the external surfaces of the compact but also within the interior. Internal pore surfaces can become exposed to the atmosphere because of interconnected porosity providing a path for the atmosphere. And chemical species from the atmosphere may diffuse into the solid metal throughout the compact to reach substances there. Cleaning of the surfaces is a very effective way to increase the driving force for sintering. In some cases very special additions can be made to the atmosphere that very quickly and effectively clean the surfaces with the result that sintering is greatly enhanced. This technique falls into the category of "activated sintering." The term applies to sintering for which special chemical additions are made to either the atmosphere or the sinter mass in order to greatly increase the driving force or material transport associated with the process. The removal of impurities from the metal itself may not be related to some effect on the sintering process but rather to an improvement in properties of the material.

(3) The provision of one or more chemical elements which may alloy with the sinter mass and promote the sintering process and/or improve the properties of the sintered material. Or an element may be present in the atmosphere in order to maintain an equilibrium condition so that no loss of an alloying element already in the sinter mass occurs.

Prevention and Reduction of Oxides Most sintering atmospheres have the capability to reduce oxides present on the surface, and possibly in the solid, of the original sinter mass, and also to prevent the formation of new oxides during the sintering. It should be noted that the reduction of oxides signifies that the chemistry of the atmosphere itself will be affected. Evaluating the ability of a given atmosphere to accomplish these goals for a specific material involves the application of some basic thermodynamic principles. These have already been discussed in section 2.2 and equations (2-7) through (2-10) may be directly applied to this aspect of sintering. The chemical reaction between a reducing component of the atmosphere and the appropriate metal oxide is considered. The equilibrium constant for the reaction is utilized to obtain a critical partial pressure ratio. For a specific sintering temperature the ratio has a unique value; maintaining the composition of the atmosphere below this value yields a reducing condition (no oxide is stable), while allowing the atmosphere to exceed this value yields an oxidizing condition (oxides will form). The critical ratios for hydrogen and carbon monoxide as a function of temperature for iron are given in Figure 4-25. Both hydrogen and carbon monoxide may be present in an atmosphere in order to maintain a reducing condition over a broad temperature range.

The reducing potential of a hydrogen bearing atmosphere is linked to the amount of water vapor in the atmosphere. Minimizing the water vapor content of an atmosphere is described in terms of obtaining a "dry" atmosphere. The dew point (in °F) is used to measure the degree of dryness. The lower the dew point, the lower the volume percent or vapor pressure of the water vapor in the atmosphere: a table of such data is given in Appendix II. Having a very dry atmosphere signifies that a relatively small percentage of hydrogen is required to maintain a reducing atmosphere. Equipment is available to control and measure the dew point of an atmosphere. Naturally, it is the dew point in the furnace that is of importance. Because of reactions between hydrogen and oxygen the dew point of the atmosphere can be increased once it enters the hot zone of the furnace and comes in contact with the sinter mass.

It should be noted from Figure 4-25 that increasing amounts of CO_2 relative to CO can be tolerated with decreasing temperature. That is, a high critical partial pressure ratio would be reducing at low temperatures. And it might appear that having such a ratio

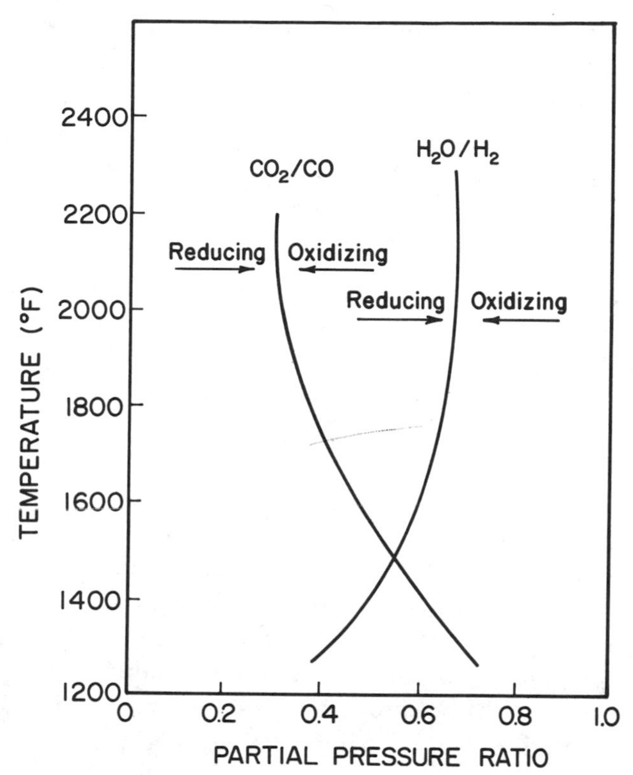

FIGURE 4-25.

Temperature dependence of critical partial pressure ratios CO_2/CO and H_2O/H_2 for iron; regions of oxidation and reducing potential indicated.

would be oxidizing at high temperatures and, thus, undesirable. However, at the higher temperatures the following reaction could take place

$$CO_2 + H_2 \rightarrow CO + H_2O \tag{4-21}$$

This could easily lower the p_{CO_2}/p_{CO} ratio to a reducing value; and for a dry atmosphere the amount of water vapor produced could be tolerated without shifting the p_{H_2O}/p_{H_2} ratio to too high a value.

The Carbon Problem for Ferrous Materials Many plain carbon and alloy steels are prepared by powder metallurgy techniques. A sintering atmosphere may be of three types: neutral, carburizing or decarburizing with respect to the composition. The evaluation of atmospheres on this basis also relies on thermodynamic analysis.

First let us consider sintering an iron-carbon alloy in an atmosphere containing CO and CO_2 (in this as in subsequent cases we assume a total pressure of one atmosphere for the sintering environment). The reaction to consider is

$$Fe + 2CO \rightarrow (Fe,C) + CO_2 \qquad (4\text{-}22)$$

where the first term on the right side represents carbon in solid solution (note that most sintering is done at a temperature which signifies that the metal is in an austenitic state). The equilibrium constant is then

$$K = \frac{p_{CO_2} \times a_c}{p^2_{CO} \times a_{Fe}} \qquad (4\text{-}23)$$

where the p terms represent the appropriate partial pressures, a_c is the "activity" of the carbon in solid solution which may be approximated by its atomic fraction, and a_{Fe} the activity of the iron which may be approximated by unity. For more complex alloys the activities would have to be more rigorously evaluated. It should be remembered that K has a specific value at any temperature at which the reaction may take place.

The application of equation (4-23) to a practical problem can be understood by applying the phase rule to the reaction; this basic principle may be written as

$$F' = c - p + 2 \qquad (4\text{-}24)$$

where F' = the degrees of freedom, or the number of independent variables
c = the number of components
p = the number of phases

Actually the number of components may be considered equal to the number or chemical species (for example, carbon dioxide would be one and not two, and carbon in solid solution would be one) minus the number of unique equations relating the species to one another. The number of phases for sintering would normally be two: the gas and the solid. For the reaction given by equation

(4-22) we have $c = 3$(Fe, CO, CO_2 and C minus one) and, hence, $F' = 3$. Two of the three degrees of freedom are already determined, the temperature and the pressure of the system. This means that *either* a_c or the ratio p_{CO_2}/p^2_{CO} may be used as a variable. Normally the ratio would be controlled in order to obtain a specific value for a_c. If the sinter mass had more carbon (usually in the form of graphite) than this critical value, then some would be lost to the atmosphere (it would be decarburizing). And if the sinter mass had less than the critical concentration, the atmosphere would provide some (carburizing). Or the atmosphere could be controlled to have exactly the same "carbon potential" as the sinter mass, and this would make it neutral. The gas ratio would have to be controlled during sintering to maintain a given potential.

Another reaction that may be appropriate is

$$Fe + CH_4 \rightarrow (Fe,C) + 2H_2 \tag{4-25}$$

for which

$$K = \frac{p^2_{H_2} \times a_c}{p_{CH_4}} \tag{4-26}$$

As in the previous case there are three degrees of freedom. The ratio $p^2_{H_2}/p_{CH_4}$ would be used to control the carbon potential of the atmosphere.

Some data illustrating the temperature dependence of the ratios p_{CO_2}/p_{CO} and p_{CH_4}/p_{H_2} (note these are not the ratios as given by equations (4-23) and (4-26), but are analogous to them) are given in Figure 4-26. The carburizing or decarburizing regions are indicated with respect to carbon saturated austenite. Even though such data are not directly applicable to lower carbon content steels they do illustrate the characteristics of these two systems. This figure should be compared with Figure 4-25. One may note that although the CO_2 to CO ratio can be fairly high at all temperatures without causing oxidation of the iron it must be very low at practical sintering temperatures to prevent decarburization. At lower temperatures high ratios would not be detrimental from either viewpoint. It can also be seen that at usual sintering temperatures very small amounts of CH_4 can cause carburization (as low as 1% concentration).

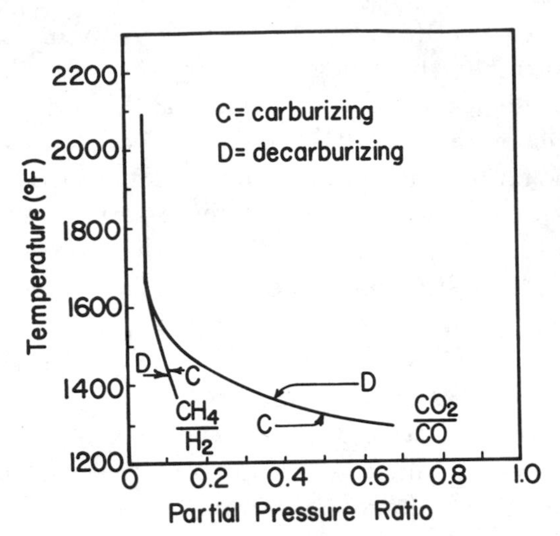

FIGURE 4-26.

Temperature dependence of critical partial pressure ratios CO_2/CO and H_2O/H_2 for carbon saturated austenite; regions of carburizing and decarburizing potential indicated.

Another possible reaction is

$$Fe + CO + H_2 \rightarrow (Fe,C) + H_2O \qquad (4\text{-}27)$$

for which

$$K = \frac{p_{H_2O} \times a_c}{p_{CO} \times p_{H_2}} \qquad (4\text{-}28)$$

This last reaction in conjunction with equations (4-25) and (4-22) allows an analysis of the complex type of widely used atmosphere termed "endogas." The six chemical species in the atmosphere are CO, CO_2, CH_4, H_2, H_2O and N_2. Hence, there are five degrees of freedom. The ones usually fixed for a given process are temperature, pressure, hydrogen content and carbon monoxide content; with the fifth one being either carbon content in the steel, water vapor content (dew point), carbon dioxide content or methane content. In practice either the dew point or carbon dioxide content is used as the controlling variable.

In Figure 4-27 the relationship between dew point and equilibrium carbon content in the steel, for several temperatures, is given for an endogas atmosphere (nominal composition of 20% CO, 40%

H_2, 1% CH_4 and 39% N_2). With increasing temperature the amount of water vapor that can be tolerated without causing decarburization decreases sharply. And at any specific temperature the decarburizing effect of the water vapor increases with increasing

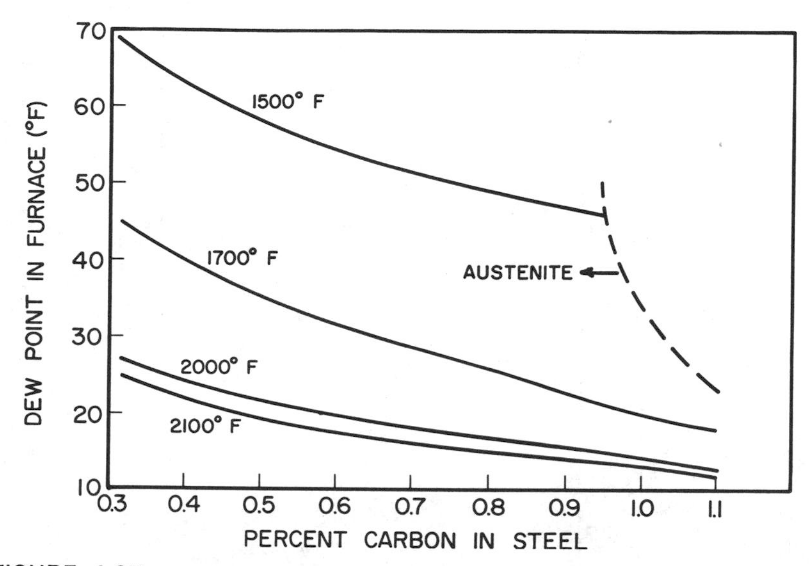

FIGURE 4-27.

Equilibrium relationship between dew point and % carbon in steel (austenite) for different temperatures; for endothermic atmosphere.

temperature; that is, having a 10% greater than desired dew point at 2100°F is more harmful (more decarburizing) than at 1700°F.

Alternatively, the equilibrium relationship between the amount of CO_2 and the percent carbon in the steel may be considered as shown by the data in Figure 4-28. Here too there is an increasing sensitivity of carbon content to the gas with increasing temperature.

One should also be aware of the following reaction

$$2CO \rightarrow CO_2 + C \qquad (4\text{-}29)$$

Iron is a very efficient catalyst for this reaction, particularly at low temperatures. It is also quite sensitive to the presence of other gases and impurities in the system. The deposition of carbon—in the form of soot—on the surfaces of the compact or within the pores between 570 and 930°F has a reasonable probability. For some systems rapid heating and cooling may be necessary to avoid this contamination. Decarburization is also a possibility with some sintering systems (the reverse of the above reaction).

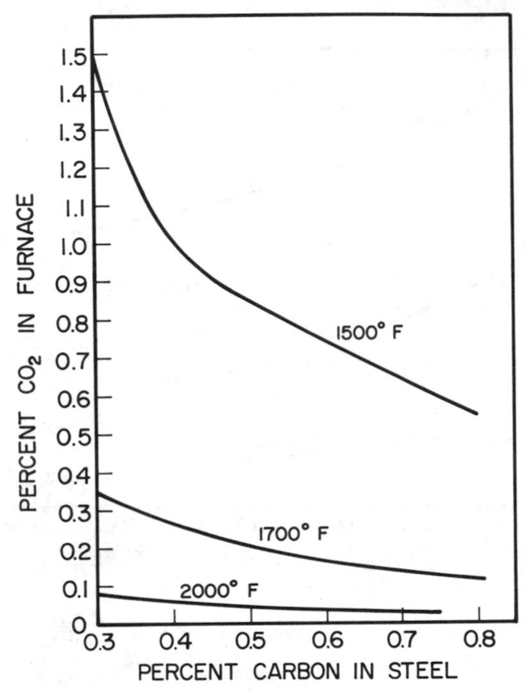

FIGURE 4-28.

Equilibrium relationship between % CO_2 and % carbon in steel (austenite) for different temperatures; for endothermic atmosphere.

We have already indicated that some of the graphite originally mixed with the iron will be lost due to reaction with oxygen or oxides in the material (note that this is one of the causes of atmosphere composition variability within the furnace). Additionally, for many atmospheres there is a decarburizing potential or species present (such as CO_2) that may react with the original free graphite. Consequently, additional graphite may be lost. The choice of the proper graphite in terms of its chemical reactivity, influenced by such factors as purity and crystal structure, is a very important aspect of the sintering and production of sintered steels. Then too, the reactivity of the iron powder is also an important factor; high purity and particle porosity often improve the kinetics of the reaction between the iron and the graphite. For most commercial powders the solutioning of the graphite in the iron is quite rapid. From 1.0 to 1.5% graphite may be added to obtain a eutectoid composition of 0.8% carbon. It should also be noted that the presence of a large amount of an essentially inert component in the atmosphere may slow down the reaction between iron and graphite. Specifically nitrogen has been shown to have this effect.

The application of thermodynamic analysis to the evaluation of sintering atmospheres has great value. However, one must be very much aware of the conditions in sintering that lead to nonequilibrium conditions. The simple fact that the composition of the atmosphere within the furnace can be very much different than that associated with the ingoing gas may have major consequences. The products of reactions between the atmosphere and the sinter mass, the inside of the furnace and within the atmosphere itself unless efficiently removed may invalidate any predictions based on simple thermodynamic analyses. And the variation in composition of the atmosphere from one end to the other and from top to bottom of the furnace chamber can lead to nonuniform reactions and effects. For example, the carbon content may vary in a large part, or soot may be deposited on only one side of the compact. Reactions between the sinter mass and the material upon which it is resting should also be considered.

Problems with Brass The sintering of brass (copper-zinc) powder represents an interesting example of how fundamental considerations yield very helpful information. Consider an atmosphere containing hydrogen as the reducing agent for which the following reaction is desired

$$\mathrm{ZnO} + \mathrm{H_2} \rightarrow (\mathrm{Cu,Zn}) + \mathrm{H_2O} \tag{4-30}$$

for which

$$K = \frac{p_{\mathrm{H_2O}} \times a_{\mathrm{Zn}}}{p_{\mathrm{H_2}} \times a_{\mathrm{ZnO}}} \tag{4-31}$$

where a_{Zn} is the activity of the zinc in the copper which may be approximated by its atomic fraction and a_{ZnO} is the activity of the

TABLE 4-10. Nature and Properties of Some Sintering Atmospheres

Atmosphere Gas	Dew Point Entering Furnace (°F)	Properties at elevated Temperatures	CO_2	CO	CH_4	O_2	H_2	N_2	A	He	Air/Nat. Gas
Hydrogen—purified bottle	−100 to −60	R, r, m	0.0	0.0	0.0	0.0	100.0	0.0	0.0	0.0	
Dissociated Ammonia											
—As reacted dry	−60 to −40	R, r, m	0.0	0.0	0.0	0.0	75.0	25.0	0.0	0.0	
—Moisture added saturated	+70 to +100	R, r, D_3	0.0	0.0	0.0	0.0	75.0	25.0	0.0	0.0	
Exothermic											
—Rich—as reacted sat.	+70 to +90	R, r, D_3	5.0	10.0	1.0	0.0	14.0	70.0	0.0	0.0	6:1
—Lean—sat.	+70 to +90	O_F, n, D_3	11.5	0.7	0.0	0.0	0.7	87.1	0.0	0.0	10.25/1
Purified Exo.—Rich	−40 or lower	R, r, C_1	0.0	10.8	1.0	0.0	15.0	73.2	0.0	0.0	6:1
Endothermic											
—Rich—Dry	−10 to +10	R, r, C_3	0.0	20.0	0.5	0.0	38.0	41.5	0.0	0.0	2.4/1
—Lean—Sat.	+70 to +90	R, r, D_3	3.0	13.8	0.0	0.0	21.5	61.7	0.0	0.0	4.5/1
Argon—bottled	−60 or lower	N, n, m	0.0	0.0	0.0	0.001	0.001	0.098	99.0	0.0	
Helium—bottled	−60 or lower	N, n, m	0.0	0.0	0.0	0.0	0.01	0.0	0.0	99.99	
Air—normal	+50 or lower	O_F, O_c, D_3	0.0	0.0	0.0	21.0	0.0	78.1	0.9	0.0	

R = reducing to iron and iron oxides
r = reducing to copper and copper oxides
N = neutral to iron and iron oxides
O_F = oxidizing to iron and iron oxides
O_c = oxidizing to copper and copper oxides
n = neutral to copper and copper oxides
D_3 = strongly decarburizing to iron-carbon
C_1 = mildly carburizing to iron-carbon
C_3 = strongly carburizing to iron-carbon
m = neutral to iron-carbon

(from Powder Metallurgy Equipment Manual—Part II, Sintering Furnaces and Atmospheres, MPIF, N.Y., 1968)

zinc oxide which may be approximated by unity. Hence, at any temperature and zinc content in the alloy there is a critical value of the H_2O/H_2 partial pressure gas ratio. An atmosphere with a ratio above this value would be oxidizing.

On the basis of this analysis a suitably dry atmosphere could be selected. However, in an actual sintering operation there would be a strong tendency to build up the concentration of water vapor. There is normally a substantial amount of oxygen or oxide on the original particle surfaces that can react with the hydrogen to form water vapor. A reasonable approach to solving this problem would be to increase the rate of flow of the atmosphere through the furnace. But another problem exists.

The vapor pressure of zinc is quite high at practical sintering temperatures. The metal would attempt to maintain its equilibrium vapor pressure of the zinc. This means that a continuously moving atmosphere would cause a severe loss of zinc—termed dezincification. Reducing the rate of flow of the sintering atmosphere can relieve this problem. On the basis of the oxidation and dezincification problems an optimum rate of flow of the atmosphere must be attained.

Actual Atmospheres The six major categories of sintering atmospheres actually used in practice will now be briefly discussed: (1) hydrogen, (2) nitrogen, (3) hydrogen-nitrogen mixtures, (4) reformed hydrocarbon gases, (4) argon and helium and (6) vacuum. The dew point range, properties at elevated temperatures, composition and for some the air to natural gas ratio associated with their manufacture of a number of atmospheres are given in Table 4-10; the list is by no means complete. Air is also included for comparison purposes and because it has been used in a few isolated cases. Typical sintering temperatures, times and atmospheres for a number of common materials are given in Table 4-11. It would be well for the reader to compare these sintering temperatures with appropriate melting points given in Appendix III if he is not already familiar with the degree of closeness of the two.

The most important characteristics of pure hydrogen are: (a) it is highly reducing to most metal oxides, (b) it is very flammable

TABLE 4-11. Typical Sintering Temperatures, Times and Atmospheres for Various Materials

Material	Temp. (°F)	Time (min.)	Atmosphere[a]
Bronze	1400–1600	10–20	H, A, X, D
Copper	1550–1650	12–45	H, A, X, D
Brass	1550–1650	10–45	H, A, X, D
Iron and Iron-Graphite-Copper	1850–2100	8–45	H, A, X, D
Nickel	1850–2100	30–45	H, A, X, D
Stainless Steel	2000–2350	30–60	H, A, V
Alnico Magnets	2200–2375	120–150	H
Tantalum	4350 approx.	480 approx.	V, argon, helium
Tungsten Carbide	2600–2700	20–30	H, V
Tungsten	4250	480 approx.	H, A, V

[a] H = hydrogen
A = dissociated ammonia
X = exothermic gas
D = endothermic gas
V = vacuum

(from Powder Metallurgy Equipment Manual—Part II, Sintering Furnaces and Atmospheres, MPIF, New York, 1968.)

and requires proper handling, (c) it is very light in weight and prone to escape from openings at the top of the furnace, (d) it is an excellent heat conductor and this leads to high heating and cooling rates and relatively high thermal losses, (e) impurity contents of oxygen and water vapor are relatively easy to remove to very low values, (f) its cost lends itself to small furnace operations but not to high quantity consumption. Note in Table 4-10 that it is usually low enough in water vapor content to make it neutral with respect to carbon.

Pure nitrogen has the disadvantages of being nonreducing and reactive with a number of elements. The latter refers to both the solid solutions nitrogen may form with some elements, such as austenitic iron which it tends to stabilize, and to compound formation. Precipitation of nitrides tends to occur with alloying elements and often results in embrittlement of the sintered material and other effects related to the loss of the alloying element from solid solution. For these reasons it has not been used extensively as a sintering atmosphere, although it is used as a purging gas for furnaces prior to and after use with flammable gases.

Mixtures of hydrogen and nitrogen may be obtained in a number of ways. The dissociation of ammonia yields a mixture of 75% H_2 — 25% N_2 with small amounts of ammonia and water vapor that are easily removed to very low values. Because of the high hydrogen content it is highly reducing and flammable. Its use is often avoided because of the deleterious effects of nitrogen already mentioned; this would be the case for stainless steel and molybdenum. Normally its water content is so low that it is neutral to iron-carbon alloys; it can be made decarburizing by the addition of moisture. Dissociated ammonia may be mixed with air and burned to yield lower hydrogen content gases, in the range from 0.5 to 24%; it too can be dried to low dew point values. Naturally they are less reducing than gases with higher hydrogen contents, but they are also less flammable and more easily handled. Similar mixtures may be made by direct catalytic oxidation of ammonia and air.

Reformed hydrocarbon gases refer to a family of relatively low cost mixtures prepared by reacting a fuel gas with air in a specific ratio. The names "exothermic gas" or "exogas" and "endothermic gas" or "endogas" are related to the reactions upon which their manufacture is based and whether the reaction gives off heat (exothermic) or absorbs heat (endothermic). Exothermic gas is obtained from the complete combustion of air and fuel gas (usually a high ratio of air to gas; the fuel gas may be natural, coke-oven, propane or butane). The largest single component is nitrogen, in the order of 70 to 90%. "Rich" gases refer to high H_2 and CO contents and "lean" ones to very low values of these reducing components. The dew points of all the varieties are rather high leading to a decarburizing potential. Only the rich types have a reducing potential, the others are oxidizing. Drying the gases is not of great help because water vapor is easily produced according to equation (4-21). Obviously the use of exothermic gases is limited; the advantages of them are low flammability and low thermal conductivity as well as the ease of their production.

Purified exothermic gases are prepared by removing CO_2 and H_2O from rich exothermic gas. It is possible to achieve gases that are either carburizing or neutral, and either reducing or neutral with respect to oxidation. This type of gas has found many applications, even though its production is considerably more complex than others.

Endothermic gases are produced by reacting a hydrocarbon gas and air (low air to gas ratios) over a catalyst with the application of heat. Either wet or dry gases can be produced, but in general the amount of hydrogen and carbon monoxide is high and the gases are reducing. They also are quite flammable. The wet gases are decarburizing and the dryer ones are carburizing. The variety of types that can be produced has led to its wide field of usefulness.

The use of the inert gases argon and helium is somewhat limited due to their lack of reducing potential and relatively high cost. Their inertness, particularly with even the most reactive metals, sometimes makes them advantageous. The thermal conductivity of argon is rather low and that of helium high.

Some sintering furnaces are specially made so that sintering may be carried out in a high vacuum. Metals or alloys that have a tendency to form hydrides, nitrides or oxides in gaseous atmospheres are often best made by this technique; these include: stainless steels, beryllium, titanium, zirconium, tantalum and metal-ceramic composites. The outgassing and decomposition of admixed lubricants may necessitate the use of a presintering treatment or special equipment and precautions for the direct vacuum sintering. Too high a vacuum can sometimes be the cause of excessive vaporization and loss of an alloying element, such as chromium in stainless steels. It should also be realized that some oxides and impurities would not be reduced or broken down during vacuum sintering.

Atmosphere Control Perhaps more than any other factor, atmosphere control has been a great obstacle to the most efficient and productive utilization of the powder metallurgy process. Optimum control of the composition of the sintering atmosphere is required to:

(1) achieve the desired degree of sintering, especially in terms of particle bonding and the nature of the porosity;

(2) achieve the desired chemical composition and metallurgical structure and, hence, final properties of the sintered material;

(3) achieve the desired dimensional tolerances, especially important are those effects directly related to the atmosphere such as the growth or shrinkage of steel compacts associated with carburization or decarburization, respectively.

The thermodynamic analyses already discussed usually are the basis for deciding what components of the atmosphere should be measured and controlled to achieve optimum results. Very sophisticated equipment is available today for direct measurement of one or more components of the sintering atmosphere in the furnace as well as for the ingoing or outgoing gases. This equipment may be used to directly control the equipment producing the atmosphere. The greatest difficulty is often the maintenance of a consistent atmosphere as a function of time for one run as well as from day to day and month to month. Changes in the raw powders, in the furnace itself, in the system conveying or supporting the compacts, in the environment of the plant itself and in the atmosphere production equipment all represent potential sources of problems with respect to maintaining the desired type of atmosphere. And when one adds the problem of variation within the furnace at any given time, the situation becomes truly complex. Because of our lack of a complete understanding of some of the aspects of the problem there are probably a great many cases where over compensation with regard to atmosphere quality is practiced; for example, using too dry or pure an atmosphere, or too great a flow rate.

4.9 SINTERING FURNACES

As in the previous section we shall not attempt to describe in detail the equipment but rather the more general principles and ideas associated with sintering furnace contruction and use. The choice of the most efficient and economical furnace must be intimately linked to specific applications. It is commonplace to carry out heat treatments of sintered materials after sintering in conventional heat treating furnaces. Perhaps some day heat treating will be accomplished as part of the sintering cycle with the obvious economical benefits making the process even more attractive.

Furnace Construction Although there are a multitude of furnace designs one generally finds three distinct zones or sections in conventional sintering furnaces; these are:

(1) a burn-off and entrance zone
(2) a high temperature sintering zone
(3) a cooling zone.

Each of these will now be briefly discussed.

The first zone of the furnace is designed to heat the green compacts rather slowly to a moderate temperature in the order of 800°F. The volatilization and elimination of the admixed lubricant usually present is one of the prime functions of this burn-off zone. A slow rate of heating is necessary to avoid excessive pressures within the compact and possible expansion and fracture or spalling. The length of this zone must be sufficient to allow complete elimination of the lubricant before the compacts enter the high temperature zone. Many problems, of a costly nature, will result if this is not accomplished; for example, the metal (such as zinc from zinc stearate) and the carbon resulting from the breakdown of the hydrocarbons that result from volatilization of the lubricant can deposit on furnace heating elements leading to premature failure, on the interior walls of the high temperature and cooling zones leading to poor heat transfer and premature failure, and on the compacts themselves leading to discoloration and possibly chemical reactions of an undesirable nature. Slow heating in this zone is also needed to avoid too rapid expansion of entrapped air in the compacts.

One should also be aware of the necessity of having a sufficient flow of a suitable atmosphere within this zone and having means to direct the flow of gas so the vapors are discharged without entering the high temperature zone. Although separation of the burn-off zone from the high temperature section is sometimes practiced, it is possible by use of air gaps and flame curtains to have proper discharge of the "dirty" atmosphere in single unit furnaces.

This first zone also serves the purpose of preheating the compacts. The heating system may be significantly different than the high temperature zone because of the presence of the products of decomposition of the lubricant and the need for a slow rate of heating.

The high temperature zone is where the actual sintering of the material takes place. It must be properly heated so that the desired temperature is reached and of sufficient length so that enough time at temperature is attained to achieve the necessary properties in the P/M parts. Because of the necessity of having a reducing atmosphere present during sintering a gas tight furnace shell or a furnace containing a gas tight muffle is utilized. For large production furnaces making use of exothermic or endothermic atmospheres nonmuffle electric or radiant tube gas fired designs are often employed. Having the atmosphere exposed to the refractory lining of the furnace may lead to the introduction of impurities in the atmosphere; however, heating through a muffle is less efficient than having the heating elements exposed to the atmosphere and furnace chamber.

A muffle is definitely required for direct gas fired furnaces in order to prevent oxidation of the compacts. Full muffle construction is also generally employed when hydrogen or dissociated ammonia atmospheres and dew points of less than −20°F are required. Reactions between hydrogen and oxides in the refractory linings of the furnace can lead to the formation of water vapor. The purging of a full muffle type furnace is usually faster and less costly; there is no entrapped air to remove from the brickwork. Usually small furnaces are of the full muffle construction. For these the high cost of the muffle and associated maintenance are not as significant as for the larger furnaces.

The cooling zone often consists of two sections: (1) a short insulated section that permits the parts to cool down from the high sintering temperature to a lower one at a slow rate so as to avoid thermal shock in the compacts as well as to the furnace; (2) a relatively long water jacketed section providing cooling to a temperature low enough to prevent oxidation of the material upon exposure to the air. Automatic water temperature control for the latter is desirable to insure that the cooling chamber does not get too cold (going below the dew point of the atmosphere would lead to condensation of water on the walls of the chamber and blue or oxidized parts might result) or too hot.

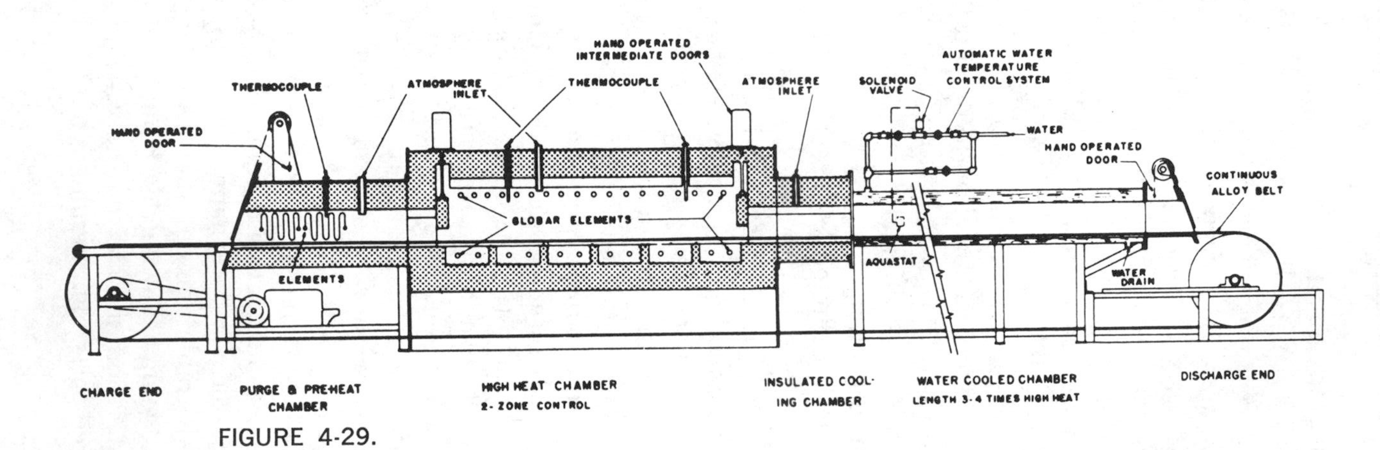

FIGURE 4-29.

Longitudinal section of a mesh belt sintering furnace showing principles of construction and means of conveying work through the furnace. (from MPIF Powder Metallurgy Equipment Manual)

It should also be mentioned that single section furnaces are also used for sintering; these include "bell" and most vacuum type furnaces. Lubricant burn-off would be carried out before sintering and normally in a different furnace. Cooling and heating times in such furnaces could be very long in comparison to the three zone types. Single zone furnaces would also be considered "batch" type furnaces.

Conveying of Compacts Most sintering furnaces are used for large volume production work and are of the continuous type; that is, there is a continuous movement of compacts through the three zones of the furnace. There are three major methods used to convey the compacts; they are:

(1) the mesh belt conveyor
(2) the roller hearth type
(3) the pusher type.

Each of these will now be briefly discussed.

The longitudinal section of a typical mesh belt sintering furnace is given in Figure 4-29. The green compacts are placed on the continuously driven alloy mesh belt (or perhaps on trays placed on the belt) and are discharged at the rear of the furnace where they may be picked off by hand or allowed to fall into a container. The speed of the belt is a very important variable that is manipulated to achieve the desired rate of movement of the compacts and times spent in each of the furnace zones. The strength of the belt limits the maximum temperature and the size of the load; it is difficult to use sintering temperatures in excess of 2100°F with this type of construction. The doors are usually left open continuously during operation and ample atmosphere production is required.

The roller hearth type of system is illustrated in Figure 4-30. The green compacts are placed on trays or similar containers that are conveyed through the three zones by riding on driven rolls. For a given length this roller hearth method can allow much higher loading than the mesh belt technique, but the maximum sintering temperature is still normally 2100°F. The charge and discharge doors are operated automatically and open only when

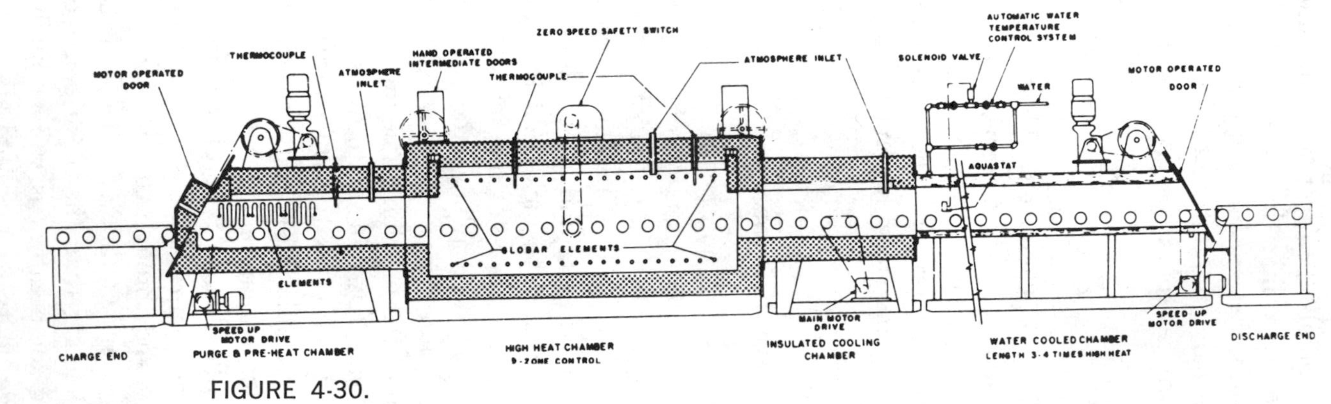

FIGURE 4-30.

Longitudinal section of a roller hearth sintering furnace showing principles of construction and means of conveying work through the furnace. (from MPIF Powder Metallurgy Equipment Manual)

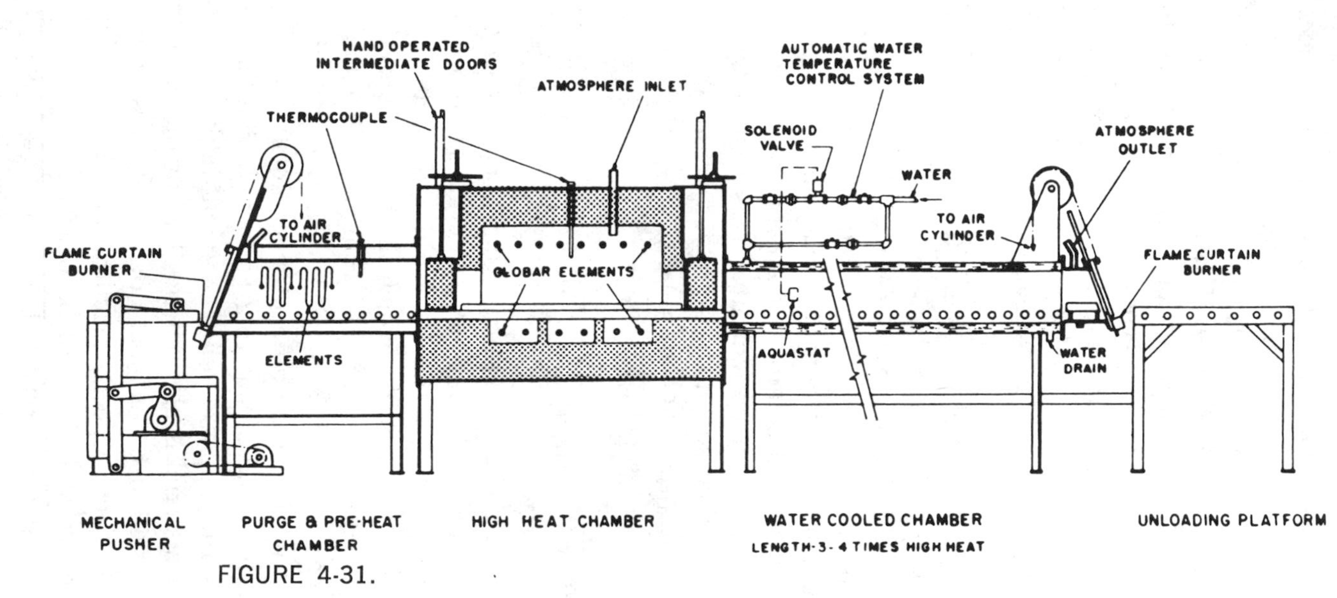

FIGURE 4-31.

Longitudinal section of a mechanical pusher sintering furnace showing principles of construction and means of conveying work through the furnace. (from MPIF Powder Metallurgy Equipment Manual)

a tray of work is charged or discharged. This reduces the quantity of atmosphere consumed and minimizes heat losses.

Figure 4-31 shows the longitudinal section of a typical mechanical pusher sintering furnace. Here too the compacts are placed on trays that are automatically pushed through the furnace zones, one against another. Two types of mechanical pusher mechanisms may be used: the intermittent pusher type generally used for most common metals, and the continuous stoker pusher type more often used for carbides. Smaller furnaces are often manually stoked. Very high sintering temperatures are possible, depending in part on the type of trays used; these may be ceramic or graphite. This type of construction is usually suited to applications involving high loading per lineal foot.

For all three of the above noted sintering furnaces the width may be manipulated to control the capacity of the furnace. The measurement and control of temperature within all zones of the furnace is a very important area. Very sophisticated instrumentation is available today to insure very accurate control of the entire temperature profile of the furnace.

4.10 LIQUID PHASE SINTERING

The presence of a liquid phase during all or part of the sintering cycle of a material represents a unique situation. One may actually consider two variations within this category: (1) normal liquid phase sintering for which the formation of the liquid phase is associated with one or more components contained in the original green compact, and (2) infiltration of the original green compact with a liquid formed outside of the compact during the very early period of sintering (although simultaneous infiltration and sintering appears to be dominant, infiltration of a previously sintered material is also practiced). For the latter case, once the liquid is within the compact the situation is very similar to the first case. Those aspects of infiltration not generally applicable to liquid phase sintering will be discussed separately later in this section. It should be clear that if the liquid phase is not present for any significant length of time during sintering, then there may be no substantial difference between this sintering and the conventional type considered initially in this chapter. We are now considering the presence of metallic liquid phases and not resins, waxes or other such materials that are sometimes used to "impregnate" sintered materials for various purposes.

In the majority of cases the use of liquid phase sintering is related to the desire to produce a very high density sintered material with little residual porosity. That is, substantial densification is usually associated with liquid phase sintering. In many cases it also yields a very desirable metallurgical structure that favors excellent mechanical properties. If the phase that was liquid during sintering retains its identity in the sintered material, then it often contributes some unique property to the composite. Although both variations yield high density materials the dimensional changes can be quite different. For the normal case there is usually substantial shrinkage of the compact during sintering. However, infiltration in which the liquid moves into the porosity may be controlled to produce shrinkage, expansion or no net dimensional change. Liquid phase sintering then represents an alternative to using high compaction pressures or very high sintering temperatures and long times (for the conventional type) to achieve high density materials. For some very hard materials, or alloys containing a hard component, liquid phase sintering may be the only reasonable way to achieve high densities. However, a number of engineering and economic factors make conventional sintering more attractive if the desired structure and properties can be achieved within the common practical limits of the operation.

System Characteristics Before delving into the stages of liquid phase sintering it is useful to summarize a number of characteristics of typical liquid phase sintering systems; they are:

(a) the composition of the alloy is such that according to the appropriate phase diagram there is a solid and a liquid phase present for a significant time at the sintering temperature;

(b) the solid phase should have a limited solubility in the liquid phase;

(c) the amount of liquid phase should be small enough so that the shape of the green compact is retained during sintering but large enough so that appreciable densification takes place;

(d) the particle size of the powder component that is the solid phase during sintering should normally be relatively fine to facilitate rapid densification;

(e) densification is achieved by sintering and, hence, the compaction pressure may be quite low and relatively unimportant; this may lead to difficulties in dimensional control and is one of the limiting factors in this type of sintering;

(f) in most cases the treatment should yield a sintered compact in which the particles that were solid during sintering are completely surrounded by the phase that was liquid.

Stages of Liquid Phase Sintering The fundamental aspects of liquid phase sintering are usually discussed in terms of three distinct stages that are based on experimental observations. These stages are given in the approximate order of their occurrence, but there may be significant overlapping for any specific system. Those driving forces and material transport mechanisms that appear to be generally valid will also be noted.

The first stage has been termed "rearrangement" or "liquid flow" and corresponds to the large scale bulk movement of particles within the liquid phase. This movement leads to a rearrangement of the particles and densification. It is assumed that the gas within the compact can easily diffuse or bubble through the liquid phase. Or one may think in terms of the liquid flowing into the porosity, displacing it, and carrying the solid particles towards the center of the compact. Increasing amount of liquid phase signifies greater densification; that is, particles may move more easily. If spherical particles are assumed, then it has been shown that complete densification by this process alone is possible if there is greater than 35 volume % liquid phase present. In any event densification by this first stage is very rapid. Solid state or liquid phase diffusion and solubility of one phase in another play no part in this first stage.

The driving force for this stage may be couched in terms of surface energies or tensions and the concept of wetting. Wetting of the solid with the liquid phase is necessary. This may be expressed in terms of the free energy change associated with the change in the kinds of interfaces present in the system:

$$\Delta F = \gamma_{sl} - (\gamma_s + \gamma_l) \qquad (4\text{-}32)$$

where ΔF = the free energy change, this should be negative for a wetting condition
γ_{sl} = the solid-liquid interfacial energy
γ_s = the solid (or solid-gas) interfacial energy
γ_l = the liquid (or liquid-gas) interfacial energy

The greater the decrease in free energy, the greater the driving force for densification (or the greater the tendency for the liquid to wet the solid).

The second stage has been termed "accommodation" or "dissolution and reprecipitation" and can only take place if there is a limited solubility of the solid in the liquid phase. It too leads to densification, but at a slower rate than the first stage. Because the solubility of the solid in the liquid increases with increasing convexity (decreasing particle size), small particles dissolve and disappear while the larger ones grow and take on a very rounded shape. Material transport is by rapid diffusion through the liquid phase. Shrinkage comes about because of the approach of the midpoints between neighboring particles; however, it has also been argued that this solutioning and reprecipitation does not in itself lead to densification but rather that it promotes particle motion associated with the first stage. One should note that this particle coarsening process does lead to a reduction in the amount of solid-liquid interfacial area and energy.

The third stage is termed "coalescence" or "solid phase bonding." If wetting of the solid with the liquid is incomplete, then there is some contact between solid particles rather than complete separation of the particles by the liquid. One may think in terms of a low grain boundary energy with respect to onehalf the solid-liquid interfacial energy. This situation leads to a skeleton of solid formed within the compact that can seriously interfere with fast densification by stage one if it occurs early in the sintering process. It should also be understood that some densification can take place at a slower rate by conventional solid state sintering processes and by stage two.

It should be noted that a liquid phase that did not wet the solid at all would tend to exude from the sintered compact; this is often termed "sweating" and is evidenced by the presence of droplets on the compact. The amount of a liquid phase present during sintering may change with time for several reasons. If the liquid dissolves in the solid and the amount present is below the maximum solubility at that temperature, then all the liquid may disappear. If this happens very quickly, then no real liquid phase sintering and densification may take place (this is the common situation noted earlier for iron-copper materials). Or because of mutual solubility the melting points of the solid and liquid phases may be changed substantially leading to an increase or decrease in the amount of liquid present.

Grain growth within the solid phase, particularly for incomplete wetting, can take place very readily as in the case of conventional solid state sintering. Finally it should be noted that the presence of closed porosity in the original green compact can seriously impede densification by liquid phase sintering. This is usually associated with the difficulty of having the entrapped gas escape to the external surfaces of the compact.

Some Actual Systems The presence of copper in iron compacts leads to the formation of liquid copper during conventional sintering. Although copper wets iron well it also dissolves rather quickly in the iron. Hence, for relatively small amounts of copper expansion rather than shrinkage can result. Increasing the amount of liquid phase present by having graphite present so that a eutectic is formed or by increasing the copper content beyond the solubility limit can promote shrinkage. Copper is often used as a means of dimensional control rather than for its actual alloying effects.

Another important application of liquid phase sintering is the production of bronze materials from compacts of copper and tin powders. At the sintering temperatures used the tin particles quickly melt and diffuse into the copper particles forming alpha bronze. The amount of liquid tin present depends not only on the amount of tin originally used but also on the size and distribution of the particles. Small particles of tin well dispersed within the copper ones will tend to melt and dissolve very rapidly. On the other hand, larger aggregates of tin will remain molten and unalloyed for longer times. The lack of uniformity of the amount of liquid phase present throughout the compact during sintering is a cause of nonuniform dimensional changes and shape distortion. The extent of densification associated directly with liquid phase sintering depends, of course, on the amount and duration of the liquid phase formed. Grain growth within the bronze itself is usually quite significant. Some interesting data for a typical copper–10% tin bronze showing the grain growth as a function of sintering temperature, time and atmosphere are given in Table 4-12. It can be seen that grain growth is definitely promoted by

TABLE 4-12. Grain Growth During Sintering of a Copper–10% Tin Powder Mixture Yielding Bronze

		Average Grain Size (microns)		
Sintering Temp. (°F)	Sintering Time (min)	Dissociated Ammonia	Endogas	Exogas
1500	5	6.7	5.9	4.9
	10	17.2	12.0	10.5
	15	20.9	23.0	16.7
1525	5	7.2	6.8	6.3
	10	18.6	17.1	16.7
	15	24.8	21.8	22.0
1550	5	6.6	7.4	7.2
	10	23.3	19.4	19.1
	15	32.2	29.0	24.2

(from E. W. Lowe and H. R. Biehl, The Microstructure of Bronze Sinterings, ASTM Spec. Tech. Publ. No. 323, 1962)

increasing the reducing potential of the atmosphere. The less the amount of liquid phase present, the greater the degree of grain growth.

The production of cemented carbide type materials is an excellent example of liquid phase sintering. One of the classical systems is tungsten carbide-cobalt. During sintering of such materials the metal component becomes the liquid phase while the ceramic component remains solid. Unlike the two previous examples the liquid phase is present through most of the sintering cycle for these cermets. However, it should be noted that the heating up of the material in the region before any liquid phase is formed is quite important. The hydrogen in the atmosphere can react with adsorbed oxygen and oxides and purify the material, and the flowing gas can remove the impurities before a liquid phase would entrap them within the compact. At relatively low temperatures solid solutions between the phases may also form; if formed such solid solutions may be the first component to melt. Densification in such systems increases with increasing metal content and decreasing ceramic particle size in a marked manner. Complete densification can often be achieved in a very short time, perhaps several minutes. It is desirable to have the metallic phase as the continuous matrix in the sintered material. This ductile phase can then impart considerable toughness and impact resistance to the otherwise brittle ceramic. In some systems it is also possible to achieve a very rounded shape to the ceramic particles in the sintered material; this is promoted by having a large amount of liquid phase formed and by having a solid-liquid interfacial energy that is not too dependent on crystallographic orientation. Such roundness aids the attainment of toughness, as will be discussed in a later section.

Infiltration Although there are a number of ways to carry out infiltration the one that is quite prevalent consists of placing a compact or piece of solid metal that will melt during sintering on or below the porous green compact to be infiltrated. Once the material is melted it will be drawn into the interconnected porosity by capillary action if there is sufficient wetting between the two. The liquid can penetrate very long distances in the compact very rapidly. A truly useful and generally applicable theory of infiltration is still lacking; however, there is some evidence to indicate that too small or large a pore size is detrimental. Obviously small initial particle sizes and high compaction pressures may lead to considerable closed porosity preventing infiltration.

If the solid metal phase is soluble to some extent in the liquid, then erosion of the surface of the green compact may take place during the initial period of sintering. This leads to undesirable pitting of the surface of the sintered compact. To avoid this the material to become the liquid phase can be alloyed with one or more elements that severely limit the solubility of the solid phase. For example, copper infiltration of ferrous compacts is widely employed and the copper infiltrant material may contain some iron, zinc or cobalt to prevent surface erosion.

Complete densification by liquid metal infiltration may be impossible because of the presence of fine porosity within the original particles of the green compact, the presence of closed porosity in the compact and the alloying of some of the liquid phase with the solid. All of these factors might lead to some residual porosity in the sintered material. Infiltration of a sintered rather than of an as-compacted material might be difficult because of the greater amount of closed porosity in the former.

4.11 HOT PRESSING

Hot pressing has been widely applied to refractory type metals and ceramic materials with high melting points and high hardness and strength, although more recently there has been a renewed interest in the more common metals and alloys. The method was originally used because of the difficulty associated with conventional compaction and sintering techniques to achieve high densities for materials exhibiting little plastic deformation during cold compaction and little shrinkage during sintering at reasonable temperatures. In hot pressing although both pressure and an elevated temperature are imposed upon the powder mass, the actual magnitude of the pressure and temperature is considerably below those values associated with conventional processing of the same powder leading to the same final density. Some data illustrating this situation are given in Table 4-13 for aluminum. Using the same time at temperature it can be seen that very much lower pressures in conjunction with about the same temperature as used in the conventional approach leads to very high densities for the hot pressing case. Using somewhat greater pressures for the hot pressing would have allowed much lower temperatures to be used to achieve those same densities.

TABLE 4-13. Densification for Conventionally Compacted and Sintered and Hot Pressed Aluminum

Pressure (psi)	Temperature (°F)	Percent Theoretical Density
Conventional Case[a]		
40,000	1150	83
60,000	1150	88
80,000	1150	93
100,000	1150	97
Hot Pressing Case[b]		
850	1100	67
	1150	69
	1200	86
	1212	96
1750	1100	82
	1150	85
	1200	92
	1212	98

[a] small cylindrical slugs single end compacted and sintered in air for one hour
[b] similar size slugs hot pressed in graphite die, with single action graphite punch, at temperature for one hour, no protective atmosphere

(from J. E. Sheehan, M.S. Thesis, University of Wisconsin, 1968)

Some additional data for copper are given in Table 4-14. Here too it is evident that very low pressures in conjunction with relatively low temperatures can lead to almost complete densification in short times. Similar results have been obtained for all types of ceramic materials.

Hot pressing is usually carried out in inert graphite or ceramic molds to avoid contamination of the powder mass. A force is applied through either a single or double punch system. Because of the intimate contact between the powder mass and the die and punches no protective atmosphere may be required. However, because there is usually considerable shrinkage during hot pressing some evacuation techniques may be necessary to facilitate removal of the air originally in the loose powder. An isostatic variation of hot pressing that has been used with much success involves placing the powder in a sealed, flexible metal envelope which is heated in an autoclave. The pressure of the surrounding gas provides the isostatic condition. Later the material is removed from the metal can. Extremely difficult materials to compact, such as spherical powder of tungsten, have been easily hot pressed to full density by this approach.

TABLE 4-14. Hot Pressing Data for Very Fine Spherical Copper Powder

Temperature (°F)	Pressure (psi)	Time (min)	Percent Theoretical Density
572	2,500	10	68
		100	70
	10,000	10	74
		100	77
1112	2,500	10	83
		100	94
	10,000	10	96
		100	98

(from J. T. Smith and T. Vasilos, The Pressure Sintering of Copper, Trans. AIME, vol. 233, pp. 1431–1433, 1965)

There has been considerable theoretical and fundamental work dealing with the mechanisms of hot pressing. Some theories appear to be valid for certain classes of materials. A detailed discussion of this area is beyond the scope of this text. However, two of the most important and relatively simple concepts that qualitatively explain hot pressing will be noted. It has already been shown that plastic deformation is largely responsible for densification during conventional cold compaction. When a material is heated its strength decreases sharply and its ability to plastically deform increases greatly. Thus, it is seen how very low pressures in conjunction with an elevated temperature can easily allow substantial plastic deformation to take place. There is considerable evidence to indicate that plastic deformation during hot pressing can account for much of the densification. Now consider conventional sintering. Material transport by solid state diffusional processes can lead to densification. It is well established that diffusion rates can be greatly increased by the presence of dislocations created by plastic deformation. Thus, during hot pressing diffusional mass transport is greatly aided, even at low temperatures.

Hence, the simultaneous application of heat and pressure tends to reduce the magnitude of these parameters necessary for very high levels of densification. There are even some cases where a liquid phase is formed during the hot pressing, and this obviously can also promote densification. One should also note that alloying during hot pressing may be enhanced because of the greater lattice defect structure introduced. From a practical viewpoint hot pressing does present a greater problem with respect to dimensional control and the large scale production of parts, especially in comparison to the more conventional approaches. Lately the concept of "warm pressing" has been looked at with great interest; in this case quite low temperatures, perhaps just a few hundred degrees for ferrous materials, would be used.

4.12 STRUCTURES AND PROPERTIES OF SINTERED MATERIALS

In this section we shall discuss the fundametnal aspects of structure and properties that are related to the unique characteristics of sintered materials. The dependence of structure and properties on the major processing variables will also be considered. And the important dependence of particular properties on structure will be critically discussed in some detail. It should be clear that it is not the purpose of this portion of the text to describe and review the structures and properties of actual powder metallurgy materials.

Residual Porosity The one structural characteristic uniquely associated with sintered materials (most of what is said in this section applies to materials made by any of the three variations of sintering) is residual porosity. Extremely few powder metallurgy materials can be produced without any porosity remaining after sintering. For many applications a complete characterization of the residual porosity is necessary; these are usually cases involving the direct use of the porosity in some fashion. For structural P/M materials the residual porosity is usually an unavoidable structural feature with undesirable effects on properties. And for this case the characterization of the porosity may be more limited. However, more than just the total amount of porosity, as indicated by the density, is required for a complete understanding of the influence of porosity on properties.

In section 4.2 we noted the important distinction between closed (isolated) and interconnected porosity in the material. Each type can be utilized in different ways and each may affect a property differently. The determination of the amount of each type is relatively simple. One of the more modern techniques of particular use for porosity characterization is "mercury porosimetry."

In this technique a sample of sintered material is exposed to mercury, at room temperature, over a very wide range of pressures. Usually the mercury is put in contact with the sample in a vacuum initially and thereafter the pressure of the mercury is increased to values as high as 15,000 psi or greater. The mercury enters the interconnected porosity. The volume of mercury penetrating the sample is obtained as a function of the pressure. The total amount of mercury accepted, in conjunction with the bulk density of the porous material, yields the proportion of interconnected porosity. A limiting factor is the smallest pore opening through which the mercury can be forced. The smaller the pore opening, actually the smallest opening the mercury must move through to reach the porosity, the greater the pressure required to have any fluid penetrate. For most materials the operating limits of mercury porosimeters allow a very accurate determination.

By assuming a somewhat ideal type of porosity it is possible to use this technique to obtain another extremely useful characteristic of the porosity. The usual assumption is that the interconnected porosity resembles a network of cylindrical channels of diameter d for which there are no small throats controlling the entrance to larger cavities. Then we may write

$$d = 4\gamma(\cos\theta)/p \qquad (4\text{-}33)$$

where $\gamma =$ the surface tension of the mercury
$\theta =$ the wetting angle of the mercury and the material being tested
$p =$ the pressure of the mercury

For most materials and conditions values of 130° for θ and 473 dynes/cm for γ are sufficiently accurate and the above equation reduces to

$$d = 175/p \qquad (4\text{-}34)$$

where d is obtained in microns if p is expressed in psi. Thus, it is relatively simple to convert data representing volumes of mercury absorbed for a narrow range of pressure to a range of pore diameters. Doing this over the entire range of pressures used allows the determination of the "pore size distribution" for the interconnected porosity. Such distributions are analogous to particle size distributions discussed in Chapter Two. It might be noted that for a 15,000 psi maximum pressure the pore diameter range that can be analyzed is from 100 to 0.012 microns. Fluids other than mercury have also been used.

Finally, the use of metallography on sections of the porous material can yield information on the true shape and surface characteristics of the porosity. Some workers have also found it useful to measure the surface area of the porous material. The greater the amount and fineness of the porosity, the greater the specific surface area of the material. The comments on surface area and its measurement made in section 2.5 are applicable to this case also. Here too the measurement refers to interconnected porosity only.

Permeability The permeability of a sintered material, usually with a relatively large amount of interconnected porosity, is of interest and importance for a number of reasons. For some applications a knowledge of the ability of a porous material to allow a fluid, either a gas or liquid, to pass through it is of paramount importance. It is also of interest because a knowledge of the permeability of a material can be used to evaluate certain characteristics of the porosity. And detailed information on the porosity can be used to calculate permeabilities.

The classical description of the passage of a fluid through a porous solid is given by D'Arcy's Law

$$P/L = Qn/Ak \qquad (4\text{-}35)$$

where P = the pressure drop across the porous mass (dynes/cm²)
L = the thickness of the material through which the fluid is passing (cm)
Q = the mean volumetric flow rate (cm^3/sec)
n = the viscosity of the fluid (poises)
A = the cross sectional area of the porous mass (cm^2)
k = the specific permeability or the permeability coefficient (cm^2)

The commonly used units have been indicated. Plots of experimental values of Q versus P should yield straight lines whose slopes in conjunction with a knowledge of L, n and A yield the values of k.

Although the above equation has been found adequate for the majority of cases there are conditions for which a more complete formulation is required. This has been shown to be

$$P/L = Qn/Ak_v + Q^2 d_f/k_i \qquad (4\text{-}36)$$

where d_f = the density of the fluid (gm/cm^3)
k_v = the viscous permeability (cm^2)
k_i = the inertial permeability (cm)

The addition of the second term on the right side of the above equation to the D'Arcy relationship provides the description of the contribution to the pressure drop under highly turbulent conditions of fluid flow. Data requiring this treatment should yield a straight line when P/LQ is plotted versus Q; the slope yields k_i and the intercept k_v.

The permeabilities may also be expressed in terms of material characteristics as follows

$$k = k_v = f^3/(1-f)^2 g S_w{}^2 \qquad (4\text{-}37)$$

and

$$k_i = f^3/g'(1-f)S_w \qquad (4\text{-}38)$$

where f = the fractional porosity
g = a constant (usually found to be from 4.0 to 5.0)
g' = a constant (usually found to be about 0.3)
S_w = the specific surface area (cm^2/cm^3)

It should be noted that the fractional porosity in the above equations should be that fraction of the porosity through which the fluid moves; this may be significantly less than the amount of porosity (both total and interconnected) that is measured. This results from the fact that some pores are closed at one end and do not "see" the moving fluid. This also explains why measured values of surface area could be higher than that truly seen by the moving fluid. For these reasons permeability coefficients calculated on the basis of the above equations can be in error.

Another method is available for the calculation of k and k_v that makes use of pore size distribution data directly; it is

$$k = k_v = 0.0416(10^{-8})f\frac{\Sigma V\bar{r}}{\Sigma \frac{V}{\bar{r}}} \tag{4-39}$$

where V = the volume contributed by n pores of average radius $\bar{r}$ in microns (V in cm^3)

With the pore size distribution expressed in terms of a bar graph one may easily envisage using the above equation. However, its derivation is based on a rather ideal model for the porosity that may lead to errors. Also, the determined values of V and $\bar{r}$ may include porosity not used by the moving fluid.

The results of a study for which k was measured directly and also calculated from the above equations with experimentally determined values of f, S_w, V and $\bar{r}$ are given in Figure 4-32. This work on loose sintered spherical copper powder indicates the normal increase in permeability with increasing interconnected porosity and also the relatively good agreement among the theoretical and experimental values.

As indicated in section 2.4 permeability measurements can be used to determine information about the particles that make up a porous bed (unsintered). Similarly, they could be used to arrive at values of f or S_w for sintered materials.

Grain Size Second to porosity with respect to uniqueness of structure is the fine grain size that many powder metallurgy materials have. Metallographic examination is required for evalua-

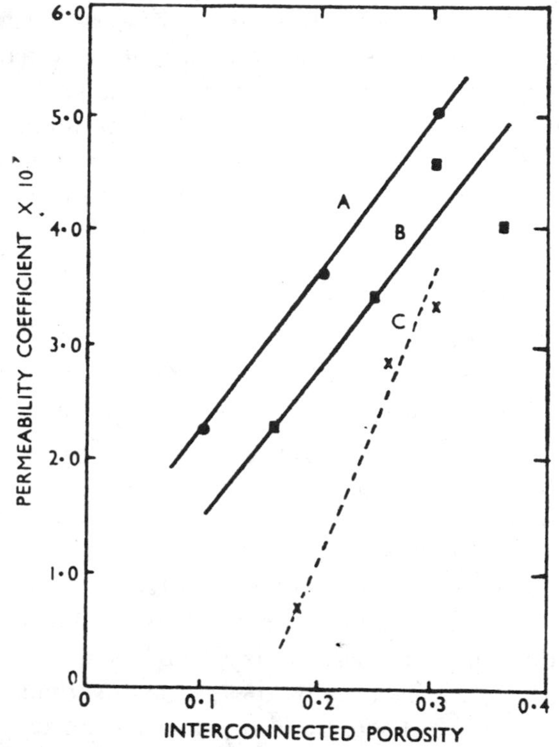

FIGURE 4-32.

Permeability coefficients for porous copper compacts as a function of fractional interconnected porosity: (A) calculated on the basis of equation (4–37); (B) calculated on the basis of equation (4–39); (C) experimental values. (from C. A. Calow and C. R. Tottle, Powder Met., vol. 8, no. 15, pp. 1–19, 1965)

tion of the grain size and other pertinent facts such as: (a) the degree of association of grain boundaries with pores; (b) variation of grain size within a compact; (c) the presence of impurities, such as oxide films, along grain boundaries; and (d) the nature of the boundary in terms of the angular misorientation it represents.

Dependence of Mechanical Properties on Porosity The dependence of various types of mechanical properties (those properties directly related to the application of stresses on a body) on the amount and nature of the residual porosity in sintered materials is of the utmost importance. Four basic types of mechanical properties will be considered: static tensile strength, ductility, dynamic strength (such as impact and fatigue) and hardness.

First, let us consider what happens to a conventional ductile metal when it is stressed relatively slowly in tension. As the load on the metal is increased from zero to positive values the material undergoes recoverable elastic deformation; there is virtually no change in its metallurgical structure. Eventually a stress will be reached at which the material will begin to deform plastically; this is termed the yield strength, or more correctly the elastic limit. The onset of plasticity signifies permanent changes in the dimensions of the material. For most applications this is undesirable, and the material and its geometry are chosen so that the applied load leads to stresses within the elastic range. During plastic deformation the metallurgical structure of the material changes substantially (notably an increase in dislocation density and reduction in grain size) in such a manner that the material becomes stronger and more resistent to further plastic deformation; this is termed work or strain hardening. During this period of plastic deformation small voids or cracks are formed in the material and grow. Eventually these growing cracks, or others nucleated at surface defects, link up to such an extent that the material fractures. The true stress (calculated on the basis of the cross sectional area at this time) at fracture is the maximum reached; however, if the stress is the engineering type (based on the original cross sectional area; much larger because no plastic deformation has reduced it), then a maximum is attained within the region of plastic deformation prior to fracture; this is termed the ultimate tensile stress or often simply the tensile strength.

For a sintered material containing porosity the situation is very undesirable. The material already has cracks throughout its entire volume. Once the material is stressed these cracks can begin to grow and link up, constantly reducing the cross section of the solid material resisting the load. Fracture is strongly enhanced by the presence of the porosity. Most powder metallurgy materials with significant amounts of porosity exhibit very little plasticity, and the stress they fracture at is considerably lower than the same metal without porosity.

The situation is really much more complex than this. Around

any geometrical discontinuity, such as a hole, crack or void, in a solid there is a stress distribution. Near the surfaces of these discontinuities the true stress in the solid is higher than in some region not associated with such defects. Thus, a *stress concentration* exists at these points. Stress concentration factors K_t can be calculated theoretically, usually for elastic stresses, or obtained experimentally; they are defined by

$$K_t = \frac{\text{maximum stress}}{\text{nominal stress}} \tag{4-40}$$

A case often considered is a plate containing an elliptical hole perpendicular to the tensile axis, as shown in Figure 4-33. The

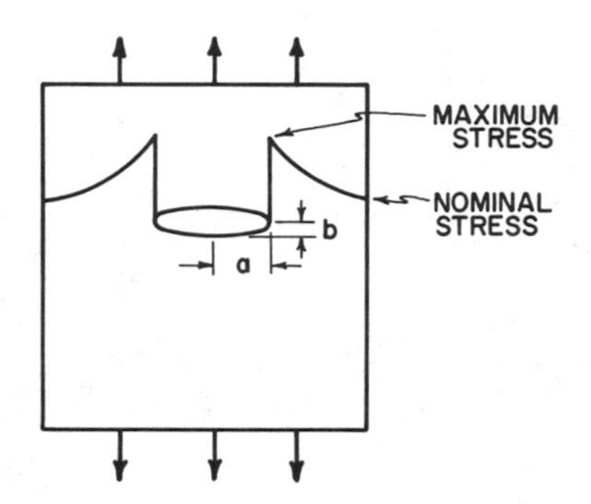

FIGURE 4-33.
Illustration of elliptical hole in a plate and associated stress distribution.

maximum and nominal stresses are indicated. For an infinitely wide plate K_t at the ends of the hole is given by

$$K_t = 1 + 2a/b \tag{4-41}$$

It is seen that as the hole becomes sharper or narrower the stress concentration increases. For a circular hole $a = b$ and $K_t = 3$. Actually for finite plates the situation is more complex. For circular holes in a finite width plate K_t depends on the hole size; it increases with decreasing size (or decreasing radius of curvature). For spherical holes K_t is less; the maximum is about 2. This is because the load not able to go through the hole has two directions in the surrounding solid in which to distribute itself, rather than one for the elliptical or cylindrical through hole.

The presence of many pores in a sintered material signifies that much of the solid metal has a much greater stress than indicated by the applied load and external dimensions. Stresses great enough to induce plastic deformation, pore or hole growth and fracture can exist at what would normally be rather low stresses in the elastic region. Thus, the yield or tensile strength is reduced. Those factors that increase the magnitude of the stress concentrations and the proportion of the material containing them will

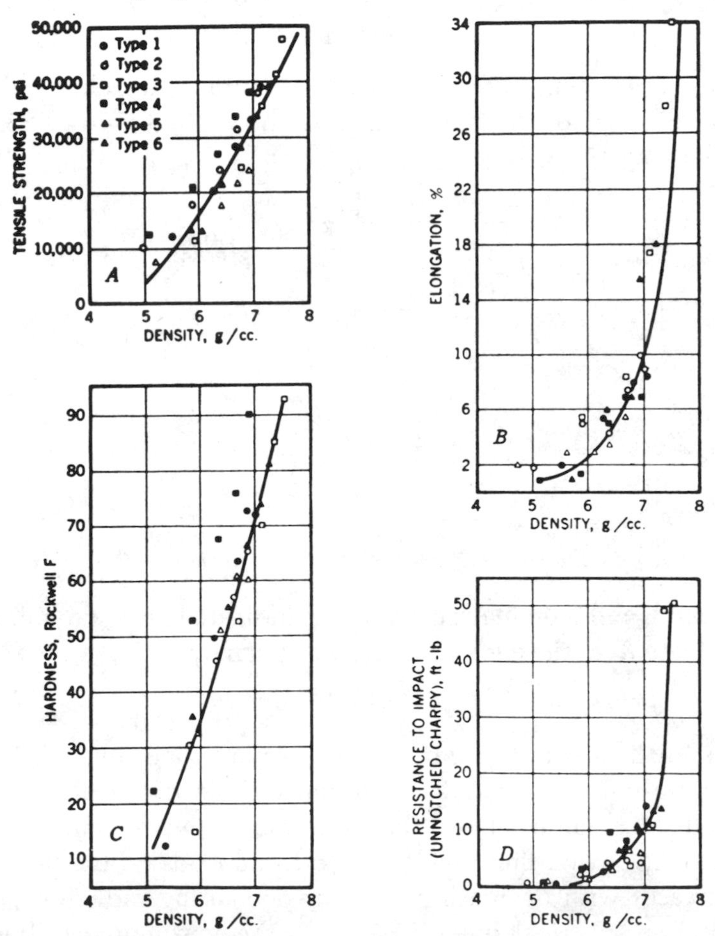

FIGURE 4-34.
Mechanical properties as a function of sintered density for iron compacts made from six different powders; sintered at 2012°F for one hour. (from A. Squire, Trans. AIME, vol. 171, pp. 485–505, 1947)

reduce the strength. These include: increasing amount of porosity, increasing angularity and irregularity of the pores, decreasing pore size, decreasing distance between pores and increasing connectivity of the porosity. *Rounding, smoothing and spheroidization of pores at a constant density are particularly effective in reducing stress concentrations and increasing strength.* Quantitative formulations for the dependence of strength on the above variables are extremely difficult to obtain because of the complexity and variability of porosity in real sintered materials. Virtually all the work in this area consists of relating strength to the total amount of porosity, and to no other characteristic of the porosity.

Some actual data illustrating the potent effect of porosity, in terms of density, on tensile strength are given in Figure 4-34. Linear relationships are often observed if the range of density is not extensive. To describe the dependence over a wide range of porosity more complex mathematical relationships are required. Many of these have been put forth; some based on theoretical derivations for ideal configurations and others on finding the equation that best fits some actual data. For example, for the case of spherical pores in a ductile metal the tensile strength T may be given as

$$T = T_s k f^{2/3} \qquad (4\text{-}42)$$

where T_s = the ultimate tensile strength of the solid metal for small porosities, and the true fracture stress of the solid metal for large porosities
k = a material constant
f = the fractional porosity

Much experimental data can be described by

$$T = T_s \exp(-kf) \qquad (4\text{-}43)$$

where T_s = the strength of the solid metal
k = a material constant

The scatter of data for a given metal with respect to a smooth curve drawn through the points is often explained by the dependence of strength on other factors. Pore shape can be affected by different compaction pressures and sintering conditions used to obtain a range of densities. The k constants in the above equations would contain these other dependencies.

It is well known that the strength of any crystalline material is dependent on its elastic modulus. The modulus is a measure of the strength of the bonding among atoms in the lattice and is the slope of the linear elastic region of the stress-strain curve. A decreasing modulus signifies greater elastic strain at a given stress. Porosity in a material allows more elastic deformation because of the reduction in strong atomic bonding associated with the metal-pore surfaces and the pores themselves. Data for a variety of ferrous materials are given in Figure 4-35. The decrease

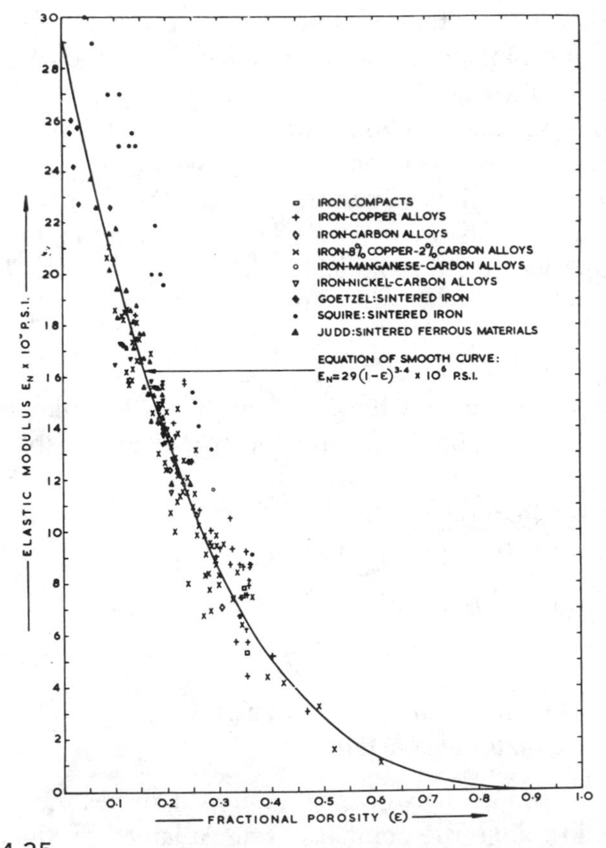

FIGURE 4-35.

Dependence of elastic modulus on porosity for ferrous sintered materials. (from G. D. McAdam, J. Iron Steel Inst., vol. 168, p. 346, 1951)

in elastic modulus E of the sintered materials is well described by the following

$$E = E_s k(1 - f)^{3.4} \tag{4-44}$$

where E_s = the modulus of the solid metal
k = a material or base metal constant
f = the fractional porosity

Here too the scatter of the data is surely due to variations in the characteristics of the porosity. The ability to control the elastic modulus for sintered materials represents a very important advantage of the process. The reduction in elastic modulus may also be associated with an increase in the damping capacity of the material. The presence of stress concentrations in the material can also be used to explain these effects.

The ductility of a material usually refers to the amount of plastic deformation achieved in a tensile test prior to fracture; it is given in terms of percent elongation. We have already pointed out that fracture depends on crack formation and growth, and that in a sintered material these processes are greatly enhanced. It is for this reason that many sintered materials exhibit essentially no ductility and are considered brittle. Some data illustrating the very strong dependence of ductility on density are given in Figure 4-34. In addition to its strong dependence on the amount of porosity, ductility is also very sensitive to pore shape. Greater roundness of pores reduces stress concentrations extremely detrimental to the deformation process and, hence, can greatly increase ductility for a given amount of porosity.

The modern theory of fracture in a ductile metal by growth of holes can be used to derive an equation describing the dependence of ductility on porosity for relatively large amounts of the latter (greater than about 10%); it is

$$e_f = k_1 - k_2 \ln f \tag{4-45}$$

where e_f = the fractional deformation
k_1 and k_2 = material constants, including dependencies on pore distribution and shape

Very few experimental data are available to test this equation because of the difficulty in obtaining measurable ductilities over a fairly broad porosity range. That data examined appear to confirm the validity of the above equation.

Dynamic properties such as impact strength or resistance and fatigue strength are very much dependent on ductility. Hence, both of these show the same strong dependence on porosity as ductility. Some data on impact resistance are given in Figure 4-34.

Hardness data for sintered materials are abundant because of the relative ease of obtaining them. The conventional macro type of hardness test, such as the Rockwell and Brinell, that make use of a relatively large indenter and high load yield data that usually follow the dependence of tensile strength on porosity. Some such data are given in Figure 4-34. The reduction in hardness with porosity is not only due to the basic weakening of the material but also due to the fact that such hardness impressions inevitably include free porosity. Hence, there is a drastic reduction in resistance to penetration of the bulk material. Of much use also is the microhardness test. Using low loads, in the order of a few hundred grams, and selectively placing the hardness indenter (using a metallurgical microscope in conjunction with the loading device) on solid material free of porosity, one obtains the true hardness of the metal. This is useful when studying the material or processing variables affecting transformations within the solid.

Ideally the situation illustrated in Figure 4-36 should prevail, with the microhardness being independent of porosity. However,

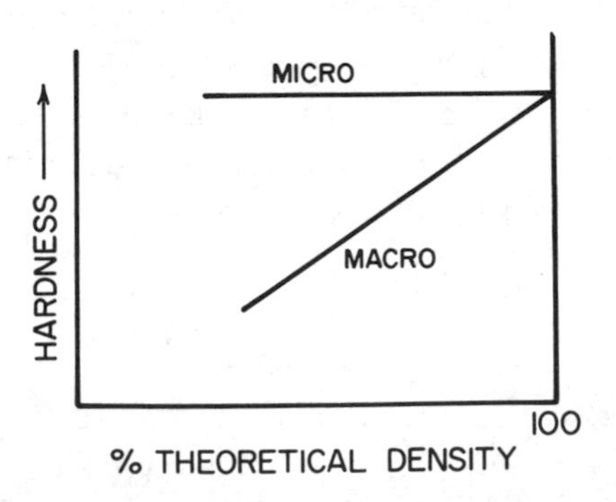

FIGURE 4-36.

Illustration of ideal relation between micro and macro hardness, for a given material, as a function of % theoretical density.

in some sintered materials the residual porosity is so fine, particularly when very fine powders are used, that even the microhardness shows a dependence on porosity. It should also be noted that certain type hardness indenters can be used over the entire range of loading (such as the vickers and knoop) and yield both micro and macro-hardness values without the necessity of converting from one system to another. Attempting the latter with standard conversion techniques obtained for solid materials can lead to errors. One may also note that it is commonplace to use the term "apparent hardness" for macro type hardness values for sintered materials. This has been done to convey the idea that the low hardness readings for these materials is not indicative of the true hardness of the solid metal within them.

It should be emphasized that it is relatively simple to achieve extremely high tensile strengths, ductilities, impact resistance, fatigue strengths and hardnesses for sintered materials completely competitive with conventional solid metals and alloys. The three most important methods of accomplishing this are: (1) increase the percent theoretical density; (2) maximize the strength and ductility of the solid metal portion of the material; and (3) achieve a high degree of roundness for the residual porosity. Both material and processing variables are manipulated to produce these effects.

Mechanical Properties Related to Material and Process Variables
Clearly the best approach to discussing mechanical properties is relate them to specific structural features. However many people find it more convenient to discuss mechanical properties in terms of original material and process variables. This is often the case because actual observations and data on the structure of the material are lacking.

It is particularly difficult to relate properties of the sintered material to original powder characteristics. Compaction and especially sintering variables can erase any effect of particle differences. For example, it is often desired to state the effect of particle size on strength of the sintered material. Consider two compacts of a given metal with the same green density but one made from powder with a much finer particle size than the other. If both were sintered in exactly the same manner, then it would be reasonable to expect a greater strength for the smaller particle size. This would be a consequence of greater sintering in terms of pore rounding and shrinkage and probably a finer grain size. However, it is relatively simple to think of situations where this conclusion would not be valid.

Very often the two compacts considered would be compacted at the same pressure rather than to the same green density. The one with the larger particle size could attain a higher green and eventually sintered density; it would then exhibit a greater strength. Or the powder may have some degree of surface contamination that can be removed by the reducing sintering atmosphere. However, the small particle size material may have its porosity in substantially a closed form and in contrast to the other with mostly interconnected porosity it may not be cleansed internally by the atmosphere. The unreduced impurities could lead to a reduction in strength by inhibiting sintering or reducing the strength of the metal itself. These examples should illustrate the necessity of very careful and intelligent analysis when attempting to relate sintered properties to original particle characteristics.

Obviously the problem exists when attempting to relate sintered properties to compaction variables. Slight differences in particle characteristics and/or sintering conditions make such attempts prone to error.

More valid and realistic are attempts to relate sintered properties to sintering variables, particularly time and temperature. The most important effects for mechanical strength are illustrated in Figure 4-37. Such curves of strength or hardness versus time at a given temperature are often used to evaluate the sintering process. The curves for the two lower temperatures represent the expected behavior. With increasing time at temperature the strength increases due to particle bonding initially and then to pore rounding and shrinkage. For T_3 the situation is somewhat different. In this case the strength first increases with increasing time and then begins to decrease. Such a decrease is often the result of grain growth occurring during the later period of sintering. And the tendency for this to happen would increase with increasing temperature. An extreme case is shown for the highest temperature. For this high temperature the inception of significant grain growth reducing strength occurs at a shorter time, and the magnitude of the rate of grain growth is so great that there is a very sharp

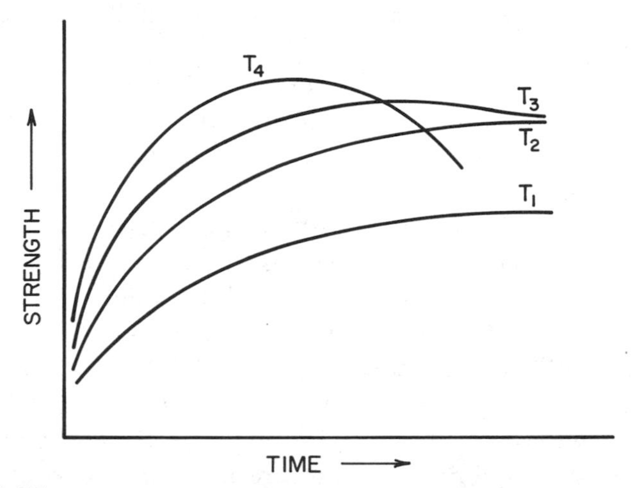

FIGURE 4-37.

Mechanical strength versus sintering time for increasing sintering temperatures (T_1 to T_4).

reduction in strength thereafter. For long times the strengths for this temperature can be lower than those obtained with sintering at a lower temperature and for a shorter time. The reduction in strength due to grain growth may also be related to less pore rounding or shrinkage due to the inhibition of material transport by grain boundary removal.

If ductility or toughness were to be considered instead of strength, the same basic effects would be observed. Increased pore rounding and shrinkage with increasing time and temperature would improve ductility, and grain growth would tend to reduce it. Sintered materials are unique in that the ductility often increases with increasing mechanical strength, whereas just the opposite is observed for conventional solid types of materials.

Alloying effects during sintering could lead to larger than expected increases in strength (and likely decreases in ductility) with increasing time and temperature. This would be a consequence of the introduction of a new metallurgical structure to the solid portion of the compact with greater intrinsic strength. Similarly, reactions with the sintering atmosphere leading to structural changes could affect the strength-time curves favorably or adversely.

The references to mechanical strength up to this point have been for room temperature behavior. The small grain size for a sintered material is not usually beneficial for elevated temperature (creep) strength. Much effort has been put into assisting grain growth for sintered materials to be used for elevated temperature applications.

It should be obvious from strength or density-time curves that different combinations of green density, sintering temperature and time could be used for a given material to obtain exactly the same density or strength. Of paramount importance is the fact that even though the density or strength may be the same, the ductility and those properties very much dependent on it would be greater for those materials sintered at the higher sintering temperatures. Increasing the sintering temperature has a potent effect on pore rounding. Some data illustrating this effect for materials with the same sintered density prepared at different temperatures are

TABLE 4-15. Dependence of Percent Elongation on Sintering Temperature for Constant Sintered Density

Sintered Density (gm/cc)	Sintering Temp. (°F)	% Elongation
5.8	2000	6.7
	2050	7.3
	2100	7.7
6.0	2000	7.3
	2050	8.0
	2100	8.5
6.4	2000	9.7
	2050	10.5
	2100	10.7

Reduced iron sintered 45 min in hydrogen.

given in Table 4-15. It is seen that relatively small increases in temperature produce substantial increases in ductility.

To a lesser extent increasing the time at a given temperature often has little effect on densification but improves the roundness of the porosity substantially. Some data showing this effect in terms of marked increases in ductility and fatigue strength with practically no change in density are given in Table 4-16. Note the

TABLE 4-16. Dependence of Mechanical Properties on Sintering Time

Time (min)	Sintered Density (gm/cc)	Tensile Strength (psi)	% El.	Fatigue Limit (psi)
30	7.42	38,800	29	17,800
120	7.44	37,400	37	20,600

Electrolytic iron powder double pressed and sintered; sintering temperature 2280°F.

(from A. Gallo and F. Utili, La Metallurgia Italiana, vol. 59, no. 7, pp. 533–540, 1967; Henry Brutcher translation No. 7381)

decrease in tensile strength for the longer time; this is due to some grain growth.

Physical Properties There are many applications for sintered materials for which their physical properties are of great importance. A complete discussion of all the major physical properties and their dependence on structure, particularly porosity and grain size, for sintered materials is beyond the scope of this text. The three most important categories are magnetic, electrical and thermal. Powder metallurgy materials used because of their magnetic properties represent a very important area. Pole pieces are a common P/M product as are magnetic cores used in electronics. However, a discussion of magnetic properties requires an extremely good background and knowledge of the subject.

The subject itself is quite complex and very much related to specific applications. Only the following few major factors will be noted: (1) for soft magnetic materials, to be easily magnetized in a magnetic field and remain so only so long as the field remains, it is undesirable to have residual porosity; the pores interfere with the movement of domain walls which is necessary to achieve a high initial or maximum permeability; (2) for many cases a small grain size would be desirable in order to reduce eddy current losses; this comes about because of the increased resistance of the material; (3) for hard magnetic materials, to remain permanently magnetized after the first application of a magnetic field, a small grain size is desirable in order to increase the coercive force; such materials may be made of mixtures of a suitable metal and nonmetallic substances that are compacted but unsintered in order to keep the metal particles separated; for the latter a small particle size is desired; (4) porosity in hard magnetic materials may serve a useful purpose with respect to magnetic properties but may lead to other problems.

Let us briefly consider electrical and thermal conductivities of sintered materials. Pores obviously represent obstacles to the conduction of electricity or heat through the material by processes associated with transport in the solid. Assuming zero conductivity for the porosity we may write

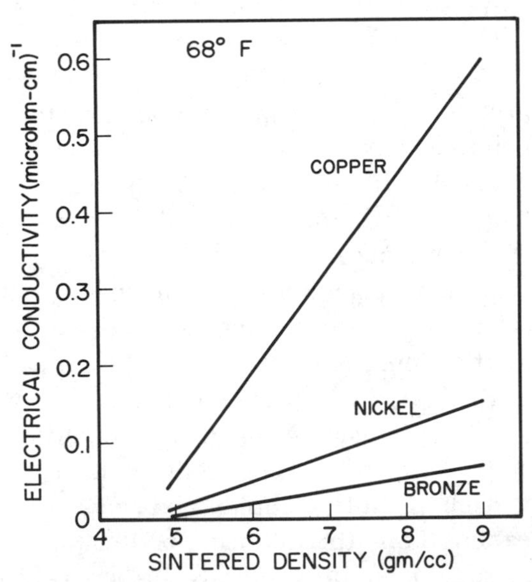

FIGURE 4-38.

Dependence of electrical conductivity on sintered density for copper, nickel and bronze (89 Cu-11 Sn) at 68°F. (from P. Grootenhuis, R. W. Powell and R. P. Tye, Proc. Phys. Soc. (London), vol. B65, pp. 502–511, 1952)

$$k = k_s(1 - f) \tag{4-46}$$

where k = the thermal or electrical conductivity
k_s = the intrinsic thermal or electrical conductivity of the solid metal
f = the fractional porosity

This simple equation is usually not strictly obeyed. Some data showing the dependence of electrical conductivity of several metals on sintered density are given in Figure 4-38. Although a linear dependence is usually found to be an accurate description of the data, one may note that the conductivity becomes zero at a finite density. This is a consequence of the fact that interconnected porosity has a greater effect on conductivity than isolated pores. Circumvention of isolated pores by electrons is possible to some extent, but for interconnected porosity relatively large portions of the metal may be made "insulated." Grain boundaries and impurities normally reduce electrical conductivity, although their effect may be small as compared to the porosity one.

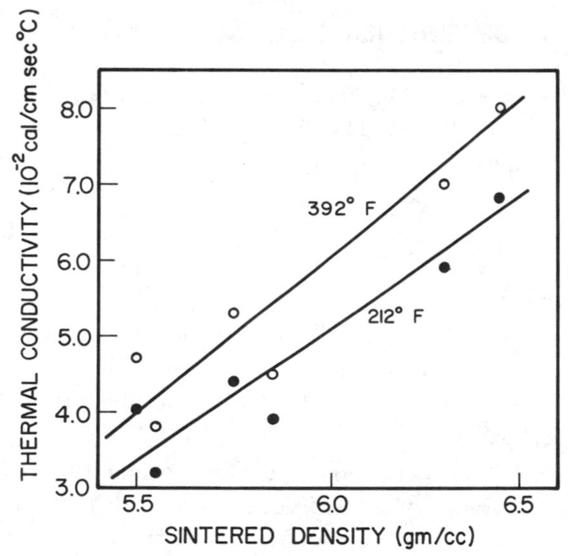

FIGURE 4-39.

Dependence of thermal conductivity at 212 and 392°F on sintered density for bronze (89 Cu-11 Sn). (from P. Grootenhuis, R. W. Powell and R. P. Tye, Proc. Phys. Soc. (London), vol. B65, pp. 502–511, 1952)

Data illustrating the dependence of thermal conductivity on sintered density are given in Figure 4-39. Here too although a linear relationship is obeyed the conductivity equals zero at a finite density. One may note that there is usually excellent agreement with the value of the conductivity, both thermal and electrical, for 100% density as indicated by extrapolating the data for the porous materials. The above equation can become inaccurate for high temperature thermal conductivity. Radiation of heat across pores can become a significant contribution to the total thermal conductivity. This method of heat conduction increases with increasing pore size and is also dependent on the third power of temperature. Fine porosity even at high temperatures remains a good obstacle to heat flow. It should be noted that there is an unusual lack of thermal conductivity data for porous metals, even though such information would be of great use in evaluating materials for certain applications as well as for analyzing the transfer of heat in such materials during various types of heat treatments.

REFERENCES FOR FURTHER READING

4-1. F. Thummler and W. Thomma, The Sintering Process, Metal. Reviews, vol. 12, pp. 69–108, 1967. An excellent contemporary review of most of the aspects of sintering (all types), particularly good for fundamental topics; has many references.

4-2. W. D. Jones, Fundamental Principles of Powder Metallurgy, Arnold, London, 1960. Chapters IV and V have much detailed information and references.

4-3. W. D. Kingery, Introduction to Ceramics, Wiley, New York, 1960. Many of the discussions on the fundamental aspects of sintering and on structure-property relationships apply very well to metals.

4-4. G. C. Kuczynski, N. A. Hooton and C. F. Gibbon, editors, Sintering and Related Phenomena, Gordon and Breach, New York, 1967. Proceedings of a 1965 conference with more advanced papers on the fundamental aspects of sintering.

4-5. H. H. Hausner, editor, Modern Developments in Powder Metallurgy, Plenum, New York, 1966. Volumes I and II contain papers on both the fundamental and practical aspects of sintering, on a more advanced level.

4-6. F. N. Rhines, A New Viewpoint on Sintering, in Plansee Proc. 1958, F. Benesovsky, editor, Metallwerk Plansee, Reutte/Tyrol, Austria, pp. 38–54, 1959 (also Proc. Metal Powder Assoc., 14th meeting, MPIF, New York, pp. 91–101, 1958). The first paper on the topological theory or interpretation of sintering.

4-7. R. T. DeHoff, R. A. Rummel and F. N. Rhines, The Role of Interparticle Contacts in Sintering, in Powder Metallurgy, W. Leszynski, editor, Interscience, New York, 1961. Contains interesting experimental data and application of the topological theory.

4-8. J. Kronsbein, L. J. Buteau, Jr., and R. T. DeHoff, Measurement of Topological Parameters for Description of Two-Phase Structures with Special Reference to Sintering, Trans. AIME, vol. 233, pp. 1961–1969, 1965. Demonstrates techniques used to apply topological theory to real materials.

4-9. F. N. Rhines, R. T. DeHoff and R. A. Rummel, Rate of Densification in the Sintering of Uncompacted Metal Powders, in Agglomeration, Interscience, New York, 1962. Further application and development of the topological theory.

4-10. R. T. DeHoff, R. A. Rummel, H. P. LaBuff and F. N. Rhines, The Relationship Between Surface Area and Density in the Second Stage Sintering of Metals, in reference (4-5), pp. 310–331, volume I. More experimental data and interpretation based on the topological approach.

4-11. L. K. Barrett and C. S. Yust, Progressive Shape Changes of the Void During Sintering, Trans AIME, vol. 239, pp. 1172–1180, 1967. Contains interesting information and ideas on evolution of structure during sintering.

4-12. R. W. Heckel, An Analysis of Homogenization in Powder Compacts Using the Concentric-Sphere Diffusion Model, Trans. ASM, vol. 57, pp. 443–463, 1964. An excellent source of data and application and development of theoretical considerations on alloying during sintering.

4-13. H. H. Hausner, Basic Studies in Linear Shrinkage Behavior During Sintering, Progr. in Powder Met. 1963, vol. 19, pp. 67–85, 1963. Contains data and discussions on dimensional changes during sintering.

4-14. Powder Metallurgy Equipment Manual, MPIF, New York, 1968. Part II on sintering furnaces and atmospheres represents an excellent source of detailed information on equipment and procedures used in sintering and some post-sintering heat treatments.

4-15. L. L. Bobo, Expanding the Application of Powder Metal Parts Through Heat Treatment, Progr. in Powder Met., vol. 24, 1968. A good discussion, on an elementary level, of material and process parameters associated with heat treatments that may or may not be part of the sintering operation.

4-16. Hoeganaes Iron Powder Handbook, Hoeganaes Corp., Riverton, New Jersey, 1962. Binders II and III contain some very useful data and discussions of practice and equipment.

4-17. J. T. Norton, Interaction Between Metals and Atmospheres During Sintering, Trans. AIME, vol. 206, pp. 49–53, 1956. One of the best discussions of the subject, on an intermediate level.

4-18. H. S. Kalish and E. N. Mazza, An Evaluation of Dissociated Ammonia and Hydrogen Atmospheres for Sintering Stainless Steel, Trans. AIME, vol. 203, pp. 304–310, 1955. A very good study of the unique problems associated with sintering stainless steels, particularly the physical metallurgy aspects of the problem.

4-19. C. G. Goetzel and A. J. Shaler, Mechanism of Infiltration of Porous Powder-Metallurgy Parts, J. Metals, Nov. 1964, pp. 901–905. A very good discussion of the fundamental and applied aspects of the infiltration variation of liquid phase sintering.

4-20. L. Ramqvist, Theories of Hot Pressing, Powder Met., vol. 9, no. 17, pp. 1–25, 1966. A good survey of the theoretical aspects of the subject with many references.

4-21. A. K. Kakar and A. C. D. Chaklader, Deformation Theory of Hot Pressing, J. Appl. Physics, vol. 38, pp. 3223–3230, 1967. A presentation of a newer theory of hot pressing.

4-22. M. Yu. Bal'shin and A. A. Trofimova, Isothermal Sintering of Metallic Powders Under Pressure, translation by U.S. Dept. of Commerce, OTS 63-21371, March, 1963. Presents interesting data and interpretations on hot pressing of copper, nickel and iron.

4-23. E. S. Hodge, Elevated-Temperature Compaction of Metals and Ceramics by Gas Pressures, Powder Met., vol. 7, no. 14, pp. 168–201, 1964. The method of gas isostatic hot pressing is well described.

4-24. R. L. Colombo, An Appraisal of Pore and Grain-Size Evolution in Sintered Bodies, Powder Met., vol. 9, no. 17, pp. 101–109, 1966. A more advanced paper dealing with grain growth during sintering, has many references.

4-25. P. Schwarzkopf and R. Kieffer, Cemented Carbides, Macmillan, New York, 1960. This book contains considerable information on the liquid phase sintering and hot pressing of this class of materials.

4-26. A. J. Shaler, Theoretical Aspects of the Infiltration of Powder Metallurgy Products, Int. J. Powder Met., vol. 1, no. 1, pp. 3–14, 1965. A more advanced paper on a theoretical level with good references.

4-27. I. Jenkins, Some Aspects of Residual Porosity in Powder Metallurgy, Powder Met., vol. 7, no. 13, pp. 68–93, 1964. A good review and discussion.

PROBLEMS

(4-1) What would be the effect of pore coarsening on grain growth during sintering?

(4-2) Explain the possible effects of stress concentrations, associated with residual stresses or gravitational stresses, near pores on the driving forces for sintering.

(4-3) Explain the possible effects of preferential adsorption of a chemical species on the surfaces (external and internal) of a sinter mass on the rate of carbon dissolution in iron.

(4-4) It has been observed that the surfaces of pores, even apparently spherical ones, actually consist of facets due to the dependence of surface energy on crystallographic orientation. Explain how this might affect the mechanical properties of the sintered material.

(4-5) Diffusion of oxygen or nitrogen from the atmosphere into a metal alloy and reaction with solute atoms can lead to oxide ("internal oxidation") or nitride particle formation. If this should take place during sintering, how would green density affect the magnitude of the reaction?

(4-6) A series of copper compacts, prepared at different compaction pressures, are sintered together in hydrogen. Dimensional change measurements on the sintered compacts indicated that the ones compacted at the highest pressures expanded, while the others underwent shrinkage. Explain.

(4-7) Consider equation (4-23); would a change in the gas composition from 5% CO_2 and 10% CO to 10% CO_2 and 20% CO be of any significance at a specific temperature with respect to the carburizing or decarburizing potential?

(4-8) How would increasing the hydrogen loss value of an iron powder affect the carbon potential of a hydrogen, dissociated ammonia and vacuum sintering atmosphere?

(4-9) Explain how a sintering atmosphere may become entrapped in a sintered material. How might this affect mechanical properties?

(4-10) Some complex materials are sintered under a pressurized atmosphere and a liquid phase is formed during sintering. What effects might this have on dimensional stability?

(4-11) Explain how the data given in Figures 4-27 and 4-28 could be used to calculate any equilibrium constants.

(4-12) Explain how initial iron particle size might influence the feasibility of using copper infiltration.

(4-13) Explain how hot pressing might promote alloying as compared to conventional compaction followed by sintering for conditions leading to the same sintered density of the material.

(4-14) Sintered materials loaded in compression often exhibit greater strength and ductility as compared to tensile conditions. Explain.

(4-15) Explain why there might be a dependence of tensile strength and ductility on orientation of the material with respect to the original direction of pressure application during compaction.

(4-16) Explain how isostatic compaction might affect the shrinkage ratio and ductility as compared to a similar compact (same powder and green density) prepared by die compaction and sintered under the same conditions.

(4-17) For a particular metal you are given sintered density-time curves for several temperatures. How would you calculate the activation energy for sintering? Could this be used to unequivocally prove what the rate controlling material transport mechanism for the sintering of this material was?

(4-18) Proper cooling of iron-copper alloys from the sintering temperature can increase the sintered strength. Explain this in terms of temperature-solubility factors.

(4-19) In order to achieve very high densities for structural applications double compaction and sintering steps are sometimes used. The first sintering, often termed "presintering," is usually carried out at a much lower temperature than the second, more normal, one. For iron-carbon type alloys explain the choice of temperatures in terms of metallurgical structure and the goals of the second compaction step.

(4-20) In order to obtain high strength and hardness in certain areas of a compact preferential copper infiltration of the ferrous material may be practiced. Discuss control of green density distribution as a means of promoting the efficient application of this technique.

(4-21) It has been observed that the weight loss of a compact during sintering, corresponding to oxide reduction, decreases with increasing green density or compaction pressure. Explain this phenomenon.

CHAPTER

FIVE

ENGINEERING CONSIDERATIONS AND APPLICATIONS

5.1 INTRODUCTION

The powder metallurgy process must be considered as an engineering endeavor. Although many atomistic processes take place during various stages in the course of converting metal powder into a useful shape, the ultimate objective is the economic production of materials which have a definite engineering application. The importance of scientific research, such as studies on the mechanism of sintering, cannot be underestimated; however, such studies must be complemented by equally sophisticated investigations on the truly engineering aspects of both the materials and methods of manufacture. In this chapter an attempt is made to introduce and synthesize the most important of these engineering considerations and applications associated with the current and future powder metallurgy processes.

5.2 PRODUCT DESIGN

The proper design of a powder metallurgy (P/M) product is a prime requisite for optimum usage of the process. There are many interpretations and definitions of the term "design." For the present discussion it is convenient to consider three fundamental design functions:

(1) materials design: the consideration of the appropriate structure-property relationships and the possible attainment by the processing technique of the properties required for the intended application;
(2) size and shape design with regard to the requirements and limitations of the manufacturing process;
(3) size and shape design with regard to the requirements of the intended application.

The genesis of a P/M part usually first comes about by the application of the third design factor. A mechanical or design engineer considers the specific details of the application and subsequently the type, and hence properties, of the material suitable for its manufacture. While not always the case, often the designer has considered a manufacturing process other than powder metallurgy and has also incorporated design features based on the known requirements and limitations of that process. Once such a design is evolved it is very likely that changes in materials and/or the size, shape and tolerances of the part must be made in order to produce this same part by powder metallurgy techniques. The overall economic advantages of making such design changes must be critically evaluated and, if favorable, additional consideration must be given to the first two design functions noted above.

Today, with increasing awareness and knowledge of the powder metallurgy process, the designer can take into account all three of the primary design functions during the original conception of the part with the full realization that it will be a P/M part. Indeed, the many unique properties available through use of this technique may form the very basis for the creation of the part.

It is the design of materials, and the size and shape of the product as they pertain to the requirements and limitations of the powder metallurgy process that will now be considered.

Materials Design In addition to the normal material considerations, such as composition and structure, there are several other factors which are particularly important when making the decision to manufacture a material by powder metallurgy. First, let us consider the fact that in the majority of powder metallurgy applications there is no melting of the material. The two main exceptions to this are the use of atomized powders and liquid phase sintering. But even for these the conditions of melting are often quite dissimilar to the more conventional melting techniques used to produce castings and ingots. This means that there may be significant differences in composition and purity between a P/M and a conventional material. Having large amounts of material molten increases the likelihood of having gaseous impurities dissolved in the metal as well as the formation of oxide or other ceramic inclusions. And these are often the cause of poor mechanical properties. Precautions such as the use of inert atmospheres or vacuum conditions during melting are possible. However, disregarding the special equipment necessary and relatively high cost of such procedures, there is still the problem of volatilization of some components. These problems become more serious with increasing melting point and chemical reactivity of the material. The high melting point and refractory metals (vanadium, niobium, tantalum, chromium, molybdenum and tungsten) are an example of materials that often can be best made into parts or ingots by powder metallurgy techniques. Similar problems exist with the manufacture of ceramic and intermetallic materials.

And another problem with fusion techniques is the possible physical separation of constituents because of differences in density. Similarly, large differences in the melting points of alloying elements and lack of mutual solubility can lead to problems in making a homogeneous material by fusion techniques. These considerations become particularly important when the best properties of an engineering material can only be achieved by having a multiphase material such as a metal-ceramic or metal-plastic combination. Many such materials can only be made by powder metallurgy techniques; for example, copper-tin-iron-lead-graphite-silica friction materials, graphite-bronze materials and copper-carbon brush parts.

A fundamental microstructural parameter is the grain size of a polycrystalline material. The grain size affects both the low and high temperature mechanical properties and is a particularly important factor for materials with a limited number of slip systems. This is the case, for example, with beryllium and magnesium which have hexagonal-close-packed crystal structures. In order to reduce anisotropy and improve the ductility of such polycrystalline materials a small grain size is highly desirable. Very small grain sizes are obtained in some powder metallurgy materials by the use of very fine powders and proper sintering conditions which avoid excessive grain growth. The grain size in the original particles may also be used to manipulate the final grain size.

Although in general a fine grain size is desirable for materials to be used at low temperatures, the strength at elevated temperatures usually increases with increasing grain size. Consequently, for materials such as superalloys the variables of the powder metallurgy process must be chosen so that a relatively large grain size is attained. However, it should be noted that this is more difficult to do than obtaining a fine grain size.

The use of heavily alloyed materials is ever increasing. The desired levels and uniformity of the engineering properties depend on homogeneity of both solid solution alloying elements and any second phase particles present. Fusion processing and hot mechanical working operations often result in gross "banding" or segregation of the alloying components within the finished material. This results in a degradation of most mechanical properties and tends to induce some degree of anisotropy. If the material can be made by powder metallurgy techniques, particularly using prealloyed powder, then such segregation effects can usually be eliminated.

Powder metallurgy has enabled the design engineer to make extensive use of multiphase materials. Four types of such materials are of particular importance: disperson strengthened, filled porosity (infiltrated or impregnated), layered and composite materials. The use of such materials depends on the contribution of each phase to one or more properties of importance for the optimum utilization of the material.

In the case of dispersion strengthened materials a dispersion of very small ceramic type of particles within a metallic matrix has been found to be an efficient means of improving the mechanical strength, especially at elevated temperatures. The particles act as obstacles to dislocation motion and the strength of the two phase material increases with increasing volume fraction and decreasing size of the particles. Relatively small amounts, from less than one to three volume percent, can yield significant improvements in strength. Improvements in strength are sometimes also related to grain size reduction and stability associated with the dispersion. Usually desired thermal or electrical properties related to the matrix material are retained.

Various powder metallurgy techniques have been used to produce dispersion strengthened materials. The simplest method is to blend the metal and ceramic powders, usually an oxide because of its strength and thermal stability, compact and sinter. This method has been used, for example, in the production of electrical contact materials where cadmium oxide particles are dispersed in silver. However, the method is not extensively used because of the difficulty in obtaining a truly uniform dispersion of extremely small (usually less than 0.1 micron in diameter is desired) particles. An extension of this method is simply the compaction and sintering of metal powders which have a tenacious oxide film on them. Sintered aluminum powder (SAP) is an example of this technique. Metal powders can be heat treated to produce varying oxide thicknesses to control the amount of dispersoid.

The current trend is to use more sophisticated chemical methods to produce powder particles with a uniform dispersion within each particle or to coat fine ceramic particles with the matrix metal. These techniques have been considered in Chapter Two. The increasing demand for higher strength, particularly at elevated temperatures, coupled with low densities has intensified both research and production efforts in this field. The mechanical working of ingots of such materials has been widely practiced to produce mill shapes.

Filled porosity type materials have already been considered to some extent in Chapter Four from the viewpoint of infiltration and liquid phase sintering. The infiltrant phase can greatly improve mechanical properties by eliminating the effects of residual porosity and by providing a ductile continuous matrix throughout the

material. Many recent advances have been made in this field for relatively specialized applications. These include the infiltration of tungsten with the much lower melting point silver allowing cooling by vaporization of the silver during high temperature aerospace applications, and the use of nickel infiltrated with various chemical compounds (such as hydroxides) for battery and fuel cell electrodes.

Also in this category is the widely used self-lubricating bearing material. In this case porosity is filled with a fluid having the desired lubricating characteristics, in the order of about 25 volume % of the material. During use the material is heated and expansion of the metal allows oil to flow to the bearing surface; during any subsequent cooling the oil is brought back into the metal mass by capillary action. For larger heavy duty bearings an oil reservoir may be provided on the non-bearing surface of the material to insure a constant flow of oil through the bearing.

It should be realized that the amount of porosity, and hence infiltrant, in filled porosity types of materials can be varied from a few percent to about 90 volume %. The dominant phase may be either the original metal skeleton or the infiltrant. These multiphase materials often provide unique properties unobtainable by any other method of manufacture and are receiving greater attention by design engineers. By suitable compaction procedures it is possible to make a portion of a part porous (subsequently infiltrated) while the remainder is a high density material. Naturally, such infiltrated materials may be fitted into or attached to conventional parts. A unique example is a composite gear design which consists of attaching an outer ring containing the gear teeth to the web and hub which are made of a porous material impregnated with oil. The exposed surfaces of the latter are coated with an oil-impervious material. A series of small passages are drilled radially inward through the gear teeth and slots deep enough to slightly penetrate the web. During use the rotation generates a centrifugal force that causes oil in the porous web and hub to flow through the passages to the gear teeth surfaces.

Considering the normal methods of cold and hot pressing it is evident that layered or laminated materials are relatively easy to produce. A die can be partially filled with one type or blend of

powder and then topped with a different powder; two or more layers may be built up. Attention must be given to the metallurgical reactions and inter-layer bonding during sintering. Often powder is applied to a solid piece of metal in order to produce a layered material. An example of this technique is the use of a sintered bronze friction material bonded to a steel base for clutch plates. Similarly, one layer may be a corrosion resistant or self-lubricating material while the other is used for structural strength.

Many multiphase materials are considered composites. One way to define a composite is to require that the minor phase be present in relatively large amounts (greater than a few volume percent) or that the size of the discontinuous phase be relatively large (greater than a micron). A number of P/M materials fall into this category. A good example is the cermet type of material consisting of a combination of one or metals or alloys and one or more ceramic phases (usually carbides or oxides). The discontinuous ceramic particles constitute the major portion and give the material its high hardness, modulus of elasticity, wear resistance and elevated temperature strength. The metallic phase (from 5 to 40 volume %) acts as a binder holding the ceramic particles together to form the composite (also called cemented carbides and oxides) and provides toughness, impact strength and thermal shock resistance.

Another type of composite is the bearing material used dry or with a fluid lubricant. Various types of powders are blended together to provide low wear rates, a low coefficient of friction, minimum welding tendency and sufficient mechanical strength. Such a material may contain from 5 to 40 volume % of solid lubricant particles such as graphite, molybdenum disulphide, tungsten diselenide or polytetrafluorethylene (PTFE) plastic or some combination of these, a continuous metallic binder phase to provide the necessary mechanical strength and possibly particles of a soft metal such as lead, tin or indium to minimize the detrimental effects of welding to the shaft, to accommodate changes in the dimensions of the shaft and to help remove hard foreign particles from wear positions. Small amounts of oxide particles or the use of metals which form a tenacious oxide film, such as aluminum, may also be used in bearing materials to reduce adhesive wearing.

The proper design of a bearing usually involves a consideration of the thermal characteristics of the various phases (thermal conductivity and melting or softening temperatures) and the "*PV*" or performance factor.

Let us consider a common sleeve bearing to illustrate the significance of the *PV* factor. If *P* is the pressure on the bearing and *V* is the surface velocity of the shaft, then

$$P = \frac{\text{load}}{\text{length} \times \text{inside diameter (projected bearing area)}}$$

$$V = \text{RPM of shaft} \times \text{inside diameter} \times \pi$$

and

$$PV = \frac{\text{load} \times \text{RPM} \times \pi}{\text{length}} \tag{5-1}$$

For a given bearing material any combination of load (below its elastic limit) and RPM will give a *PV* value, and this is then related to the life time of the bearing as shown in Figure 5-1. The

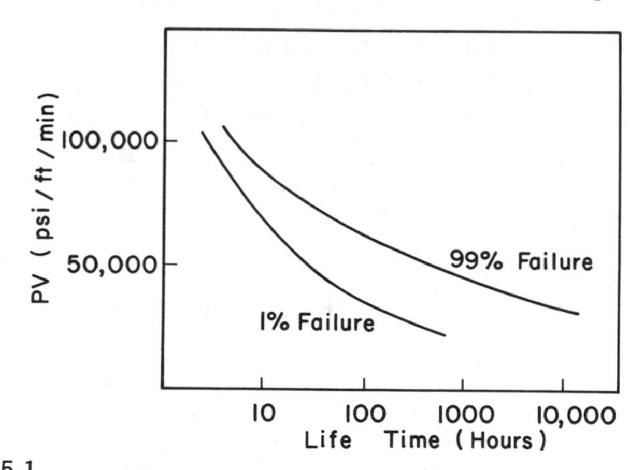

FIGURE 5-1.

Schematic illustration of dependence of PV factor on life time of bearing for 1% and 99% failure.

higher the *PV* factor the lower the life time of the bearing. These considerations also apply to self-lubricating bearing materials. Actual bearing design is based on a knowledge of the permissible value of *PV*, corresponding to a specific material, desired life time and the operating conditions.

Yet another type of composite which promises to be of great value is the fiber reinforced metal. It has been found that large additions (10 to 80 volume %) of very strong and thermally stable fibers or whiskers of refractory types of materials, such as boron, silicon carbide, silicon nitride, alumina and tungsten, to a metal or alloy yield very high values of mechanical strength, elastic modulus and structural stability up to temperatures very near the melting point of the metallic phase. Much attention has been given to directionally aligned fibers, continuous or discontinuous, which yield the highest possible strengths; however, the production of composites with a random arrangement of discontinuous fibers (with diameters of a few thousandths of an inch) also offers significant improvement in properties, possibly with less manufacturing difficulties. The properties of the latter type would also be highly isotropic in comparison to the aligned types and this may be desirable for some applications. The basic problems in producing such composites by powder metallurgy techniques include: the difficulty in obtaining a truly uniform and dispersed arrangement of fibers, the attainment of good contact and fiber-matrix bonding without the formation of other compounds, the retainment of the required lengths of fibers in order to maximize the transfer of stress between the matrix and fibers, and the attainment of very high sintered densities. Some data are given in Table 5-1 to illustrate the strengthening effect of continuous aligned fibers (in

TABLE 5-1. Increased Strength with P/M Fiber Composites

	Tensile Strength (ksi)			100-hr Rupture Stress (ksi)	
Material	400°F	1200°F	2200°F	1200°F	1800°F
Hastelloy X	105	85	5	43	4.6
Hastelloy X + W wires	110	96	55	79	34

Materials vacuum hot pressed at about 2150°F and 4250 psi for 30 min; 37 and 33 volume % tungsten in composites for tensile tests and stress rupture tests, respectively.

(from G. F. Davies and R. J. MacDonald, Metal-Filament Reinforced P/M Composites, given at Spring Powder Metallurgy Clinic Conference of MPIF, Cleveland, 1967)

this case actually wires) at elevated temperatures; in this case hot pressing was employed.

The very important effects of porosity on mechanical and physical properties have already been considered from a fundamental viewpoint in Chapter Four. The positive use of interconnected porosity in terms of the permeability of a porous material was also discussed. A few additional remarks are in order with respect to the engineering use of porosity. Porosity is often used simply to control the density of a material and if desired, by control of the compaction operation, to prepare a part in which the density varies according to prescribed design specifications. In this way the weight-to-density ratio is highly controllable and such parts as counterbalances and governor weights can easily be made. Such free porosity may also be used to control the damping (energy absorbing) characteristics of a material. The porosity serves to damp mechanical vibration and noise and, hence, can improve mechanical fatigue strength and wear resistance, and reduce the operational noise in consumer products such as typewriters.

Widespread use of metallic filter materials is based on the combination of controllable permeability, mechanical strength and endurance. There is usually at least 50 volume % porosity with the actual amount being determined by: the desired rate of flow of the filtrate, the minimum mechanical strength needed for structural stability and processing limitations. The size of the porosity is determined by its requirement to be an effective obstacle to the solid species to be eliminated from the liquid or gaseous stream, to cause sufficient diffusion of the flowing fluid, to cause the desired pressure drop in the fluid flow, or to provide sufficient cooling of the fluid. The filter material is chosen for inherent strength requirements and usually chemical inertness with respect to the filtrate. Very high volume fractions of porosity, over 0.9, and extremely uniform pore sizes are obtainable by using uniformly shaped powders (not necessarily spherical) with a very narrow size distribution, non-mechanical compaction techniques and limited sintering conditions, and possibly pore-forming agents that are volatilized during or before sintering. Such filter materials can be made in many configurations, including sheets, tubes and discs.

Lastly, we may note that the guiding principle in the design of multiphase materials to be produced by powder metallurgy is the recognition of the multiplicity of required engineering properties for a particular application and the possible economic attainment of these properties by two or more phases, each with its own particular contribution to the complete set of desired properties. The concept of a phase must be broad and include both solid and liquid, both metal and nonmetal, both material and porosity. And one must consider the size, shape and distribution of the phase in addition to its volume fraction. Not only the properties of each phase when in its pure state but also the properties of each phase when in its application environment must be known.

Size and Shape Design The successful adaptation of powder metallurgy as a major manufacturing technique will continue to critically depend on a thorough knowledge by engineers of the limitations on part size and shape inherent in the conventional process. The term conventional refers particularly to cold compaction of powder within a solid die, this of course represents the most widespread usage. Some variations of the process, including isostatic compaction, slip casting and powder rolling and extrusion, present fewer (or perhaps different) limitations associated with the processing and usually this is why they are used.

The most fundamental design principle is that the shape of the part must permit ejection from the die. The usual objective is to design a part which can be compacted directly into an accurate finished shape. Many P/M parts have replaced assemblies of many smaller components and costly machined parts. However, there are some parts which require certain shapes that can only be achieved by subsequent machining. Figure 5-2 illustrates several important examples of designs not acceptable for direct production by powder metallurgy. In some cases a real understanding of the process can yield a good alternative, such as the replacement of a diamond knurl configuration with straight serrations, as shown in Figure 5-2.

Multilevel parts with uniform density can be made with the number of levels (diameters) being equal to the number of pressing actions available in the compacting press. In some cases it may be necessary to machine some of the smaller levels in order to

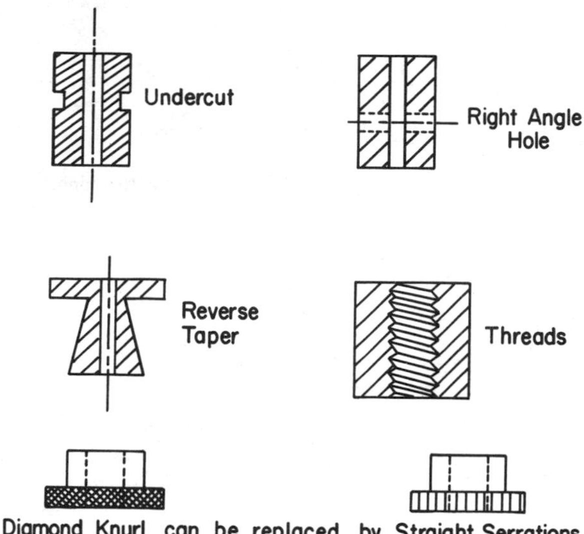

FIGURE 5-2.

Illustrations of part designs not acceptable for direct production by powder metallurgy.

retain sufficient green strengths or because of a lack of press motions as shown in Figure 5-3. Often a minimum of 0.032 in. is considered necessary between steps. Axial variations, such as slots, are most economically produced, without multiple punch action, when the depth is less than about 1/4 of the length, as shown in Figure 5-3.

Powders do not flow with great ease into small cavities and the preferred design attempts to eliminate thin walls, narrow splines and flutes, and sharp corners. The life and cost of tooling are also improved if such features are avoided. It is usually considered best to have side walls bordering a depression or hole greater than about 0.032 in. as shown in Figure 5-4. Abrupt changes in wall thickness are also undesirable. Feather edges such as those shown in Figure 5-4 should be replaced by rounded corners. Rounded corners are also preferred in routine designs of flanges and holes as shown in Figure 5-4 also. It should be noted that observation of these rules facilitates handling of the green compact without spalling and promotes uniform density and strength within the part.

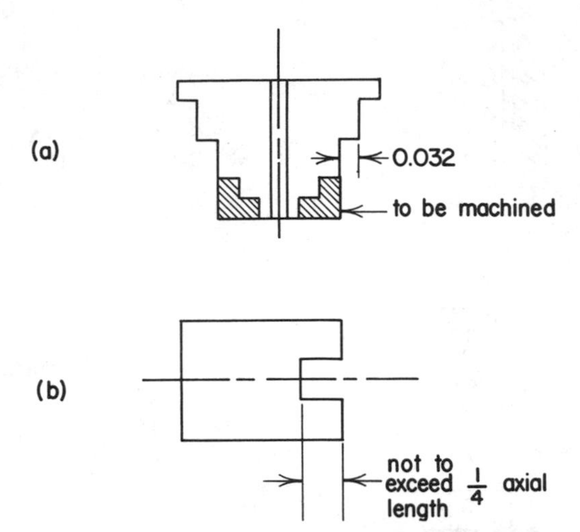

FIGURE 5-3.

Proper design of: (a) a multi-level part, (b) a slotted part.

Several other design features should be employed if strong and efficient tooling is to be achieved. A good design principle is to allow a reasonable clearance between the top and bottom

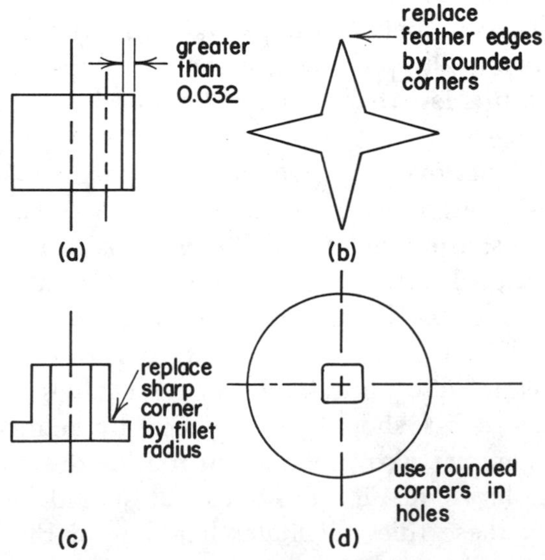

FIGURE 5-4.

Proper part design for holes, sharp edges and corners.

punches during compaction. Sharp edges should be avoided in both punches and dies if dimensional changes due to tool wear are to be minimized. Sharp edges can often be eliminated by the introduction of flats as shown in Figure 5-5. Flats on spherical surfaces, as shown in Figure 5-5, are desirable for optimum tool

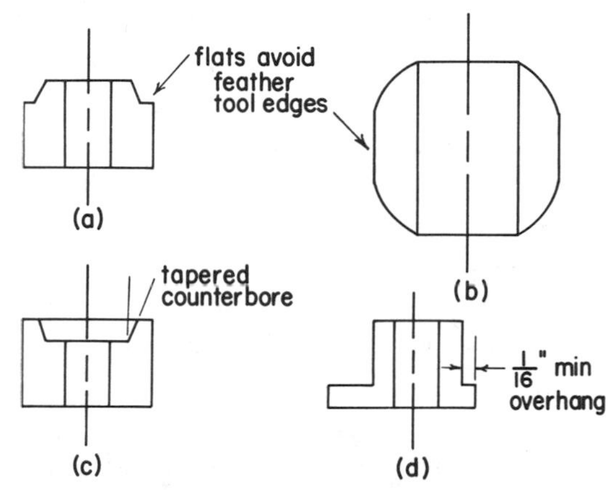

FIGURE 5-5.

Proper part design for strong and efficient tooling.

performance. The design of tapered rather than straight counterbores, as shown in Figure 5-5, assists in tool removal and reduces tool wear and possible damage to the compact. Similarly, tapering of the external sides of the part reduces ejection pressures and reduces tool wear.

When holes are desired in a part they can be most economically produced as round rather than odd-shaped with flat surfaces, and they should be kept reasonably large (greater than about 3/16 in.) in order to avoid excessive core pin breakage. In many instances a flange eliminates sharp corners or edges and the minimum flange overhang should be about 1/16 in. as shown in Figure 5-5. Similarly, holes not closer than 1/16 in. to the edge of a part are easiest to prepare.

It is often desirable to have a constant density along the axial (vertical) direction of the compact. As the length of a part increases density variations become an important consideration. With conventional compaction in which both the lower and upper punches compact the powder a minimum in density in the center of the part will result, as discussed in Chapter Three. This effect is minimized by using length to diameter ratios that are relatively low, in the order of two to four. Other factors which also determine the thickness of a part are: the press stroke, clearance in the press for the tooling, available ejection pressure and tool strength.

The limits of part size with respect to lateral dimensions (such as diameters) are dictated by the compaction pressure necessary to reach the desired level of green density. For structural parts high green densities are desired and compaction pressures may reach several hundred tons per square inch, although 50–60 tsi is a common maximum operating value. The green density-compaction curve for the particular powder, as discussed in Chapter Three, is necessary for proper evaluation of the required compaction pressure. With the use of high tonnage capacity conventional presses (in the thousands of tons range) or HERF machines large parts having lateral dimensions in the order of several feet and a weight of at least 30 to 50 pounds can be produced on a production basis. Because many facilities are limited to pressures of 50–60 tsi and tonnages of 100–500 the maximum cross-sectional areas are in the order of 2–10 sq. in. for high strength structural parts. The use of infiltration techniques could increase these limits somewhat.

Several types of configurations can be produced by powder metallurgy which are either impossible, impractical or considerably more expensive to produce by other manufacturing techniques. A good example is the true involute gear form. Such gears are difficult to accurately produce by casting or machining methods. Since pressure is applied axially during compaction, radial contours that do not have axial length variations can easily be produced by powder metallurgy. Much success has been achieved in the production of gears of various shapes.

A critical gear design consideration is the tooth strength T which is given by

$$T = SWF(1200 + V)/P(800) \qquad (5\text{-}2)$$

where T = the dynamic load transmitted at the pitch diameter
S = the safe working stress (usually about 1/3 of the ultimate tensile strength)

W = the face width
F = the tooth form factor which is a function of the number of teeth and the configuration of the teeth, available in handbooks; usually in the range of 0.2–0.5.
P = the diametrical pitch
V = the velocity within the limits of 1000–4000 ft/min

A knowledge of the necessary load transfer capability and data on the inherent strength of the powder metallurgy material can allow proper selection and design of the gear dimensions. In general powder metallurgy gears do not compete favorably with gears that can be stamped, cast or cut from pinion rod.

Another example of a configuration particularly suited to powder metallurgy is the production of keys and keyways for gears, pulleys and other devices. As shown in Figure 5-6 the key can be made integral with the part.

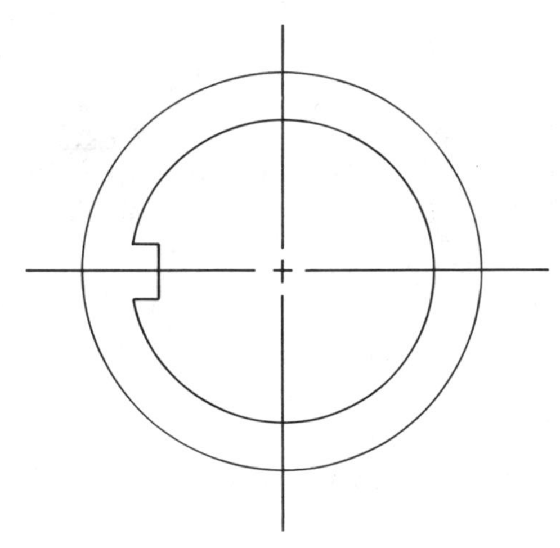

FIGURE 5-6.
The integral key design is well suited for powder metallurgy processing.

A major manufacturing consideration is the dimensional tolerance that can be obtained. It is good practice to specify tolerances only as close as is absolutely necessary for the proper utilization of the part. There is a tendency for engineers to require unnecessarily close tolerances and this can cause significant increases in the production costs. For P/M parts closer tolerances are possible for radial as compared to axial dimensions. This results from the radial dimensions being controlled by the accuracy imparted to the dimensions of the tooling, whereas axial dimensions depend on the motion of the press, the accuracy of die filling and the presence of any vibrations which tend to cause powder settling in the die. Factors that can influence tolerances and tolerance control are outlined in Table 5-2. In general it can

TABLE 5-2. Tolerances

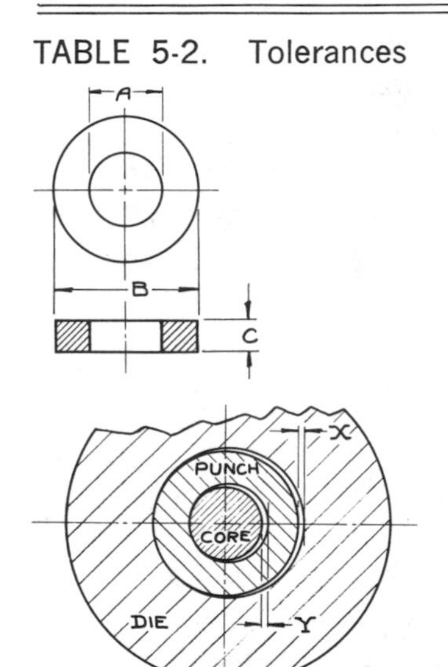

CONCENTRICITY OF "A" TO "B" AFFECTED BY:

1. Clearance between punch and die "X".
2. Clearance between punch and core "Y".
3. Relative stack-up of X and Y.
4. Amount of X and Y needed as function of tool design, complexity, and size.
5. Variation of X and Y due to wear.
6. Uniformity of size change in sintering.
   a. Density variation.

ABSOLUTE SIZE OF "A" AND "B" AFFECTED BY:

1. Original size of die and core.
2. Wear on die and core.
3. Size change of part from die size.
   a. Pop-out.
   b. Size change in sintering.
      1. Type of material.
      2. Density of material.
      3. Sintering conditions.

THICKNESS "C" AFFECTED BY:

1. Variations in fill weight.
   a. Flow rate of powder.
   b. Density of powder.
   c. Speed of operation.
   d. Die Design.
2. Stress variation in press (stretch).
3. Wear and mechanical variations in press.
4. Heat-ups.

(Based on data presented at 1968 P/M Parts Design Workshop, Powder Metallurgy Parts Association)

be said that tolerances depend on the nature and quality of the press and tooling, control of raw materials and compaction and sintering procedures. Tolerances tend to vary significantly among producers and become more difficult to hold as the part size increases.

A more subtle advantageous feature of P/M parts is the absence of tool or cutter marks and burrs and chips (especially in holes) in those parts that do not have to be machined. Consequently, in applications involving close contact between parts significant improvements in performance have been achieved that were not envisaged in the original design of the P/M part.

One approach to eliminate some of the limitations of the powder metallurgy process is to compact two or more parts, which present no difficulties, and then to sinter these compacts together in such a way that a complex part, impossible or impractical to produce by itself, is economically made. This is usually termed the "green assembly" technique. A quality bond between the component parts must be achieved and for many applications sufficiently strong bonds may be obtained under normal sintering conditions. Making use of a liquid phase during sintering can facilitate bonding. Similarly, it is possible to insert one part into another and under appropriate sintering conditions and proper sintering behavior of the materials (the outer one undergoing shrinkage and the inner one expanding slightly) to obtain a shrink type of fit.

Considerations of size and shape design of P/M parts should always include a complete knowledge of the elastic expansion of a compact upon removal from the die, the amount and kind of dimensional changes upon sintering and particularly the dependence of these changes on: the direction of measurement (either parallel or perpendicular to the compaction direction), variations in the size and composition of the original powders, sintering conditions and green density.

5.3 PROCESSING AFTER SINTERING

The ultimate objective in the utilization of powder metallurgy techniques is to produce a finished part or product after sintering except for those parts requiring infiltration of some kind. In practice, parts may require additional processing after sintering which does not necessarily detract from the overall economic advantages of using the process. It is this processing which will now be briefly discussed.

Repressing A common treatment, alluded to previously, involves repressing of a part after sintering. Usually it is necessary to use different tooling than that used for the original compaction and also a different press. One objective of this treatment is to provide very close dimensional control and the term *sizing* is often used to describe this treatment. Sizing may also be accomplished by burnishing, reaming, ball broaching and boring. Other reasons for repressing include: increasing the density, increasing the mechanical strength (by cold work in addition to densification) and improving the surface finish. The term "coining" is often used when repressing is done for these purposes. Parts in which porosity is desired to serve some special function must be given special consideration in order to avoid closing surface porosity during repressing. Repressing is often a very practical alternative to alloying or heat treatment in order to increase mechanical strength.

Machining It is not possible to state many useful rules or principles for the machining of P/M materials because of the diversity of materials, machining techniques and objectives. It is obvious that a machining operation may close surface porosity and, hence, interfere with an intended function. In general the machining characteristics of many P/M materials are similar to cast iron and other cast materials, and it has been found that they machine best by using dead sharp tools, high speeds and light feeds. Good grinding results are often produced with hard, fine-grain wheels operating at conventional speeds and with light feeds. The use of coolants in machining operations may be detrimental if they are retained in the porosity. Volatile coolants can be removed by subsequent heating. Compressed air is also useful for chip removal and tool cooling. It should be noted that scrap losses due to machining of a well designed powder part are usually trivial as compared to such losses from machining of bar stock, rod or castings which may run as high as 50% or more.

Surface Treatments On some occasions the surfaces of P/M parts are desired to be cleaned or finished and this can be accomplished by liquid blasting, belt sanding and tumbling. The purpose of such treatments is to impart a smooth, bright finish to the sintered part and, in some cases, to remove sharp corners, eliminate burrs and control dimensions. It is possible to carry out such treatments without significant surface pore closure. A common operation is the plating of P/M parts. This is done to improve resistance to corrosion or abrasion, or for decorative purposes by the use of chromium, nickel, cadmium or zinc plates. Additionally, silver or copper plating may be used to improve electrical conductivity and tin plating to increase solderability. The amount of porosity in the part dictates the surface preparation necessary for optimum plating. Infiltrated and high density parts having more than 90–95% theoretical density have isolated surface pores and can be plated by standard procedures used for wrought materials. With lower densities surface porosity, interconnected to interior porosity, is a problem because of the possible entrapment of the plating solution and special surface preparation treatments are necessary. The pores may be closed by impregnation with a metal (such as copper for ferrous parts) or with a plastic, mechanical working of the surface by burnishing or shot peening, or by heat treatment. If any electrolyte is trapped in the material, then "bleeding," discoloration and flaking of the plate may result. Recently mechanical plating techniques have been introduced that eliminate the problems associated with electrolyte filling of porosity.

Steam Treatment Ferrous parts may be given a steam treatment to increase hardness, compressive strength, wear resistance and corrosion resistance. The treatment consists of heating the parts to about 1000–1100°F and subjecting them to superheated steam under pressure. A layer of black magnetic iron oxide is formed on all external and internal surfaces, including interconnected porosity. The surface finish obtained is very attractive, smooth and may be quite reflecting. If necessary oil impregnation can be done after this treatment. It should be noted that excessive oxidation can lead to internal stress generation, decreasing mechanical strength and possibly fracturing the material. Other oxidizing and phosphating treatments have also been used with success.

Heat Treatment With increasing demand for parts with high hardness, wear resistance, tensile and fatigue strength many P/M materials are heat treated after sintering. Metal infiltrated and high density parts may be heat treated by conventional methods. Low and medium density ferrous parts become highly carbidic by solid carburizing and liquid carburizing is undesirable because of the possible entrapment of the corrosive salt in the pores. Gas carburizing will produce a well-defined case in parts having densities of over about 85% theoretical. Parts of lower densities exhibit a diffuse transition form core to case because of the penetration of the carbonaceous gas through the interconnected porosity. Carbonitriding may lead to a similar condition but is used to produce higher hardness and hardenability. Such treatments are often very fast as compared to solid materials because of the interconnected porosity serving as a route for material transport. Quenching of parts is often carried out, but because of the lower thermal conductivity of porous materials more severe quenching mediums may be necessary. The entrapment of a quenching medium in the residual porosity can be a source of trouble, especially since such parts are usually heated or tempered again at an elevated temperature where volatilization of such substances may contaminate the material or the atmosphere. Relatively little work has been done on combining sintering and heat treating operations to achieve the obvious economic advantages.

Joining In some applications P/M parts can be economically used when they are welded or brazed to other components. Virtually all welding techniques, including projection, resistance, arc and friction, have been used. Electron beam welding is more difficult because of the release of air from residual porosity and contamination of the vacuum. Copper and copper base alloy infiltrated parts are particularly suited for brazing. Conventional brazing and soldering is effective on infiltrated and high density parts where flux and metal absorption into the residual porosity is absent.

Powder Forging The combination of powder metallurgy and forging technologies is increasing in importance and scope. In actual fact there has long been a strong link between the two. Much of the refractory metals and alloys are fabricated from ingots that are initially made by compaction and sintering of powder. Such fabrication may not only involve forging but also extrusion and rolling. However, what offers more promise for more conventional materials is the use of P/M preforms, most likely in a sintered or partially sintered state, that are warm or hot forged (cold forging may also be possible for some cases) in order to obtain the desired shape, dimensions and properties. Such a process offers the following advantages:

(1) a reduction in forging energy (less blows or pressure) necessary to achieve the final desired form as compared to the use of cast or wrought forging stock;
(2) a reduction in forging scrap losses;
(3) improvements in properties due to the elimination of alloy inhomogeneities and impurities associated with conventional forging stock;
(4) improvements in properties, as compared to conventional P/M materials, due to improvements in density and metallurgical structure resulting from the forging treatment;
(5) increases in the size and complexity of parts as compared to conventional P/M parts;
(6) introduction of novel alloy and composite materials not readily available as conventional forging stock but easily prepared by powder metallurgy techniques;
(7) reduction in manufacturing costs as compared to using either forging or powder metallurgy processes to produce an equivalent product.

Active research and development work in this area has already begun; some results from an early study are given in Table 5-3 for a nickel base superalloy. There are clearly substantial improvements with the powder forged materials in terms of strength and ductility as compared to the costly vacuum melted and cast material.

Conclusions It is evident that the proper method of carrying out a post-sintering operation on a P/M part must be based on a consideration of the nature of the porosity present. Several effects are possible: foreign materials may become entrapped in the porosity hindering treatment or use of the part; surface porosity may become closed and interfere with the proper functioning of the part; and the porosity may be utilized in some fashion so as to promote some aspect of the treatment, such as by increasing the

TABLE 5-3. Comparison of Mechanical Properties of Powder Forged and Cast Inconel 713C

Condition	Elastic Limit (psi)	Tensile Strength (psi)	% El	% Reduction in Area
Vacuum melted, Vacuum cast	106,600	123,000	7.9	11.6
Compacted,[a] Forged[b] 19% in one pass	202,000	237,000	6.5	5.5
Compacted, Forged 30% in four passes	186,000	218,000	10.3	11.7
Compacted, Forged 31% in one pass	216,000	242,000	2.5	2.3
Compacted, Forged 37% in four passes	185,000	206,000	5.7	7.0

[a] Prealloyed −80 mesh powder compacted at 40 tsi, sintered for $1\frac{1}{2}$ hours in vacuum at 2370°F to about 95% of theoretical density.
[b] Forging done on sintered compacts reheated to 2100°F, rapidly press-forged at 95 tsi without side restraint; deformation is reduction in height in forging direction.

(from K. Farrell, Int. J. Powder Met., vol. 2, no. 1, pp. 3–5, 1966)

speed of a case hardening technique or reducing strength so as to facilitate a mechanical working operation.

5.4 TOOL DESIGN AND MATERIALS

The importance of proper tool design and material selection is best shown by the contribution of tooling to the total cost of producing P/M parts—typically 10 to 60%. The actual value increases with increasing hardness of the powder particles, increasing density of the compact, increasing complexity of part shape, and tighter dimensional tolerances. These factors are used to determine the necessary tooling materials and their required performance characteristics. Obviously, the tooling cost increment in the final piece cost is lessened by the length of the production run. The more parts produced on a given set of tools the lower the unit tool cost.

It is important to realize that the actual cost of the material is small (probably less than 10%) compared to the total cost of tool making. It is the cost of the actual design, with respect to shape, dimensions, mechanization and press adaptability, and the corresponding machining and heat treatment operations that make up the bulk of the tooling costs. Tool design and production is a highly specialized field in itself, and there are relatively few qualified people to cope with the complex tooling required in powder metallurgy operations. Only the rudiments of the subject will be considered here. Intelligent design and use of P/M parts will depend to some extent on a knowledge of these.

A basic tooling consideration is the magnitude of the clearances between moving tools, particularly between punches and the die. Powder particles are very small and abrasive in nature and necessitate clearance in the order of 0.0002 to 0.0005 in. to avoid excessive tool wear resulting from trapping of particles in these spaces. Tool wear is also improved by highly polished surfaces.

The proper functioning of a set of tools depends on the resistance of the tool materials to wear and breakage. The die requires the highest wear resistance and this is related to a high hardness in the order of 60 R_c. Punches and core rods require greater toughness and are therefore used at lower hardness values of about 50–60 R_c. This decreases wear resistance, but wear is less on these components due in part to limited movement of the powder across the punch faces. Dies and punches must possess the proper level of tensile and compressive strengths in order to avoid bursting and buckling, respectively. Fatigue strength is necessary for dies and punches and is promoted by proper tool design which eliminates stress concentrations, such as sharp corners and notches and inclusions within the tool material.

Many tool materials must be heat treated to achieve the desired levels of hardness, strength and toughness. It is necessary to avoid distortion and this depends on careful material selection and good design and heat treatment practice. Another critical factor is the machinability of the tool material which depends on its composition and condition. It must be realized that high wear resistance corresponds to increasing difficulty and cost of conventional machining. Hence, only the actual necessary level of wear resistance, dependent chiefly on the powder hardness, production quantity and desired part tolerances, should be specified. The newer non-mechanical machining methods, such as chemical and electrical techniques, have greatly facilitated tool making and are being widely employed.

A broad variety of tool materials are in use today. These range from alloy steels with relatively high carbon contents and major amounts of chromium, molybdenum, vanadium and tungsten which are hardened by quenching and tempering (producing a dispersion of carbide particles) to maraging steels with 15 to 20% nickel and many other alloying elements and very low carbon contents (strengthened by producing a disperson of intermetallic compounds within a martensitic matrix). For extremely high wear resistance the cermet type of material may be used, either singly or as a coating on a metal. Powder metallurgy techniques are being used extensively to manufacture all types of tool materials.

5.5 PROCESS AND ECONOMIC CONSIDERATIONS

The broad application of powder metallurgy techniques is based on two principles: (a) the process should be used to produce parts whose required engineering properties can only be achieved by the use of this process and (b) the process should be used to produce products with adequate properties when there is an economic advantage in comparison to cast, wrought, machined and other conventional materials with the ability to perform the same engineering function. Applications based on either of these principles can only be achieved after a comprehensive evaluation of the complete process with regard to choice of the optimum technique and equipment, attainment of necessary material properties, potential production rates and basic economic considerations.

Materials The choice of raw materials is basic to any manufacturing operation. The lowest cost iron powder, used in great quantities for P/M parts, has been available for the past several years for about 8 to 12 cents per pound when ordered in large quantities. The relative cost of various common and exotic powders are given in Table 5-4. The cost of powders increases with: reduction of impurity levels, addition of alloying elements, restric-

TABLE 5-4. Relative Powder Costs

Material	Relative Cost Index
Iron, sponge	1.0
Iron, atomized	1.2
Prealloyed steel	1.4
Iron-copper-carbon	1.4
Copper infiltrated iron	2.0
Zinc	2.5
Iron, electrolytic	2.7
Aluminum	4.3
Brass	5.2
Nickel-silver	6.0
Bronze	6.8
Nickel	7.0
Iron, carbonyl	7.4
Nickel coated graphite (25%)	15.0
Nickel coated tungsten (50%)	30.5
Nickel coated WC (80%)	56.5

tion of particle size distributions requiring special sizing operations, increased compressibility requiring additional annealing of the powder, increased flow rates and apparent density requiring special production treatments, and incorporation of second phases or coatings. Selection of a powder is based primarily on four factors: (a) the engineering properties which must be obtained, (b) the limitations of available processing facilities, (c) part shape and dimensions, (d) the cost, availability and consistency of the powder.

The first factor is simply based on the inherent properties of any powder and the sintered material, variation of sintered properties with density and subsequent processing, and the requirements of the intended application. Major limitations of conventional equipment include the maximum clearance in the press and size of available tooling which limit the apparent density of the powder. Similarly, the press stroke permits only certain compressibilities and press tonnages restrict powders which do not yield high enough green densities. In isostatic compaction the chamber size would place some limitations on apparent density. Some thought would yield several other simple equipment limitations which affect the choice of a powder.

Part shape and dimensions may also influence powder selection. For example, extremely close tolerances are difficult to maintain with large dimensional changes due to sintering. In this case the part dimensions should be largely determined by compaction, and factors such as apparent density, compressibility and chemical composition are very important. Intricately shaped parts with thin walls, flanges, holes or various levels require high green strength to eliminate cracking and spalling during ejection and transport to the sintering furnace. Parts with large thicknesses increase the relative importance of die fill height limitations and usually tend to place greater emphasis on the use of high apparent density powders.

The cost of powders is an obvious consideration. The majority of applications involve the production of many thousands or even millions of parts and even a very small difference in powder cost, amounting to only a fraction of a cent per pound, can be significant to the total cost of production. Naturally, the amount of powder per part is the basis for determining the material cost. Additionally, many applications involve the use of lubricant additions and this adds a further small increase in material cost; and infiltration would necessitate the use of additional materials. The infiltration of ferrous materials with copper and copper base alloys is particularly costly and should only be used when improvements in properties cannot be achieved by more economical and practical techniques.

A prime consideration in the selection of a powder is the consistency of the powder quality. It should be evident that many of the process variables are adjusted to produce the desired product when using a powder with a definite set of properties. Any change in these properties from one lot to another can completely invalidate the use of the original parameters. The properties or characteristics of prime importance are: the particle size distribution, the chemical composition, the apparent density and the particle shape. It is because of the importance of this factor that adequate quality control of the incoming powders should be carried out. If such variations are not detected, then significant quantities of inadequate and rejected parts and inefficient use of equipment and manpower will result.

Blending Prior to most compaction operations a blending or mixing step is utilized. The necessary equipment and manpower are a significant contribution to the total production cost, and many powder manufacturers offer to perform this service at an additional cost of about 0.5 to 0.75 cents per pound for simple lubricant or graphite additions. And of course there are numerous commercial preblends consisting of several metal powders. It should be noted that blending done in advance of actual usage, including transport of the mixture, may be inefficient due to settling of various components due to size, shape or density differences leading to segregation within the mixture. This situation results in degradation and lack of uniformity of part properties and changes in part dimensions unless re-blending is carried out prior to use.

Compaction The various methods of compaction have been reviewed in Chapter Three; however, the criteria for choosing the optimum method for the production of a particular material are important process considerations. Previous discussions have been oriented towards the conventional method of compaction used for structural parts manufacture. The vast majority of porous materials are also made by this technique, but the compaction pressures are much lower. To a lesser extent, hot pressing is used for the refractory metals and ceramic materials, and isostatic compaction for large and/or complex shape metal and ceramic materials. Pressureless and exotic compaction techniques represent a very small amount of use at present.

Considering the conventional pressing method the task is to establish some guidelines for proper selection of a press. A basic decision to make is the choice between mechanical and hydraulic presses. An advantage of an hydraulic press is that the compaction pressure can be varied within the minimum and maximum capacities of the press, and this pressure is directly indicated. Maximum pressure can be applied at almost any point in the stroke. In contrast to this most mechanical presses operate at lower power consumption but must expand their entire energy against whatever resistance they meet. The maximum pressure is exerted at the bottom of the stroke. The output of the press also differs for these two types. Regardless of the proportions of a component, a fixed-stroke mechancial press will deliver its rated load at a prescribed rate (cycles per minute). On the other hand, an hydraulic press has a cycle time which varies with its stroke. High pressures and thick components require a proportionately longer cycle. In general, hydraulic presses rarely permit cycle times comparable with mechanical presses at pressures approaching the maximum rating of the press.

The guideline to use in selection of a press, omitting tooling, is a difficult factor to determine. Comparison of presses must be based on the assumption that all the presses being considered can actually make the component or range of components that is anticipated. One method to use is to calculate the capital cost per ton of pressure; this ignores several other important factors. A somewhat better approach is to calculate and minimize the capital cost per unit output and time. This takes into account dimensional capacity, pressure capacity and cycle speed. The part weight can be given as

$$W = (0.5F)(0.75L)D/CP \qquad (5\text{-}3)$$

where $0.5F$ = the practical usable fraction of the maximum fill height
$0.75L$ = the practical usable fraction of the maximum pressing load
D = the green density
C = the compression ratio
P = the actual compaction pressure

If an efficiency factor of 80% is given to the production time of a press, R is the press cycles per minute and Q is the price of the press, then the press value rating (PVR) is

$$PVR = Q/WR = CPQ/(0.3)DFLR \qquad (5\text{-}4)$$

The factor Q/FLR is the basis for comparison of various presses which can use a powder and produce a part corresponding to CP/D. In general this press value rating decreases with increasing press tonnage.

Because the cost per hour of operation increases with increasing tonnage capacity, while the number of parts per hour decreases, the tendency is to install a range of presses to cope with a maximum variety of applications. Two factors which are then introduced are the cost of tool interchangeability and press maintenance. In order to spread the work load it may be necessary to have adaptors which can accommodate tools from other size presses, and this can be costly. Maintenance costs usually increase with increasing variety of press sizes and types.

It is also necessary to consider the powder supply equipment associated with a press. This involves the use of a hopper located near the top of the press which feeds the powder into a feed shoe. The shoe then delivers the powder to the die. The factors to consider are: the mechanization of the feed shoe as it relates to punch movement, the uniformity of powder feed, the capacity of the hopper as related to the press cycle and volume of powder per part, and the flow rate of the powder. Efficient powder handling is essential to the economy of the compaction operation. The quantity of powder fed to the die must be well within 1% of the optimum quantity if parts with the proper dimensions and density are to be produced with a high degree of precision. In some cases vibratory attachments may be added to the feeding apparatus to improve powder flow.

The choice of tooling must be related to the particular application. However, more complex tooling requires more press motions; the two factors are intimately related. Simple components lend themselves to ejection tooling, while withdrawal tooling may be advantageous for parts of complex form and section. Small porous and structural materials are well suited for low tonnage ejection, rotary mechanical presses. The added cost of using many die sets can be justified for relatively simple tooling or very high production rates. In any event, one must also consider another contribution to press efficiency. During the manufacture of parts one or more items of tooling may become unusable. This results from actual breakage or excessive tool wear. The time required for tool adjustment or, in the case of a completed job, changeover of the tooling should be assessed. This varies with the type of tooling used. Ejection tooling requires adjustment or removal of 4 or 5 main items, each attached to different parts of the press. Adjustment and accurate positioning of the upper punch can be a time consuming task. The use of complete die sets, in which the complete tooling is assembled prior to fitting into the press, offers improvements in accuracy and changeover time. This is also the advantage of withdrawal tooling. For optimum press utilization a different or replacement die set or tool should be on hand so that the press is kept in almost continuous operation.

In the previous section the importance of the cost of tooling to the total manufacturing operation was noted. The above discussion illustrates that not only the initial cost but also the operational costs of maintaining tooling are of importance. One guideline to use in evaluating tools is to consider the cost to replace worn out tools. Table 5-5 gives some examples of various classes of tools,

TABLE 5-5. Evaluation of Tools

	Class A	Class B	Class C
Life expectancy	good	fair	low
Danger of breakage	nil	moderate	high
Replacement costs	low	high	high
Example			
Product	bronze bearing	ball joint bearing	gear and pinion
Expected die life	1 million parts	1 million parts	1 million parts
Die replacement cost	$185	$900	$1,000
Expected punch life	300,000 parts	150,000 parts	70,000 parts
Punch replacement cost	$90	$400	$1,100
Expected core life	100,000 parts	1 million parts	70,000 parts
Core replacement cost	$25	$50	$30
Tool replacement cost per 100 parts	$0.07	$0.36	$1.71

(from R. A. Bagby, Progr. in Powder Met. 1966, MPIF, New York)

indicating the method of analysis based on the replacement cost concept. The basic principle is that tool life is the most single important factor and tool materials should be chosen by performance rather than price.

Sintering The choice of a sintering furnace is also a difficult and critical decision to make. The two most important factors to consider are the temperature of operation and the type of atmosphere employed, and to a lesser extent time and cooling rates. Sintering temperatures vary according to the materials being produced. Several furnaces covering a range of temperatures and atmosphere capability may be appropriate for operations preparing large volumes of a variety of materials. The two basic methods of heating are gas and electric. Electric heating with Nichrome or Kanthal type elements is generally limited to 2100°F; for high temperatures the more costly Globar (silicon carbide), molybdenum or graphite elements must be used.

The influence of the type of heating on the selection of an atmosphere is an important consideration. As noted in the previous chapter gas heated furnaces usually necessitate a muffle construction to separate the sintering atmosphere from the atmosphere generated by the heating burners. Similarly, molybdenum and graphite windings must be protected from any gas containing oxygen, and even Globar elements should be protected from reducing atmospheres at high temperatures. Muffle construction adds a significant amount to the cost and maintenance of a sintering furnace. Electric furnaces are more economical if the design allows rapid replacement of the heating elements.

The economic operation of a sintering furnace, in terms of capital and operational costs per pound of sintered material, is improved by observation of the following factors:

(1) all parts should be sintered in the shortest time necessary to develop the desired dimensions and properties;

(2) the parts should be packed at the highest loading density in pounds per square foot of furnace space;

(3) to reduce power (gas or electric) consumption the conveying supports (belts, slabs or boxes) for the parts should be made of low heat capacity materials, and the ratio of part weight to conveying material weight should be as high as possible;

(4) to reduce power consumption and loss of heat due to the thermal conductivity of the gas, the furnace design should be based on a minimum amount of gas to be used;

(5) measures should be taken in furnace design and environmental plant layout to minimize heat losses from radiation and convection.

The two guidelines helpful in furnace selection, assuming that all furnaces under consideration are capable of performing the intended sintering, are: (a) minimize the capital cost per unit output and time and (b) minimize the maintenance costs (particularly heating element replacement and power consumption) per unit output. It should also be noted that heating and cooling rates are being given more attention, and control of these may affect both furnace design and cost. In general the cost per pound of sintered parts increases with increasing temperature. For example, there may be an increase of 10 to 15% when changing from 1600 to 2100°F and, because of the drastic changes in construction and heating element materials, a change from 2000 to 2500°F might mean a 150% increase in costs. It should be clear that the advantages of high sintering temperatures with regard to improvements in density and mechanical properties must be great enough to offset the higher sintering costs.

The other cost factor to consider is the maintenance of the desired sintering atmosphere. Some materials are very tolerant to wide variations in sintering atmosphere conditions, while others demand very close control of chemical composition or pressure (for vacuum sintering). The latter types require measurement and control instrumentation which increase the total sintering costs. They may also necessitate muffle construction and furnace design which eliminate any possible gas leakage. Naturally, the basic cost of the atmosphere per cubic foot is of primary importance. This involves the consideration of the capital and maintenance costs associated with the appropriate generator or source of atmosphere. This can be a very significant percentage (5 to 20%) of the total sintering costs and if the nature of the part material allows a choice of atmospheres, then the one chosen should have the minimum total capital and maintenance costs of direct and indirect atmosphere equipment per cubic foot of atmosphere. Bottled gases are the most expensive on a volume basis but of course require no capital equipment costs. Hydrogen and dissociated ammonia atmospheres tend to be the most costly plant produced atmospheres and should only be used when absolutely necessary to attain the desired sintered material properties. Atmospheres derived from hydrocarbon gases are much less costly. The presence of impurity or alloying elements which form oxides either difficult to reduce (such as Cr, Si, V, Ti, Al, Nb, Zr, B) or volatile and corrosive to furnace refractories and heating elements (such as P, Mo, B) or which may interact chemically with a gaseous component (such as Cr, V, Al) like nitrogen to form an internal precipitate increase costs by requiring low levels of water vapor and carbon dioxide or the absence of a particular gas.

Post-sintering Operations Depending on the exact nature of a post-sintering operation, the contribution of such a step towards the total manufacturing costs can be extremely high. It is outside the scope of this text to evaluate the costs of all the treatments discussed in section 5.3. It is sufficient to emphasize that such secondary operations as machining, repressing, finishing, plating and heat treatment require additional capital equipment, maintenance and manpower expenditures if carried out in the powder metallurgy plant, which is highly desirable.

The repressing operation presents somewhat different problems to the plant engineer than the initial compaction operation. Although existing compacting presses can be used for sizing or coining (usually less complex and costly presses are used) different tooling is normally required. Ejection tooling is most efficient and economical for this operation. In most cases repressing is not done on a continuous basis, but is carried out on a single cycle basis relying on hand or semiautomatic feeding. This is due to the necessity of positioning a shaped part into the die and the problem of lubrication. The latter must be done in such a way that the lubricant remains on the surface of the component and is not absorbed into the pores. If the latter occurs, then problems may arise during subsequent heat treating operations, or possibly a second sintering treatment. Fluid lubricant in the porosity also acts as a hydraulic cushion and increases dimensional variations and may cause tool failure.

Productivity and Total Costs One of the most interesting aspects of the powder metallurgy process is its ability to be highly automated. There is little doubt that products which must be mass produced are particularly suited to this process. Highly automated operations are being built to rapidly process very large quantities of powders through the blending, compaction and sintering treatments with a minimum of direct human involvement. This approach is being aided by advanced conveyor systems for powder and parts, high production rate presses, large capacity continuous sintering furnaces and automated property (such as density and hardness) measurement systems.

Even without a consideration of highly automated mass production operations, powder metallurgy has traditionally been considered a high volume production technique. This results from the high cost of tooling and the rapid rates of production possible with even the simplest equipment. A widely quoted figure is 50,000 parts for minimum total production but there are many exceptions to this guideline. The minimum number of parts will decrease with: reduced tool costs, use of some or all of the tooling for the production of more than one part, careful part design originally based on the use of powder metallurgy, minimization of post-sintering operations, and the number of machining operations required for production of the part by more conventional techniques. When these factors are considered, production rates as low as a few hundred parts, so called "short runs," may be practical.

In determining the production rate of an operation, one must be aware of the slowest step. All processing steps must be done in sequence. It is not efficient to have a very rapid compaction capability in conjunction with a much slower sintering production rate. Green compacts remaining in plant atmospheres for long periods are prone to moisture pickup, oxidation and contamination from the environment.

A number of economic factors have been discussed with regard to the technical aspects of the process. However, the total costs of manufacture involve many other considerations. These are extremely important in evaluating the possible adoption of the process for a specific manufacturing problem. Some of these factors are often considered the indirect costs of manufacture. These include the cost of administration, selling and marketing operations. The actual costs for any part will depend on both the nature and complexity of the part, and the efficiency of the entire production operation.

There are several factors which are often difficult to evaluate quantitatively but are of great importance in deciding the competitive position of the process. For example, utilizing a P/M part in a component may reduce factory floor space requirements and capital investment in machining or assembly equipment, allow machining or assembly labor to be used elsewhere, allow more rapid design changes with shorter lead times, allow a lower cost plant location, or provide a capability for a more diversified product line.

Although the buyer of a P/M part from a manufacturer may only be interested in the selling price and the ability of the part to perform its function, a better understanding of the complete economics of the process may lead to a better appreciation of those factors dictated chiefly by the requirements of the buyer, which determine the costs and, hence, selling price and which may be considerably changed without affecting the engineering performance. The broad economic considerations are also important for evaluating the potential benefits of in-plant operations, in which a company can produce its own powder metallurgy products. In most cases the economic advantages favor the purchase of P/M parts from an experienced and properly qualified custom P/M parts manufacturer rather than attempting to make them on an in-plant basis.

Continuous Forming One of the greatest innovations in our modern materials technology may be the direct use of powders to continuously produce sheet or bar (mill) forms. The most investigated technique is powder rolling, and a variety of metals are being made today by this process; these include nickel sheet and strip for electronic applications and coinage, and aluminum base materials. The use of this technique to produce ferrous materials could radically change our entire economy. The basic point is that our current technology involves the costly process of melting raw materials, producing large cast ingots and the use of large break-down mills and expensive soaking pits to produce sheet and bar stock. Although it must be admitted that new advancements in fusion technology, such as continuous casting, attempt to improve the traditional approach. In many cases it is possible to produce the pure metal directly from its ore in the form of powder. The concept of continuous powder metallurgy operations is simply the direct use of such powder (or even powder economically produced from the molten state) to continuously produce sheet or bar stock by rolling or extrusion techniques.

The basic economic advantages include the elimination of large amounts of very costly equipment, elimination of much of the scrap losses, and greater flexibility of product specifications. Many complex alloys and multiphase materials, including layered types, can only be economically made by such techniques. It is also possible to produce any length desired because of the continuity of the process. For sheet materials coil end-scrap losses have been drastically reduced. Mechanical properties for even the simplest materials have been improved by powder metallurgy techniques. Many variations have been developed for rolling and extrusion processes, but the essential aspect of all the processes is their basic simplicity and use of relatively inexpensive capital equipment. The ultimately used techniques will probably make extensive use of the hot compaction concept. It should also be noted that porous materials are being made by these continuous techniques.

The single most important obstacle to making large scale use of such processes has been the cost of powders. In recent years advances in process metallurgy techniques, enabling more economic production of large amounts of powder, have changed the entire complexion of the situation. It is safe to say that large scale production of iron powder could, and probably will, allow the complete development of these processes and greatly influence the entire iron and steel industry and subsequently all the other metals oriented industries.

5.6 ENGINEERING PROPERTIES

It is not the purpose of this section to attempt to reproduce large quantities of data on the properties of powder metallurgy materials (although some representative data will be given in the next section). This information, when needed, is best obtained from the most direct and current sources or, for critical or large scale operations, obtained in the laboratory under known conditions. The availability of new materials and the development of newer techniques and process equipment are constantly broadening the engineering properties of powder metallurgy products. One should be aware of the material specifications published by the MPIF and standards of the ASTM. There are several basic factors, however, which should be recognized when in pursuit of engineering properties of powder metallurgy materials.

Comparisons with Other Types of Materials In Chapter Four the effect of residual porosity on properties of the sintered material was thoroughly discussed. It is usually uneconomical to attempt to eliminate all the porosity in a sintered material. Therefore, a comparison between two materials of the same composition in which one is made by powder metallurgy and the other is a cast, wrought or machined product is quite invalid. The powder metallurgy material will often appear inferior on this basis. Table 5-6 contains some comparative data which show how powder metallurgy materials may not differ very much with regard to yield or tensile strengths (for some materials there is an improvement due to a finer grain structure or higher purity) but usually exhibit much lower tensile elongations. Toughness, as indicated by impact tests, is also usually lower. It is for this reason that many new materials have been developed within the powder metallurgy industry. By manipulation of the composition and metallurgical structure, the properties of a powder metallurgy product with less than its theoretical density can equal or exceed those of similar more conventional materials. Part of the problem in expanding the use of powder metallurgy is the necessity to educate engineers that a change in composition, and possibly secondary treatments, will usually be required to make a comparable part by powder metallurgy.

Mechanical Property Determination Dealing with powder metallurgy materials often presents unique problems with respect to testing and property evaluation. For example, a basic decision to make is whether to test a specimen which has been given its shape and dimensions by the powder metallurgy process only, or to machine the desired specimen from a sintered material. Although it may be argued that no machining should be done for testing whose results will be used to evaluate products that will not be machined, this does place limitations on the types of specimens that can be produced. That is, a conventional round type

TABLE 5-6. Comparison of Mechanical Properties of Powder Metallurgy, Cast and Wrought Materials

Material	Manufacturing Process	Density (g/cc)	Yield Strength (psi)	Tensile Strength (psi)	% Elongation
copper	powder metallurgy	8.5	15,000	30,000	29
	wrought	8.92	10,000	32,000	45
nickel	powder metallurgy	8.6	—	73,000	34
	wrought	8.9	25,000	75,000	40
bronze (90Cu-10Sn)	powder metallurgy	8.0	30,000	45,000	11–15
	cast	8.8	26,000	46,000	15–25
	wrought	8.8	65,000	85,000	68
brass (80Cu-18.5Zn-1.5Pb)	powder metallurgy	8.0	28,000	37,000	21
	cast	8.8	17,000	34,000	25
	wrought	8.8	12,000	38,000	53
iron	powder metallurgy	7.5	27,500	41,000	30
	ingot iron	7.86	29,000	45,000	45
316L stainless steel (Fe-18Cr-12Ni-2Mo)	powder metallurgy	6.65	51,000	58,000	8
	wrought	7.9	32,000	78,000	50
4660 steel (Fe-1.5Ni-0.5Mo-0.6C)	powder met.-heat tr.	7.2	120,000	140,000	0.5
	wrought-heat tr.	7.9	250,000	275,000	12

(from M. Feir, P/M Parts—Today's Properties, Progr. in Powder Met., 1966, MPIF Note: Since the above comparison was made P/M properties have been increasing steadily as a result of improvements in powders, process techniques and equipment. In many instances they are now equivalent or can be made equivalent to the comparable wrought material)

of tensile test bar, for example, could not be prepared by conventional compaction and sintering. It is conceivable that machined specimens might yield significantly different results than as-sintered ones because of the modification of the surface structure of the material. In particular, surface porosity could be closed, eliminating detrimental stress concentrations. Some comparative data for tensile testing of as-sintered and machined specimens are given in Table 5-7; it should be noted that relatively

TABLE 5-7. Effect of Machining Tensile Test Specimens of High Density Ferrous Materials

		Standard As-sintered[a]		Machined From Bars[b]		Machined From Blanks[c]	
Material	Density (g/cc)	Tens. Str. (psi)	% El.	Tens. Str. (psi)	% El.	Tens. Str. (psi)	% El.
iron	7.0	32,000	24.5	32,500	25.6	32,000	26.0
	7.2	34,500	28.4	35,000	32.4	35,500	30.0
	7.4	37,500	37.4	40,000	35.8	41,000	35.4
iron-2% copper	7.0	54,000	9.7	54,000	10.6	56,000	12.0
	7.2	60,000	13.4	59,000	15.3	61,000	17.0
	7.4	64,000	18.6	60,000	20.5	62,000	22.2

[a] standard flat test bars 0.225 in. wide, 0.200-0.250 in. thick
[b] cylindrical test bars 0.2756 in. dia. machined from sintered bars
[c] as in (b) but machined from large flat sintered compacts; both (b) and (c) specimens annealed at 1697°F for 15 min to relieve stresses due to machining

(from I. Ljunberg, Precision Metal Molding, Feb. 1955)

high density materials were examined and that an annealing treatment was given to the machined specimens in order to relieve any stresses introduced during machining. Although there were no significant differences in tensile strengths between the two types of specimens, there was a greater ductility observed in about 83% of the cases for the machined specimens, with the average increase being about 2% elongation. For lower densities the tensile strengths might be different, but in general greater ductility and toughness would probably be observed for machined type specimens. And the nature of the machining operation as well as the absence of a special annealing treatment could affect such findings.

Tensile and other tests may be affected by the somewhat brittle nature of many powder metallurgy materials, particularly ones with more than 10–15% porosity. Such materials tend to be quite susceptible to premature failure due to poor specimen alignment and preparation. Because of the difficulty in performing accurate tensile tests on powder metallurgy materials compression tests are often used (some reported "tensile" data are actually obtained from compression tests); greater strengths and ductilities are usually observed in compression tests. Also, transverse rupture tests are frequently used because of the easier specimen preparation and economy and rapidity of the test; however, the results are not valid when more than about 1–2% plastic deformation is exhibited. An often used generalization, that is useful, is that the tensile strength is about onehalf the transverse rupture strength. It should also be noted that the determination of elastic modulus and elastic limit or yield strength is difficult, and not usually carried out, during the tensile testing of powder metallurgy materials, even though such properties are of extreme importance and usefulness.

It has already been pointed out in the previous chapter that the macro type of hardness test is indicative of both the hardness of the metal and the amount of porosity present. The use of microhardness testing is often warranted when information on the metallurgical structure of the metal is desired. For example, evaluating the extent of a case hardening heat treatment definitely requires microhardness testing.

Non-destructive Testing The problems inherent in obtaining accurate and meaningful data useful in quality control have prompted the development and application of non-destructive tests particularly suited for powder metallurgy materials. In one method the specimen is excited by a piezoelectric or electromagnetic transducer. At the fundamental resonant frequency the amplitude of vibration reaches a maximum. This frequency is related to the thin-rod sonic velocity by the following equation:

$$V_o = 2Lf \qquad (5\text{-}5)$$

where V_o = the thin-rod velocity in in./sec
L = the sample length in in.
f = the resonant frequency in cycles/sec

This equation is useful for tests on specimens with varying lengths. In tests on electrolytic iron powder materials the tensile strengths for a number of specimens sintered at various temperatures and times, with densities ranging from 5.6–7.3 g/cc, where correlated with V_o. The degree of correlation was significantly better than the dependence of tensile strength on sintered density.

Another technique consists of measuring the ultrasonic velocity by placing transducers on opposite faces of a specimen and measuring the time to transmit a pulse; the bulk sonic velocity is calculated by use of

$$V_u = T/p \qquad (5\text{-}6)$$

where V_u = the bulk velocity in in./sec
T = the sample thickness between transducers in in.
p = the pulse travel time in sec

Excellent correlation has been obtained between V_u and the tensile strength of sintered iron materials. This parameter is also sensitive to the shape of the pores.

Both V_o and V_u are indirect measures of the elastic modulus of the bulk material; the modulus is of course dependent on both the nature of the solid material and the amount and nature of the porosity. Other quantities such as damping factors may be similarly employed; and eddy current testing has also been applied with success. Some of these non-destructive tests are especially useful because they can be applied to localized regions of P/M parts, and may sense differences for different directions of testing within a part. They also may be automated and appear to be more reliable than density or hardness measurements to determine the inherent quality of a material without resorting to actual destructive testing.

Other Properties There are of course numerous other properties pertinent to many applications. These may be put into the following classes: (a) chemical properties such as corrosion resistance and oxidation behavior; (b) wear properties such as coefficient of friction and weight loss behavior; (c) electrical and magnetic properties such as resistivity and hysteresis losses; (d) permeability properties of porous materials; (e) nuclear properties of importance to nuclear fuels and shielding materials; and (f) thermal properties. There have been no signficant departures from normal testing procedures for obtaining such properties of powder metallurgy materials. As indicated in Chapter Four, the one significant factor influencing all properties is the presence of porosity. Its effect on the validity of any testing procedure must be evaluated.

5.7 APPLICATIONS

The variety of applications of powder metallurgy materials is remarkable. They range from the most exotic and sophisticated innovations which enable rockets to reach for the stars to parts in our mundane washing machines and automobiles. The materials being processed include our oldest known metals, such as iron and copper, to the newest alloys, composites and nonmetallic materials emerging from the research laboratories. It would be impractical to attempt to describe all these applications; instead, some of the more important materials, properties and applications will be briefly discussed. That much of what is said now will be obsolete within a very short time speaks well of this dynamic materials processing field.

Ferrous Materials As in most other metals oriented fields powder metallurgy is strongly linked to the use and development of ferrous materials. The least expensive materials are the low density, as-sintered, iron parts with no alloying additions. Although the mechanical properties are low, many applications actually do not require high strengths. For example, lightly loaded gears and structural parts may be efficiently lubricated and do not necessitate high strength and hardness. Some applications allow considerable freedom with regard to part dimensions and larger sizes can be used to offset the low strengths. Medium density (6.2–6.6 g/cc) iron-carbon, iron-copper-carbon and iron-nickel-carbon materials with tensile strengths of 40,000 to 70,000 psi in the as-sintered condition are widely used. Almost every conceivable type of part has been made from these materials in applications ranging from toys to typewriters to industrial conveyor systems.

High density (over 6.8 g/cc) iron and iron alloy materials are also used in a broad range of applications. The higher costs are usually justified for applications requiring: close tolerances, high strengths, high wear resistance, low porosity and good surface finish. Infiltrated parts are relatively expensive because of the large amount of copper used, but very high strengths and hardnesses can be obtained.

Some representative data for the aforementioned types of un-heat treated ferrous powder metallurgy materials are given in Table 5-8. It is clear that strength and hardness increase with

TABLE 5-8. Typical Properties of Some As-sintered Ferrous Powder Metallurgy Materials

Material	Density (g/cc)	Condition	Tensile Strength (psi)	% Elong.	Apparent Hardness (Rockwell)
Fe, sponge	5.8	S	19,500	1.5	54 F
	6.2	S	26,000	1.5	66 F
	6.6	S	31,000	2.0	71 F
Fe, electrolytic	6.9	S	30,000	10.0	78 F
	7.3	R	38,000	15.0	—
	7.5	R	41,000	25.0	—
Fe, atomized	6.7	S	25,000	4.0	61 F
	7.3	S	36,000	7.0	78 F
Fe-1.0C	5.8	S	34,000	0.5	20 B
	6.2	S	41,000	1.0	42 B
	6.6	S	52,000	1.0	60 B
Fe-1.5Cu-1.0C	6.6	S	58,000	1.0	65 B
	7.0	S	76,000	1.4	80 B
Fe-2.0Cu-0.75C	6.7	S	78,000	3.0	79 B
	7.2	S	95,000	3.0	89 B
Fe-2.0Ni-0.5C	7.0	S	50,000	3.5	74 B
Fe-2.0Ni-0.8C	7.0	S	65,000	3.0	79 B
Fe-4.0Ni-0.8C	7.0	S	77,000	3.0	88 B
Fe-7.0Ni-0.8C	7.0	S	80,000	2.5	88 B
Fe-8.0Cu-0.9C	7.5	I	115,000	1.0	24 C

S = as-sintered R = repressed I = infiltrated

increasing density and alloy content, while ductility increases with increasing density but decreases with increasing alloy content. Relatively high strengths and hardnesses can be achieved without heat treating.

Many plain carbon and alloy steels are being used in the heat treated condition; both prealloyed atomized powders and blends of the component metals are being used. Increasing applications requiring unusually high strengths, coupled with high toughness, or an exceptionally high value of some other property are placing greater emphasis on these materials. Some alloying elements which are common in cast and wrought steels, such as manganese, have not been widely used in powder metallurgy materials. The new class of maraging steels, with very high strength and toughness, and a simple heat treatment might be of considerable use in some aerospace and heavy industry applications. High alloy steels, including the maraging type, are being made into machine tools by powder metallurgy techniques. Some representative data

TABLE 5-9 Typical Properties of Some Heat Treated Ferrous Powder Metallurgy Materials

Material	Density (g/cc)	Condition	Tensile Strength (psi)	% Elong.	Apparent Hardness (Rockwell)
Fe-1.5Cu-0.8C	7.0	Q + T @ 450°F	124,000	0.5	64 30N
Fe-1.0Cu-4.0Ni-0.7C	6.8	Q + T	90,000	0.5	38 C
	7.2	Q + T	135,000	0.5	45 C
Fe-2.0Ni-0.75C	6.8	Q + T @ 400°F	75,000	0.5	33 C
		500°F	118,000	0.5	29 C
		600°F	121,000	0.5	21 C
	7.25	Q + T @ 400°F	89,000	0.5	46 C
		500°F	144,000	0.5	41 C
		600°F	161,000	0.5	34 C
Fe-4.0Ni-0.5C	7.0	Q + T @ 600°F	154,000	1.0	39 C
Fe-7.0Ni-0.5C	7.3	Q + T @ 600°F	168,000	1.5	40 C
Fe-1.8Ni-0.5Mo-0.3Mn-0.6C	6.2	Q + T	85,000	0.5	30 C
	6.8	Q + T	112,000	0.5	40 C
Fe-16Cu-1.0C (infiltrated)	7.7	Q + T	165,000	2.0	40 C

Q = quenched (usually from 1600°F into oil)
T = tempered (usually at 400–600°F)

on currently used heat treated ferrous materials are given in Table 5-9. The most current P/M property data and that which is typical of the industry's capabilities is published in MPIF Standard No. 35, "P/M Materials Standards and Specifications." It may be secured from the Metal Powder Industries Federation at 201 E 42nd Street, New York, N.Y. 10017. The usual levels of high strength and hardness associated with conventional heat treated steels are readily attained with the powder metallurgy materials, but the ductilities are somewhat low.

In recent years there has been increased use of nickel, in the order of 2–7%, in conjunction with carbon and possibly copper to achieve high strengths in the heat treated condition. Such materials are particularly competitive with copper infiltrated iron-carbon materials (without heat treatment). The large amounts and high cost of the copper used, the equipment and manpower used to compact the copper slugs used for infiltration, the manpower used to place the infiltrating compacts on the iron ones prior to sintering, and the somewhat superior toughness and fatigue strength for the nickel steels at equivalent levels of strength have all promoted this change.

Another alternative to the copper infiltration technique, yielding similar properties but eliminating some of its disadvantages, is the use of pre-infiltrated iron powder. The individual particles of such powders consist of an intimate mixture of iron and copper —each similar to a copper infiltrated compact. The amount of copper can be controlled over a broad range. Such powder when compacted and sintered, and possibly heat treated, yield structures and properties completely analogous to conventionally infiltrated materials with the same composition and density. The one major disadvantage is that there is a very large amount of shrinkage because of the formation of the liquid copper phase within the original compact during sintering. Some representative data for materials made from this pre-infiltrated powder are given in Table 5-10. As expected, the amount of shrinkage increases with increasing copper content. Of course one does have the advantage, as with conventional copper infiltration, of using relatively low compaction pressures, thus facilitating the production of large parts with high strengths.

The stainless steels have been successfully used for a number of years in a broad variety of uses, including high density structural parts and porous filter materials. Although more costly due to the basic raw material costs, which are high because of the alloying elements and the use of carefully controlled processing conditions, their use is justified in applications requiring good strength and corrosion resistance. They are widely used in marine, pharmaceutical, chemical, food processing and medical applications.

TABLE 5-10. Properties of Some Materials Made from Pre-infiltrated Iron-Copper Powder

Material	Condition	Compaction Press. (tsi)	Density (g/cc)	Tensile Strength (psi)	% Shrinkage
Fe-4Cu-1.2C	S	40	6.63	51,800	0.48
Fe-7Cu-1.0C	Q + T	40	6.48	113,900	0.80
Fe-12Cu	S	50	7.14	77,500	1.60
Fe-12Cu-1.2C	S	40	6.95	94,800	1.10
Fe-20Cu-1.0C	S	50	7.46	124,900	1.96
Fe-22Cu-1.0C	S	40	7.54	102,000	2.20

S = as-sintered Q = quenched T = tempered

(from A. Adler and F. Emley, Int. J. Powder Met., vol. 3, no. 1, pp. 7–15, 1967; and technical data sheets, Minerals, Pigments and Metals Div., Chas. Pfizer and Co., New York.)

Increasing attention is being paid to the fatigue strengths of powder metallurgy materials, particularly the relatively high strength ferrous alloys. Some representative data are given in Table 5-11. One may note that high fatigue limits are obtainable and, as expected, tend to increase with increasing density, alloy content and heat treatment. The fatigue ratio (ratio of fatigue limit to tensile strength) is usually from 0.3 to 0.5 for tensile strengths up to 70,000 psi, and decreases with higher strengths. This behavior is similar to wrought and cast materials. Because of the potent effect of stress concentrations on fatigue strength, notches are often put into fatigue specimens and the "notched fatigue limit" determined. The stress concentration factor K_t was defined in equation (4-40) and the fatigue notch factor is defined by the following equation:

$$K_f = \frac{\text{fatigue limit with no stress concentration}}{\text{fatigue limit with a stress concentration}} \tag{5-7}$$

TABLE 5-11. Fatigue Limits of Some Ferrous Powder Metallurgy Materials

Material	Condition[a]	Density (g/cc)	Fatigue Limit (psi)
Fe-5.0Cu-0.75C	S	5.8	17,400
	S	6.2	21,100
	S	6.3	23,000
	S	7.0[b]	30,000
	Q + T	5.8	22,500
	Q + T	6.2	30,000
	Q + T	6.3	32,500
	Q + T	7.0[b]	38,000
Fe-1.8Ni-0.4Mo	S	6.8	16,000
Fe-1.8Ni-0.4Mo-0.2C	S	6.8	21,000
Fe-1.8Ni-0.4Mo-0.6C	S	6.8	25,000
Fe-1.8Ni-0.4Mo-0.8C	S	6.8	27,000
Fe-1.8Ni0.4Mo-0.4C	Q + T	7.0	44,000
	Q + T	7.2	46,000
Fe-19.0Cu-0.75C (infiltrated)	S	7.0	22,000
	Q + T	7.0	27,000

[a] S = as-sintered   Q = quenched   T = tempered
[b] extrapolated from actual data

(from S. W. McGee, Progr. in Powder Met. 1966, MPIF, New York; A. F. Kravic, Progr. in Powder Met. 1967, MPIF, New York)

And the fatigue notch sensitivity q is defined by

$$q = (K_f - 1)/(K_t - 1) \tag{5-8}$$

Some additional fatigue data both for notched and un-notched (smooth) specimens for some powder metallurgy and conventional materials are given in Table 5-12. Sintered ferrous materials possess low notch sensitivity factors similar to cast iron.

Copper Materials High density pure copper materials are used in applications requiring high electrical conductivity and, in some cases, nonmagnetic behavior. P/M parts are more economical than conventional materials requiring substantial forging and machining. Bronze parts are used because of their corrosion resistance, stability and relatively good mechanical strengths. They are also made with the self-lubricating feature. Typical applications include clutches with sintered bronze acting as a friction material and gears. Brass and nickel silver parts have good machinability, strength, ductility and corrosion resistance and

TABLE 5-12. Effect of an External Notch on Fatigue Behavior of Sintered and Conventional Materials

Material	Density (g/cc)	Tensile Strength (ksi)	Smooth Fatigue Lim. (ksi)	Fatigue Ratio	Notched Fatigue Limit (ksi)	K_f	K_t	q
Fe-4.0Ni-4.0Cu-1.0C	6.6	97.5	30.0	0.31	18.5	1.64	3.0	0.32
Fe-6.5Cu-1.0C	6.4	64.0	25.0	0.40	15.0	1.69	3.0	0.35
Fe-4.0Ni-0.4C	7.0	67.0	26.0	0.39	18.0	1.44	2.2	0.36
Fe-4.0Ni-0.4C*	7.0	105.0	38.0	0.36	25.0	1.52	2.2	0.43
Fe-22.0Cu (infiltrated)	7.3	49.0	20.5	0.42	11.2	1.81	3.0	0.40
Wrought 1045	—	120.0	67.0	0.56	27.0	2.72	3.1	0.82
Gray Cast Iron	—	51.4	24.6	0.48	15.6	1.57	3.1	0.27
Nodular Cast Iron	—	89.5	42.5	0.48	24.6	1.73	3.1	0.35

* quenched and tempered, all others in sintered condition

(from A. F. Kravic, Progr. in Powder Met. 1967, MPIF, New York)

are widely used for structural applications such as gears, cams and spacers. Brass nuts and washers made by powder metallurgy are also produced. Porous parts have also found wide use in many different applications, including strips for the leading edges of aircraft wings through which anti-freeze is exuded to prevent icing. Some representative properties of some common copper base materials are given in Table 5-13.

Copper and copper base alloys have also been successfully made into sheet and strip by powder rolling techniques. Multiphase materials with copper as the continuous phase have been developed for special applications requiring high thermal and/or electrical conductivities. For example, refractory metal carbides or tungsten are dispersed in a copper matrix for use as electrodes for electrical discharge machining, and solid lubricant particles may be dispersed for bearing material applications.

TABLE 5-13. Typical Properties of Some Copper Base Powder Metallurgy Materials

Material	Density (g/cc)	Condition	Tensile Strength (ksi)	% Elong.	Apparent Hardness (Rockwell)
Cu-16.5Zn-18.0Ni-1.5Pb (nickel-silver)	7.6	S	27.6	8	76 H
	8.0	R + A	35.0	15	80 H
Cu-20.0Zn-1.5Pb (brass)	7.8	S	28.4	15	74 H
	8.1	R	40.9	3	97 H
	8.1	R + A	34.5	20	82 H
Cu-9.5Zn-0.5Pb	7.9	S	33.7	29	69 H
	8.2	R	40.8	7	96 H
	8.2	R + A	38.5	43	78 H
Cu-30Zn	7.5	S	27.5	8	81 H
Cu (elect. cond. = 90% IACS min.)	8.6 min.	R	35.0	18	70 F min.

S = as-sintered R = repressed A = annealed

(from E. I. Larsen and E. F. Swazy, Progr. in Powder Met. 1967, MPIF, New York.)

Nickel Materials As already indicated nickel is being used extensively as an alloying element in powder metallurgy materials. Dispersion strengthening of nickel has been very effectively carried out. The most promising class of materials consist of two or three volume percent of very small particles of thoria (a few hundred angstroms in diameter) in nickel or nickel base alloys prepared by selective reduction of the oxides or by salt-decomposition techniques. These materials have very high mechanical strengths at both room and elevated temperatures (to 2400°F), excellent structural stability at elevated temperatures, high thermal conductivity, very good thermal shock resistance and relatively good corrosion resistance. Fabrication of these materials into sheet and bar stock includes various types of mechanical working operations.

One of the major methods of obtaining pure nickel from its ore results in the production of nickel powder. For this reason nickel sheet is now commercially produced by powder rolling. Complex composite materials are also feasible because of the production of composite powders in which a core material, such as graphite or tungsten carbide, is coated with nickel. Solid lubricants are being dispersed in nickel to produce bearing materials. The conventional class of nickel base superalloys widely used for elevated temperature applications have also been successfully prepared by a variety of powder metallurgy techniques. Significant efforts are being expended on developing unconventional processing methods, such as slip casting and direct extrusion, so that large parts or mill shapes may be produced. Probably the two major problems with fully exploiting such processing are the elimination of impurities from the original powders and those introduced during processing, and the need to produce a relatively large grain size.

Pure nickel powder has been widely used for manufacturing highly porous nickel sheets and plates for use in alkaline battery and fuel cell electrodes, including the popular nickel-cadmium rechargeable battery. Its chemical and electrical properties make it ideal for such applications; some data for differently prepared materials are given in Table 5-14. Very sophisticated continuous

TABLE 5-14. Properties of Some Porous Nickel Electrode Materials

Processing	% Porosity	Bend Strength (psi)	Electrical Resistivity (micro-ohm-cm)
loose sintered	88	256	444
loose sintered with woven nickel mesh	84	384	126
slurry sintered	78	1252	109

Note: Type 255 carbonyl nickel powder used, sintered 15 min in hydrogen at 1652°F.

(from V. A. Tracey and N. J. Williams, Electrochem. Technology, vol. 3, pp. 11–19, 1965)

pressureless processing methods have been developed for producing these sheet materials. The use of pore forming agents permits the attainment of very high levels of interconnected porosity coupled with good mechanical strength.

Aluminum Materials The use of aluminum powder to make shapes via P/M has just recently been perfected commercially. By maintaining careful control over sintering conditions (especially temperature and dew point), the use of about 1.5% lubricant and the addition of small percentages of such strengthening elements as Mg, Si or Cu singly or in combination, aluminum P/M parts can be made readily. Some properties for an aluminum P/M alloy containing 4.4% Cu, 0.8% Si and 0.4% Mg are shown in Table 5-15. Success has also been achieved with aluminum self-lubricating bearings. Excellent results have been obtained for continuous powder rolling and extrusion of pure aluminum and aluminum base alloys. Some very novel sheet products with attractive surface finishes due to a multiphase structure have been made.

Dispersion strengthening of aluminum has also been quite successful, but no substantial commercial development of these materials has taken place. The classical example is sintered aluminum powder (SAP) which is usually manufactured from flake aluminum powder having an initial oxide content of about 10–13%.

TABLE 5-15. Sintered Properties of Aluminum Alloy[a]

Green Density Percent	Green Density g/cm³	Thermal Condition[b]	Tensile[c] Strength psi	Yield Strength psi	Elongation Percent in 1 in.	Apparent Rockwell Hardness
85	2.36	T1	24,500	21,000	2.0	60/65 R_e
		T4	30,500	26,000	3.0	70/75 R_e
		T6	36,000	—	—	75/80 R_e
90	2.50	T1	29,200	24,600	3.0	70/75 R_e
		T4	35,600	29,800	3.5	75/80 R_e
		T6	46,800	—	—	85/90 R_e
95	2.64	T1	30,300	26,200	3.0	70/75 R_e
		T4	38,000	31,000	5.0	80/85 R_e
		T6	48,100	47,500	2.0	85/90 R_e

[a] Sinter 30 minutes at 1100 F in N_2 (average dew point—45 F)
[b] T1—as sintered; cooled from sintering temperature to 800 F in N_2, air cooled.
T4—heat treat 30 min. at 940 F in air, water quench and age 4 weeks at R.T.
T6—heat treat 30 min. at 940 F in air, water quench and age 18 hours at 320 F.
[c] Determined with flat tension test bar (MPIF Standard 10).

(from J. H. Dudas and W. A. Dean, Internat'l Journal of Powder Metallurgy, Vol. 5, No. 2, pp. 21–36, 1969)

The powder is usually hot-worked by extrusion directly or after a normal compaction and sintering operation. The mechanical properties and structural stability at both room and elevated temperatures are exceptionally good.

Recently considerable interest has been shown in using aluminum slugs prepared by powder metallurgy techniques for forging or extrusion raw materials. Also boron fiber reinforced aluminum composites have been made by powder metallurgy techniques with considerable success.

Refractory Metals Extensive use of powder metallurgy techniques has been made in the production of the refractory metals tungsten, molybdenum, tantalum and niobium, and alloys based on these metals. The fact that these metals have high melting points and are chemically reactive, as noted earlier, make them particularly suited to nonfusion processing. These materials are used in a variety of industrial applications and especially within the aerospace industry. Their high melting points and good elevated temperature mechanical properties make them well suited for elevated temperature applications. Because they are relatively hard at room temperature processing often consists of isostatic compaction, hot pressing or hot working (extrusion or forging) of powders to achieve the desired shapes and densities. Care must be taken to avoid contamination due to absorption of gaseous elements, such as oxygen and nitrogen, that tend to embrittle these materials. Ingots and billets of these materials are often made by powder metallurgy techniques and subsequently broken down by conventional types of operations.

A good example of an important industrial class of such powder metallurgy refractory materials is the "high density" or "heavy metal" tungsten base alloys. These materials offer very high densities coupled with good strength, machinability and other properties of interest for specific applications. The four major fields of applications include: weights and counterbalances, radiation shielding, rotating inertia members and hypervelocity members. Some typical compositions and properties for this class of materials are given in Table 5-16. The high ductilities of some of these materials should be noted.

TABLE 5-16. Properties of Some High Density Tungsten Base Powder Metallurgy Materials

Material	Density (g/cc)	Yield Strength (ksi)	Tensile Strength (ksi)	% Elong.	Fatigue Limit (ksi)	Hardness (Rockwell C)
W-6.0Ni-4.0Cu	16.9	75	112	6	40	24
W-3.5Ni-1.5Cu	18.0	85	110	5	43	27
W-7.0Ni-3.0Fe	17.0	88	125	18	62	25
W-3.5Ni-1.5Fe	18.0	90	130	15	67.5	28
W-4.0Ni-2.0Fe-4.0Mo	17.25	140	150	2	65	36

(from E. I. Larsen and E. F. Swazy, Progr. in Powder Met. 1967, MPIF, New York)

Another class of widely used powder metallurgy refractory materials are used as electrial contact devices. Usually porous compacts of tungsten or tungsten carbide are infiltrated with copper or silver. The latter provides a continuous high conducting phase, while the refractory material provides resistance to electrical arc erosion and mechanical strength. The refractory materials are not soluble in the copper or silver and, hence, do not affect the desired properties. Some data for several of these materials are given in Table 5-17.

Cermets The application of these metal-ceramic composites has been eminently successful for high speed machining of metals. Widespread use of cermet tools is based on their resistance to deformation at elevated temperatures, low edge wear and high strength and hardness. Their use has drastically reduced machining times and costs, and resulted in improved surface finish and tool life. The WC-Co type is widely used to machine nonferrous metals, nonmetallic materials and most cast irons. More complex carbide alloys containing two or more carbide phases (such as WC and a solid solution of WC, TiC and TaC) are used to machine steels and alloy cast irons. There are many varieties of these cermet materials, designed with specific applications in mind. Major recent developments include the use of heat treatable steels as the metallic binder phase to improve fabrication of the tool (the cer-

TABLE 5-17. Properties of Some Powder Metallurgy Electrical Contact Type Materials

Material	Density (g/cc)	Tensile Strength (ksi)	Hardness (Rockwell)	Electrical Conductivity (% IACS)
W-27.5Ag	15.6	70	90 B	49
W-35.0Ag	14.8	50	85 B	51
W-49.0Ag	13.5	35	55 B	65
W-15.0Ag	17.0	65	26 C	38
W-13.0Cu	16.7	90	26 C	33
W-26.0Cu	14.7	90	98 B	46
W-45.0Cu	12.6	63	79 B	55
WC-50.0Ag	12.4	40	91 B	47
WC-44.0Cu	11.6	75	99 B	43
Mo-39.0Ag	10.2	60	82 B	47
Mo-50.0Ag	10.2	—	75 B	52

(from E. I. Larsen and E. F. Swazy, Progr. in Powder Met. 1967, MPIF, New York)

met is machined in the unheat-treated condition) and properties, and the use of smaller carbide particle sizes to improve tool life. Actually the cermet class of materials is a technology in itself.

Automotive Applications The use of P/M parts for automotive applications is important for two reasons: (1) the automotive industry uses about 50% (on a tonnage basis) of all the ferrous and nonferrous parts produced, and (2) major innovations in materials design and processing procedures are likely to be developed within this industry and ultimately affect all other applications. Although P/M parts have been used in automobiles for several decades, today they still represent a very small fraction of the material in an automobile. However, there is now a major redevelopment of powder metallurgy materials for a multitude of automotive uses. This has come about because of improved materials and processing techniques, increased awareness and knowledge of powder metallurgy techniques by design engineers and reductions in manfacturing costs of mass produced quantities of P/M parts. The use of high tonnage compaction presses and high compressibility powders, allowing higher densities and larger parts to be obtained, larger sintering furnaces and advanced techniques in automation procedures have also spurred this new growth.

The number of automotive parts being made today by powder metallurgy are great; they include: oil pump gears, transmission seals, transmission gears and parts, clutch plates and discs, brake linings, valve seat inserts, electrical contacts, camshaft sprockets and connecting rods. If continued improvements are achieved and if costs can be reduced, and this is likely, then many additional parts could be made; these might include: cylinder liners, crankshafts, camshafts, wheel hubs, flywheels and universal joint parts. The advent of powder rolling could drastically increase the consumption of powders for automotive applications, as should increased development of alloy steels and new compaction techniques. Forging preforms made from powder can offer great opportunities in the automotive industry because of economic advantages attainable without sacrificing engineering performance.

Consumer Products and Business Machines Virtually every type of powder metallurgy material is used in the multitude of consumer products, such as all types of appliances, lawn mowers, snow blowers, rifles, toys, outboard marine engines, ball point pens, fishing reels, air conditioners and cameras, and business machines, including typewriters, computers and dictating machines. The development of materials used because of their electrical and magnetic properties and secondary manufacturing operations such as plating and surface finishing has been very much linked to these two important kinds of applications.

Aerospace Applications The applications of powder metallurgy materials in aerospace systems are of great interest because of the nature of the materials used, which have created major process innovations, and the uniqueness of the applications, which have resulted in radically new material designs. On a tonnage basis these materials might appear insignificant, but on a cost basis these materials clearly represent a major category. In most of these applications powder metallurgy techniques are used because: the material used cannot be cast in an economical or practical manner, there is a need for controlled porosity, or there is some unique property which can only be obtained by using this method. Two metals which are good examples of the first case are beryllium and tungsten. The former has the advantages of a high strength-to-weight ratio, high modulus of elasticity and high heat capacity. The use of isostatic and vacuum hot pressing have helped to minimize brittleness problems. Applications of beryllium include heat shields for space capsules, gyroscope parts, antennas for Telstar space vehicles and some structural parts.

Tungsten is the only metal capable of being used in the high thermal environments encountered in many aerospace applications. Parts with uniform porosity are used in plasma jet engines and ion engines at operating temperatures near 3000°F. Infiltrated composites, such as tungsten-silver, with exceptional physical and mechanical properties are used for rocket nozzles. Isostatic pressing and the use of ultra fine powders have been successfully developed for these materials.

Molybdenum and tantalum alloys are produced by powder metallurgy techniques for a variety of applications. Molybdenum has been used to protect silicon semiconductors in rectifiers used in space, for some nozzles on liquid fuel rockets and is under development for leading edges of supersonic aircraft. Tantalum is widely used for capacitors in the complex controls and communications of space satellites and vehicles, and for heat shields of propulsion units of missiles.

Many conventional powder metallurgy products are extensively used in aerospace systems; these include: sintered bronze bushings in equipment in Explorer satellites, magnetic materials such as Alnio in communications systems, numerous ferrous parts in motors, solid lubricant type bearing materials for use in space vehicles and satellites, and ferrite cores for inductor coils and toroid transformers in the Telstar satellites.

Atomic Energy Applications Powder metallurgy techniques have been widely applied to material fabrication problems associated with nuclear power reactors. Some general features of powder metallurgy processing of particular importance to this field are: the ability to control grain size, especially the production of fine grain size materials; the ability to make alloys of elements with large differences in density or melting point; the ability to make multiphase materials, especially metal-ceramic types; the ease of making layered or clad types of materials. Certain metals are of particular importance in nuclear applications and can be effectively processed by powder metallurgy methods. Uranium, UO_2, UC, Al-UAl_4 and thorium are fuel materials; beryllium is a moderator (controls the speed of neutrons); and zirconium and its alloys are useful as cladding materials to inhibit corrosion in reactors.

Although these materials can be readily produced in powder form, some present several severe handling problems. Beryllium is highly toxic and zirconium, in fine particle sizes, is highly pyrophoric; and uranium powder is both toxic and pyrophoric. Many conventional materials have also been used for nuclear applications. Aluminum, magnesium and stainless steel alloys have been used for cladding purposes (to separate the fuel and coolant); many of the more exotic techniques such as hot pressing, isostatic compaction and slip casting have been successfully applied to nuclear applications.

REFERENCES FOR FURTHER READING

5-1. Powder Metallurgy Design Guidebook, MPIF, New York. A good basic review of the process and basic engineering considerations, including part design.

5-2. W. D. Jones, Fundamental Principles of Powder Metallurgy, Arnold, London, 1960. Chapters five through seven give detailed information on various applications, economic and design factors, and processes; also many references.

5-3. D. Feinberg, Surface Finishing of P/M Parts, Progr. in Powder Met. 1968, MPIF, New York. A good review of the many surface finishing operations applied to powder metallurgy materials.

5-4. D. A. Armstrong and L. R. Hilderbrand, Tolerance Factors in P/M parts Production, Int. J. Powder Met., vol. 4, no. 2, pp. 35–41, 1968. A good discussion of the variables of the process and how they affect the control of dimensional tolerances.

5-5. R. L. Forbes and D. W. Pantano, Achieving Quality Assurance with P/M Parts, Progr. in Powder Met. 1967, MPIF, New York.

An enlightening discussion of the procedures and equipment used to achieve high quality parts production.

5-6. R. A. Vanatt, Expanding P/M Parts Applications Through Secondary Machining, Progr. in Powder Met. 1967, MPIF, New York. A good review of secondary operations now used extensively for powder metallurgy materials.

5-7. A. F. Kravic, The Fatigue Properties of Sintered Iron and Steel, Progr. in Powder Met. 1967, MPIF, New York. An excellent contemporary review of this important topic, with good references.

5.8. R. A. Bagby, Factors Influencing the Economic Design and Application of Powder Metallurgy Parts, Progr. in Powder Met. 1966, MPIF, New York. General discussion of part design, economic considerations and applications.

5-9. H. G. Taylor, A Critical Review of the Effect of Press and Tool Design Upon the Economics of Sintered Structural Components, Powder Met., vol. 18, pp. 285–318, 1965. An excellent discussion of process and economic considerations.

5-10. D. C. Major and J. E. Hammond, A Review of Metallurgical and Economic Aspects of Tooling Materials for the Compaction of Powder-Metal Parts, Powder Met., vol. 8, pp. 319–334, 1965. A good discussion and useful data.

5-11. M. Feir, What Properties Can Users Expect from P/M Parts, Materials in Design Engin., pp. 88–90, June, 1966. Contains a significant amount of reliable mechanical properties.

5-12. R. H. Brockelman, Evaluating Properties of Powder Iron Compacts by Sonic Tests, Metal Progress, pp. 95–98, July, 1966. Basic discussion and results of some unique nondestructive tests.

5-13. R. Talmage, Potential of Powder Metallurgy Is Tied to New Strength and Versatility, Soc. Auto. Engr. J., vol. 73, pp. 30–35, October, 1965. A good discussion of automotive applications and a table of mechanical properties.

5-14. J. A. Vaccari, P/M Parts, Materials and Processes Manual No. 242, Materials (in Design) Engineering, pp. 85–100, July, 1967. An excellent modern review of the process including considerable useful data.

5-15. H. H. Hausner and M. C. Kells, The Role of Powder Metallurgy in the Design of Nuclear Power Reactors, 2nd Plansee Proc., F. Benesovsky, editor, pp. 287–304, 1956. Elementary treatment of the topic.

5-16. H. H. Hausner, editor, Modern Developments in Powder Metallurgy, Plenum, New York, 1966. This three volume set is the proceedings of the 1965 International Powder Metallurgy Conference and contains many useful papers, most on a more advanced level.

5-17. H. H. Hausner, K. H. Roll and P. K. Johnson, editors, Iron Powder Metallurgy, Plenum, New York, 1968. Contains much classical information now difficult to obtain in original form. This is part of a continuing series called "New Perspectives in Powder Metallurgy." Excellent reference source.

5-18. P/M Materials Standards and Specifications. MPIF Standard No. 35. All of the essential property and performance data necessary for the proper specification of P/M parts. Periodically up-dated to reflect latest industry practices. A necessary publication for all powder metallurgists and P/M parts users.

PROBLEMS

(5-1) Discuss the design and manufacture of a two inch long cylindrical part in which the inner core section (3/4 inch in diameter) is a porous filter material and the outer shell (1/4 inch wall thickness) is a high density structural material providing mechanical rigidity and strength to the part. Consider material design and the possible methods of compaction, sintering and any useful post-sintering operations.

(5-2) Discuss the significance of compaction pressure with regard to the closest obtainable tolerances.

(5-3) Under what conditions can a compaction die be used for repressing of the part after sintering?

(5-4) Discuss the relative merits of macro and microhardness testing of powder metallurgy materials with regard to evaluation of wear resistance, corrosion resistance and yield strength.

(5-5) Very high density parts can be prepared by using high compaction pressures or infiltration techniques. Discuss the relative merits of each approach for producing a very large part from prealloyed atomized powder.

APPENDIX I

Density-Porosity Data for Iron (based on theoretical density of 7.87 g/cc)

Density (g/cc)	Porosity (%)
5.00	36.47
5.05	35.83
5.10	35.20
5.15	34.56
5.20	33.93
5.25	33.29
5.30	32.66
5.35	32.02
5.40	31.39
5.45	30.75
5.50	30.11
5.55	29.48
5.60	28.84
5.65	28.21
5.70	27.57
5.75	26.94
5.80	26.30
5.85	25.67
5.90	25.03
5.95	24.40
6.00	23.76
6.05	23.13
6.10	22.49
6.15	21.86
6.20	21.22
6.25	20.58
6.30	19.95
6.35	19.31
6.40	18.68
6.45	18.04
6.50	17.41
6.55	16.77
6.60	16.14
6.65	15.50
6.70	14.87
6.75	14.23
6.80	13.60
6 85	12.96
6.90	12.33
6.95	11.69
7.00	11.05
7.05	10.42
7.10	9.78
7.15	9.15
7.20	8.51
7.25	7.88
7.30	7.24
7.35	6.61
7.40	5.97
7.45	5.34
7.50	4.70
7.55	4.07
7.60	3.47
7.65	2.80
7.70	2.16
7.75	1.52
7.80	0.89
7.85	0.25
7.87	0.00

% theoretical density = 100 − % porosity

APPENDIX II

Water Vapor Content of Atmosphere in Terms of Dew Point

Dew Point (°F)	Water Vapor*	
	% by volume	partial pressure (atm)
100	6.45	.0645
90	4.75	.0475
80	3.46	.0346
70	2.47	.0247
60	1.75	.0175
50	1.21	.0121
40	.827	.00827
30	.553	.00553
20	.367	.00367
10	.236	.00236
0	.150	.00150
−10	.093	.00093
−20	.0558	.000558
−30	.0328	.000328
−40	.0188	.000188
−50	.0104	.000104
−60	.0056	.000056
−70	.0029	.000029
−80	.0015	.000015
−90	.0007	.000007
−100	.0003	.000003

* for total atmosphere pressure of one atmosphere

APPENDIX III

Melting Points and Densities of Some Metals and Alloys

Metal	Melting Point (°F)	Density at 68°F (g/cc)
aluminum	1220	2.70
antimony	1167	6.62
brass (65 Cu-35 Zn)	1710	8.47
bronze (90 Cu-10 Sn)	1830	8.78
cobalt	2718	8.9
copper	1981	8.94
gold	1945	19.3
iron, pure	2797	7.87
iron, cast	2327	7.03
lead	621	11.34
magnesium	1202	1.74
manganese	2300	7.44
nickel	2647	8.9
palladium	2826	12.0
platinum	3216	21.45
silver	1761	10.5
titanium	3150	4.5
tungsten	6115	19.3
zinc	787	7.14

INDEX